PARAMAGNETIC RESONANCE

VOLUME I

Sponsors of the Symposium

THE HEBREW UNIVERSITY OF JERUSALEM
THE INTERNATIONAL UNION OF PURE AND APPLIED PHYSICS
THE ISRAEL ACADEMY OF SCIENCES AND HUMANITIES

PARAMAGNETIC RESONANCE

PROCEEDINGS OF THE FIRST INTERNATIONAL CONFERENCE HELD IN JERUSALEM, JULY 16–20, 1962

Edited by

W. LOW

Department of Physics
The Hebrew University of Jerusalem, Israel

Volume I

1963

ACADEMIC PRESS · NEW YORK · LONDON

PHYSICS

ACADEMIC PRESS INC.
111 Fifth Avenue
New York 3, N. Y.

United Kingdom Edition
Published by
ACADEMIC PRESS INC. (London) Ltd.
Berkeley Square, London, W. 1

Library of Congress Catalog Card Number 63−21409

PRINTED IN THE UNITED STATES OF AMERICA

Contributors to Volume I

Numbers in italics indicate the page on which the author's contribution appears.

P. Auzins, Department of Chemistry, University of Minnesota, U.S.A. (*90*)

Y. Ayant, Institut Fourier, Grenoble, France (*267, 279, 290*)

J. M. Baker, Oxford University, Oxford, England (*202*)

E. Belorizky, Laboratoire d'Electrostatique et de Physique du Métal, Grenoble, France (*290*)

R. Bersohn, Department of Chemistry, Columbia University, New York 27, U.S.A. (*305*)

W. E. Blumberg, Bell Telephone Laboratories, New Jersey, U.S.A. (*125*)

A. Bose, Indian Association for the Cultivation of Science, Cal-32, India (*155*)

H. A. Buckmaster, Physics Department, University of Alberta, Calgary, Alberta, Canada (*217*)

G. Burns, International Business Machines Corporation, Thomas J. Watson Research Center, Yorktown Heights, New York, U.S.A. (*260*)

B. A. Calhoun, International Business Machines Corporation, J. Watson Research Center, Yorktown Heights, New York, U.S.A. (*224*)

A. S. Chakravarty[1], Indian Association for the Cultivation of Science, Cal-32, India (*155, 305*)

R. Chatterjee, Indian Association for the Cultivation of Science, Cal−32, India (*155*)

G. A. deMars, Raytheon Research Division, Waltham, Massachusetts, U.S.A. (*51*)

M. deWit, Texas Instruments Incorporated, Dallas 22, Texas, U.S.A. (*144*)

G. H. Dieke, The Johns Hopkins University, Baltimore, Maryland, U.S.A. (*237*)

J. C. Eisenstein, National Bureau of Standards, Washington, D.C., U.S.A. (*253*)

J. Eisinger, Bell Telephone Laboratories, Murray Hill, New Jersey, U.S.A. (*125*)

R. Englman, Massachusetts Institute of Technology, Cambridge, Massachusetts, U.S.A. (*329*)

T. L. Estle, Texas Instruments Inc., Dallas 22, Texas, U.S.A. (*144*)

V. J. Folen, U.S. Naval Research Laboratory, Washington, D.C., U.S.A. (*68*)

A. J. Freeman, Materials Research Laboratory, Massachusetts, U.S.A. (*373*)

M. J. Freiser, International Business Machines Corporation, Thomas J. Watson Research Center, Yorktown Heights, New York, U.S.A. (*224*)

H. J. Gerritsen[2], Chalmers University of Technology, Gothenburg, Sweden (*3*)

S. Geschwind, Bell Telephone Laboratories, Murray Hill, New Jersey, U.S.A. (*113, 125*)

E. A. Giess, International Business Machines Corporation, Thomas J. Watson Research Center, Yorktown Heights, New York, U.S.A. (*224*)

J. L. Hall[3], Carnegie Institute of Technology, Pittsburgh 13, Pennsylvania, U.S.A. (*206*)

---

[1] Present address: Department of Chemistry, Columbia University in the City of New York, New York 27, N.Y., U.S.A.

[2] Present address: RCA Laboratories, Princeton, New Jersey, U.S.A.

[3] Present address: Joint Institute for Laboratory Astrophysics, Boulder, Colorado, U.S.A.

v

F. S. HAM, General Electric Research Laboratory, Schenectady, New York, U.S.A. (*130*)

W. HAUSER, Northeastern University, Boston, Massachusetts, U.S.A. (*297*)

W. HAYES, The Clarendon Laboratory, Oxford, England (*163*)

D. HORN[1], Technion–Israel Institute of Technology, Haifa, Israel (*329*)

V. W. HUGHES, Yale University, New Haven, Connecticut, U.S.A. (*382*)

J. P. HURRELL, Oxford University, Oxford, England (*202*)

D. F. JOHNSTON, Theoretical Physics Division, Atomic Energy Research Establishment, Harwell, England (*374*)

D. KIRO, Department of Physics, The Hebrew University of Jerusalem, Israel (*44*)

P. KISLIUK[2], Bell Telephone Laboratories, Murray Hill, New Jersey, U. S.A. (*113*)

L. S. KORNIENKO, Institute of Nuclear Physics, Moscow State University, Moscow, U.S.S.R. (*126*)

G. F. KOSTER, Massachusetts Institute of Technology, Cambridge, Massachusetts, U.S.A. (*362*)

M. J. M. LEASK, Clarendon Laboratory, Oxford, England (*261*)

W. LOW, Department of Physics, The Hebrew University of Jerusalem, Israel (*44, 59, 79, 167, 314*)

G. W. LUDWIG, General Electric Research Laboratory, Schenectady, New York, U.S.A. (*130*)

W. MARSHALL, Atomic Energy Research Establishment, Harwell, England (*347*)

K. A. MÜLLER, Battelle Memorial Institute, Geneva, Switzerland (*17*)

M. C. M. O'BRIEN, The Clarendon Laboratory, Oxford, England (*322*)

R. ORBACH, Division of Engineering and Applied Physics, Harvard University, Cambridge, Massachusetts, U.S.A.(*261*)

J. W. ORTON, Mullard Laboratories, Salfords, Surrey, England (*90*)

J. OVERMEYER, International Business Machines Corporation, Thomas J. Watson Research Center, Yorktown Heights, New York, U.S.A. (*224*)

P. P. Pashinin, P. N. Lebedev Physical Institute, U.S.S.R. Academy of Sciences, Moscow, U.S.S.R. (*197*)

M. J. D. POWELL, U.K. Atomic Energy Research Establishment, Harwell, England (*261*)

A. M. PROKHOROV, Institute of Nuclear Physics, Moscow State University, USSR (*13, 126, 197*)

U. RANON, Department of Physics, Israel Atomic Energy Commission Laboratories, Rehovoth, Israel (*167*)

J. P. REMEIKA, Bell Telephone Laboratories, Murray Hill, New Jersey, U.S.A. (*113, 125*)

J. G. RENSEN, Philips Research Laboratories, N. V. Philips' Gloeilampenfabrieken, Eindhoven, Netherlands (*105*)

L. RIMAI, Raytheon Research Division, Waltham, Massachusetts, U.S.A. (*51*)

G. ROSENGARTEN, Department of Physics, The Hebrew University of Jerusalem, Israel (*314*)

R. S. RUBINS, Department of Physics, The Hebrew University of Jerusalem, Israel (*59, 79*)

R. T. SCHUMACHER, Carnegie Institute of Technology, Pittsburgh 13, Pennsylvania, U.S.A. (*206*)

I. R. SENITZKY, U.S. Army Signal Research and Development Laboratory, Fort Monmouth, New Jersey, U.S.A. (*380*)

H. STATZ, Raytheon Company, Waltham, Massachusetts, U.S.A. (*362*)

---

[1] Present address: Department of Physics, University of Tel-Aviv, Tel-Aviv, Israel.

[2] Present address: Aerospace Corporation, El Segundo, California, U.S.A.

J. Thomas, Laboratoire d'Electrostatique et de Physique du Métal, Grenoble, France (*279*)

Reuben S. Title, International Business Machines Corporation, Thomas J. Watson Research Center, Yorktown Heights, New York, U.S.A. (*178*)

J. W. Twidell, The Clarendon Laboratory, Oxford, England (*163*)

G. K. Walter, Texas Instruments Incorporated, Dallas 22, Texas, U.S.A. (*144*)

R. E. Watson, Atomic Energy Research Establishment, Harwell, England (*373*)

J. E. Wertz, Department of Chemistry, University of Minnesota, Minneapolis, Minnesota U.S.A. (*90*)

J. S. van Wieringen, Philips Research Laboratories, N. V. Philips' Gloeilampenfabrieken, Eindhoven, Netherlands (*105*)

F. I. B. Williams, Oxford University, Oxford, England (*202*)

W. P. Wolf, Clarendon Laboratory, Oxford, England (*261*)

D. L. Wood, Bell Telephone Laboratories, Murray Hill, New Jersey, U.S.A. (*113*)

A. Yariv, Bell Telephone Laboratories, Murray Hill, New Jersey, U.S.A. (*189*)

A. Zusman, Department of Physics, The Hebrew University of Jerusalem, Israel (*44*)

G. M. Zverev, Institute of Nuclear Physics, Moscow State University, Moscow, U.S.S.R. (*13*)

PREFACE

This volume contains a collection of papers of the First International Conference on Paramagnetic Resonance held at the Hebrew University of Jerusalem, Israel on July 16–20, 1962. The conference was sponsored by the Hebrew University of Jerusalem, Israel, the International Union of Pure and Applied Physics, and the Israel Academy of Sciences and Humanities.

This conference summarized the advances which have taken place during the last 16 years since the discovery of electron spin resonance by Zavoisky. It also indicated the areas of major interests in this particular field. The topics in this conference were restricted essentially to solids. The major sections of these papers dealt with the electron spin resonance in the iron group and the rare earth groups, the theory related to these spectra, the effects of electric fields, pressure and temperature on these spectra. It discussed the advances in our knowledge of the relaxation phenomena which seem to be now reasonably well understood. Review papers on electron spin resonance in semi-conductors and in biological materials summarizes the results of the last few years in this field. Finally, there were a few selected papers on spin resonance of F centers, organic materials and in glasses.

About 180 scientists from 16 countries participated in this conference. The organizing committee wishes to express its gratitude to all the institutions which have generously assisted in making this conference possible. In addition to the three sponsoring bodies, valuable assistance has been extended by the Charles F. Kettering Foundation, the Office of Naval Research and the Israel National Council for Research and Development. We are also indebted to the National Science Foundation, the Royal Society and other national organizations for the travel support given to many of the scientists.

It is a pleasure to acknowledge the efforts of the Local Arrangements Committee, the Department of Physics of the Hebrew University, and in particular of Mrs. H. Lehrer in planning and running a smoothly conducted conference and in providing an interesting series of social events.

W. Low

Jerusalem, December, 1962

בע״ה׳ עיה״ק׳ ירושלים׳ תשכ״ג

VOLUME I — CONTENTS

PART III: THEORY RELATED TO ESR

VOLUME II — CONTENTS

PART IV: PARAMAGNETIC RELAXATION, LINE WIDTH AND EXCHANGE PHENOMENA

C. EXCHANGE PHENOMENA

PART V: EFFECTS OF ELECTRIC FIELD, EXTERNAL PRESSURE ON ESR SPECTRA AND EXPERIMENTAL TECHNIQUES

A. Effects of Electric Field and External Pressure on ESR

PART VII: ESR OF BIOLOGICAL MATERIALS, ORGANIC CRYST ALS
AND GLASSES

PART I

ESR SPECTRA OF IRON GROUP ELEMENTS

A.

Paramagnetic Resonance of Transition Metal Ions in Rutile (TiO_2)

H. J. GERRITSEN
*Chalmers University of Technology, Gothenburg, Sweden**

ABSTRACT
A review and discussion of paramagnetic resonance on eighteen different ions in TiO_2 will be given, with emphasis on charge, lattice site and crystal field considerations.

Introduction

Rutile (TiO_2) is a crystal with tetragonal symmetry. Thick crystals are slightly yellow due to the fundamental absorption of the crystal which sets in at about 4300 Å [1]. There are two lattice sites at which the Ti^{4+} ions are located. These sites are identical except for a 90° rotation around the tetragonal axis (see Figure 1a). The local surroundings of this site has cubic symmetry with a rather small orthorhombic distortion. The lines

Part of rutile lattice showing the two substitutional Ti^{4+} positions.

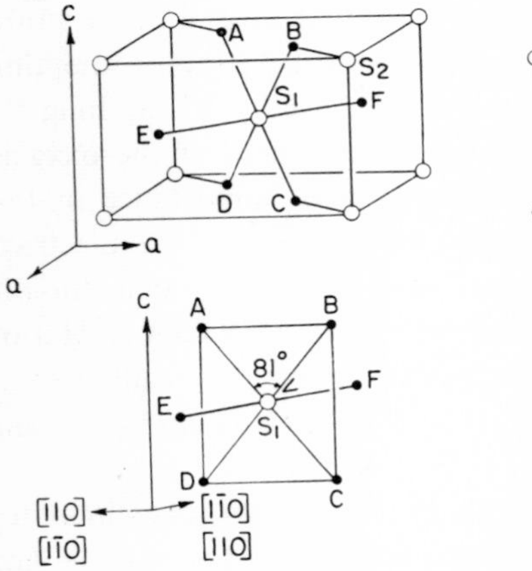

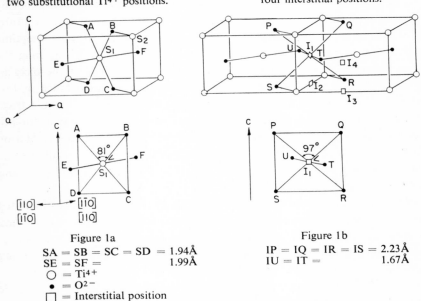

Figure 1a

$SA = SB = SC = SD = 1.94Å$
$SE = SF = 1.99Å$

Part of rutile lattice showing the four interstitial positions.

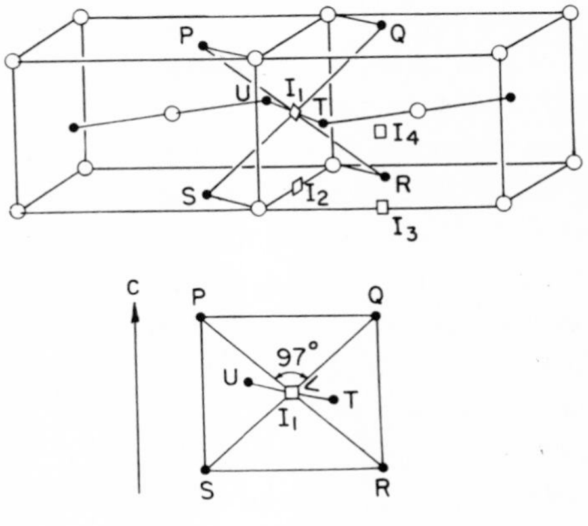

Figure 1b

$IP = IQ = IR = IS = 2.23Å$
$IU = IT = 1.67Å$

○ = Ti^{4+}
● = O^{2-}
□ = Interstitial position

Substitutional and interstitial lattice positions in TiO_2

* Present address: RCA Laboratories, Princeton, N. J.

connecting the Ti^{4+} with its neighboring O^{2-} ions are the magnetic symmetry axes. They are: $[1\bar{1}0]$, $[110]$ and $[001]$. Many di-, tri- and tetravalent ions have been observed to occupy this substitutional site. In no cases was there found a charge compensating missing O^{2-} near such ions and, the oxygen vacancy, necessary when the charge of the doping ion is less than four seems to be distributed almost statistically in the lattice. Some work is in progress on a Cr^{3+} ion with probably an oxygen vacancy nearby, but this spectrum is much weaker than that of the undisturbed Cr^{3+}. The second location where doping ions can fit is sketched in Figure 1b. It is an interstitial position and there are four such equivalent sites, obtainable by rotations of $\pm 12.5°$ and $90° \pm 12.5°$ around the c axis counting the $[110]$ direction as $0°$. The only ions known so far to occupy this site are Ti^{3+}, Ni^{3+} and Ni^{2+}.

Optical work is rather disappointing in rutile since all ions broaden and shift the fundamental absorption from the uv into the visible and in particular Cr^{3+}, Ti^{3+} and V^{4+} do so in very low (0.05%) concentration, giving rise to completely black crystals. Several other ions show this effect to a much lesser degree and it is fairly weak for Cu^{2+} in which Al Starr and the author at Chalmers Institute, Gothenburg, have measured the absorption bands due to transitions from $d\gamma$ to the three $d\varepsilon$ levels.

Since O^{2-} has no nuclear moment, the charge transfer to the neighboring negative ions as was observed by Tinkham in ZnF_2, also a rutile structure, in which case the paramagnetic electron spends only 60% of the time near the paramagnetic ion could not be studied directly. If anything the large dielectric constant of rutile and the closer approach of the oxygens would probably increase the charge transfer. It is of importance in this respect to mention the work of Dr. E. Yamaka (in progress) at the Electrical Communication Laboratory, Tokyo, Japan who has observed a complicated super hyperfine structure on Ti^{3+} and V^{4+} in TiO_2 in high resolution EPR work, which he ascribes to the effect of the electron spending some time near the nuclear moments of Ti^{47} ($I = 5/2$; 7.8% abundance) and Ti^{49} ($I = 7/2$; 5.5% abundance).

To a large extent the work done on rutile in recent years was stimulated by its excellent performance as a maser. After chromium doped rutile had pushed the frequencies available for maser amplification by a factor of two over ruby [2], the study of iron in rutile [3] led to masers operating at a signal frequency of 72 kmc [4]. The high dielectric constant of rutile—around 200 at microwave frequencies [5]—made novel structures possible [6]. From the laser application point of view it seems doubtful whether TiO_2 is a useful crystal, in view of the fact that—as mentioned—most ions make the crystal rather absorptive in the visible region due to a smoothing out of the band gap absorption. No systematic study of this interesting phenomenon has to my knowledge been undertaken.

Iron group ions

For reference Table I is included containing all the information available up till December 1962 on different ions in rutile.

α is the angle which one of the magnetic axes in the plane $\perp$ to the c axis makes with the [110] direction. In view of the 90° symmetry in this plane, the two complexes in the Ti^{4+} site could be distinguished by labelling them: $\alpha_I = 0$; $\alpha_{II} = 90°$, where α then would specifically stand for the angle between say the magnetic x axis of complex I resp. II and the [110] direction. This will not be done and, keeping this symmetry in mind, the substitutional (Ti^{4+}) site referred to by $\alpha = 0$. The interstitial position would in the undistorted lattice give rise to four complexes with $\alpha_I = +12.5°$, $\alpha_{II} = -12.5°$, $\alpha_{III} = (90° + 12.5°)$ and $\alpha_{IV} = (90° - 12.5°)$. They will be presented in the table under $\alpha = 12.5°$. The ions will now be discussed individually.

$3d^1$, Ti^{3+} and V^{4+}

Ti^{3+} was the first ion in rutile known to be in the interstitial (though somewhat distorted from $\alpha = 12.5°$) position [7] in reduced rutile. Though this is the usual spectrum to be observed, we have seen in one crystal of rutile simultaneously with the interstitial spectrum, a spectrum of comparable strength representing substitutional Ti^{3+}. In addition both spectra show a complicated hyperfine structure and more study is needed to understand this problem. The Ti^{3+} ion makes the rutile quite conducting and thus lossy for microwaves and as a consequence no studies of spin lattice relaxation at elevated temperatures have been made.

V^{4+} occupies the substitutional site [8]. At 77°K the spin lattice relaxation starts to visibly broaden the paramagnetic resonance lines. Since an excited level of the orbital triplet state is nearby, the dependence could either be represented by an energy difference of 490 cm^{-1} between ground state and excited state, if a Finn-Orbach-Wolf type mechanism [9] is assumed or a T^{-7} law if Raman processes would cause this broadening. The data [11] do not permit a choice between the two possibilities.

In contrast to Ti^{3+}, V^{4+} does not make the crystal conductive to any appreciable extent at room temperature.

$3d^3$, Cr^{3+} and Mn^{4+}

Cr^{3+} has been studied quite extensively [10]. It shows a fairly isotropic g-value and hyperfine splitting constants—as is usual and to be expected

TABLE I

Tetragonal axis	Ion	Conf.	T (°K)	S_{eff}	g_c	g_{110}	$g_{1\bar{1}0}$	α	D_z (cm^{-1})	E_z (cm^{-1})	Δ_0 (kMc)	A_c	A_{110}	$A_{1\bar{1}0}$	P	P'	Ref.
													×10^{-4} cm^{-1}				
c	Ti^{3+}	$3d^1$	4.2°	1/2	1.940	1.972	1.975	20°									[7]
c	Ti^{3+}	$3d^1$	4.2°	1/2	1.953	1.975	1.978	0									[11]
$1\bar{1}0$	V^{4+}	$3d^1$	4.2–77°	1/2	1.913	1.915	1.956	0				43	31	142			[8]
$1\bar{1}0$	Cr^{3+}	$3d^3$	4.2–350°	3/2	1.97	1.97	1.97	0	−0.68	−0.14	43.3	isotropic: 16.7 (for Cr^{53})					[10]
–	Cr^{3+}	$3d^3$		3/2		?		0?	eight sites ?		36.5						[11]
c	Mn^{4+}	$3d3$	4.2–300°	3/2	1.99	1.99	1.99	0	0.40	0.13	27.8	isotropic: 72					[12]
$1\bar{1}0$	Mn^{3+}	$3d4$	4.2–77°	2	2.0	2.0	2.0	0	0.33	0.15	3,20	78	78	51			[11]
$1\bar{1}0$	Fe^{3+}	$3d5$	4.2–300°	5/2	2.00	2.00	2.00	0	0.68	0.07	43.3,81.3						[3]
$1\bar{1}0$	Ni^{3+}	$3d7$	4.2–300°	1/2	2.085	2.084	2.254	9.1°									[15]
$1\bar{1}0$	Ni^{3+}	$3d7$	4.2–200°	1/2	2.237	2.272	2.050	0°									[15]
$1\bar{1}0$	Co^{2+}	$3d7$	4.2°	3/2($\frac{1}{2}$)	3.75	5.88	2.19	0°				26	150	(−)40			[13]
$1\bar{1}0$	Ni^{2+}	$3d8$	4.2–77°	1	2.1	2.1	2.2	5.4°	−8.3	0.14	8.2, 250						[15]
$1\bar{1}0$	Cu^{2+}	$3d9$	4.2–77°	1/2	2.093	2.106	2.344	0°				(−)28 (−)19	(−)88 (+)11	(−)1			[15;11]
c?	Nb^{4+}	$4d1$	4.2–25°	1/2	1.948	1.973	1.981	0°				2.1	1.75	8.04			[7;11]
$1\bar{1}0$?	Mo^{5+}	$4d1$	4.2–77°	1/2	1.788	1.812	1.912	0				30.5	24.7	65.8			[22]
c	Ta^{4+}	$5d1$	4.2–10°	1/2	1.945	1.979	1.979	?				2.7	<2.5	<2.5			[7]
$1\bar{1}0$	Ce^{3+}	$4f1$	4.2°	1/2	3.866	4.394	2.069	0°									[7]
c	Er^{3+}	$4f11$	4.2°K	1/2	15.1	<0.1	<0.1	0?							495		[11]

for this ion. The paramagnetic resonance widens slightly at higher temperature but is still quite sharp up to 350°K.

A weak spectrum (about 5% of the main spectrum in crystals containing about 0.1% Cr) is observed probably due to Cr^{3+} with an oxygen vacancy or an O^- ion nearby. The zero field splitting of this center is 36.5 kmc as compared to 43.3 kmc for the ordinary spectrum. There are at least 4 sites, probably 8, and it seems rather unlikely from the data available at present that it represents Cr^{3+} in the interstitial position [11].

Mn^{4+} has a ground state quite similar to Cr^{3+} [12]. The g-values are closer to 2.00 than for Cr^{3+}, as is to be expected since the increased charge tends to pull the ligands closer around the paramagnetic ion, resulting in an increased electrical field and a g-value closer to two. The splittings in the ground quadruplet is 2/3 of that observed for Cr^{3+} again pointing to an increase in the electrical field. The spectrum has the symmetry of the substitutional site, just as Cr^{3+}. The hfs is isotropic and the resonances observable at 300°K. Below 77°K a second spectrum occurs to be discussed below.

$3d^4$, Mn^{+3}

At and below 77°K a second Mn spectrum appears [11]. It is very anisotropic and could at 8 kmc and 35 kmc be described by a g-value $g_y \approx g_x \lesssim 0.2$ and $g_z = 8.0$. The center occupies the substitutional position. There seem to be two explanations for this peculiar ion: 1) It is Mn^{4+} with $3d^5$. In that case it could be spin quenched, in which case it seems unlikely to obtain such a large orbital contribution to lead to $g_{||} = 8.0$. It could also be like Fe^{3+} but with zero field splittings outside our range. The spectrum would then be comparable to Fe^{3+} in haemoglobin and the g-values could be accounted for. However, no resonance at 77°K was detected due to any other doublet and it is hard to believe that the zero field splitting should be so large as to leave the higher doublets empty at 77°K. I am thus inclined to believe at present that we might have: 2) Mn^{3+}, with $S_{eff} = 2$ or 1 (depending on whether it is not or is partially spin quenched) and that the line we have observed so far originates from a state with a zero field splitting equal or less than 2 kmc. More work is in progress in cooperation with Ed Sabisky (RCA Laboratories)*.

Note added in proof: Very recent work both at RCA Labs and Chalmers University has verified the second assumption. The preliminary figures are: Mn^{3+} with $S = 2$ and $g = 1.97$ (± 0.04) $|E| = 0.15$ cm^{-1} (± 0.03); $|D| = 0.33$ cm^{-1} (± 0.03) in line with the values for Cr^{2+}, also $3d^4$ (K. Ono, S. Koide, H. Sekiyama and H. Abe. *Phys. Rev.* **96**, 38 (1954).

---

* Prof. W. Low mentioned to the author that he has also observed this spectrum and believes it to be Mn^{3+}.

$$3d^5$$

Fe^{3+} has this configuration. The ion is substitutional [3] and has all the values normal for Fe^{3+} in crystals. It is observable at 350°K and below and apparently not spin quenched, since $S_{eff} = 5/2$.

$3d^7$, Co^{2+} and Ni^{3+}

Co^{2+} occupies the substitutional site [13]. The very anisotropic g-values and hyperfine splittings are in good agreement with the other Co^{2+} salts in particular with Co^{2+} in ZnF_2 (a crystal which has the rutile structure) [14]. There is no doubt that the electronic configuration represents the non spin quenched state $\varepsilon^5\gamma^2$. There is a very large effect of charge transfer [13] which is also observed in Cu^{2+} (see below).

Ni^{3+} is a peculiar ion [15]. In fact two spectra were observed, both representing spin quenched Ni^{3+}, corresponding to $\varepsilon^6\gamma^1$ and $S_{eff} = 1/2$. The presence of spin quenched Ni^{3+} was also observed at about the same time in nickel doped Al_2O_3 [16] and is an illustration of the fact that increase of charge on the paramagnetic ion ($Co^{2+} \rightarrow Ni^{3+}$) can increase the crystal electric field enough to go from a non spin quenched ground state ($\varepsilon^5\gamma^2$) to a spin quenched one ($\varepsilon^6\gamma^1$). The Ni^{3+} ion should be quite susceptible to Jahn Teller effects, since it contains a single electron in an orbital doublet state.

The normally observed Ni^{3+} spectrum (observed at 300°K and below) occupies the interstitial position, The spectrum is shown in Figure 2 together with the Ni^{3+} in the substitutional site (so-called "light generated" nickel) in the plane $\perp c$ axis and serves as an illustration of the typical behavior of interstitial versus substitutional spectra.

The g-values of the interstitial nickel, $g_\perp = 2.08$ and $g_\parallel = 2.25$ are of importance here. These g-values are comparable to those observed for usual Cu^{2+} salts in tetragonal surroundings [17]. It turns out that in the case of copper in crystals the Jahn Teller effect tends to distort an octahedral surroundings in all cases known in such a fashion that along one direction two of the six ions are pushed out, this axis is called the z axis, and the other four ions in, resulting in a tetrahedral field which has as the highest orbital level a wavefunction $(x^2 - y^2)$. This level has in Cu^{2+} one electron in it, and the g-values of this level are $g_\perp = 2(1 - (\lambda/\Delta))$; $g_\parallel = 2(1 - (4\lambda/\Delta))$ [18].

The other doublet level with wavefunction $(2z^2 - x^2 - y^2)$ is lower in energy since it has a large electron density along the z axis, where the ligands are pushed out and has in the case of Cu^{2+} two electrons in it.

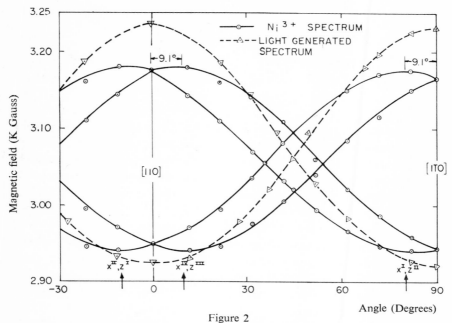

Figure 2

Narrow line spectra of nickel doped rutile in (001) plane at 77°K and 9242 MC.

One calculates for it: $g_\perp = 2(1 - (3\lambda/\Delta))$ and $g_\parallel = 2$. In case of Cu^{2+} in crystals λ is about -700 cm^{-1}.

In the case of Ni^{3+} the situation is the following. The substitutional site has one direction ($\perp$ to the rectangle) along which the two oxygens are further away from the paramagnetic ion than the four oxygens in the plane. For the interstitial site just the opposite holds; the two oxygen ions are now quite close to the center as compared with the four in the plane (see Figure 1). It is therefore to be expected that Cu^{2+} would prefer the substitutional site since it moves the single electron in the $(x^2 - y^2)$ wavefunction which agrees with the Jahn Teller tendency of the Cu^{2+} ion observed in surroundings with six water dipoles. If Ni^{3+} would like to place its unpaired electron in a $(x^2 - y^2)$ wavefunction, it has to go in a surrounding where two oxygens are quite close by that is in an interstitial site. There the energy for the $(x^2 - y^2)$ wavefunction is probably quite low. This loose argument may make the observed tendency of Ni^{3+} preferring the interstitial site somewhat plausible. In any case once it occupies this site, one expects g-values: $g_\perp = 2(1-(\lambda/\Delta))$, $g_\parallel = 2(1-(4\lambda/\Delta))$ in rough agreement with the values observed: $g_\perp = 2.08$, $g_\parallel = 2.25$. Good agreement can be obtained by introducing second order terms in the expressions for g.

Ni^{3+} in the substitutional site can be created by illumination of the crystal. In contrast with the interstitial Ni^{2+}, whose resonances are sharp up to 300°K, the substitutional Ni^{3+} shows resonances that widen appreciably above about 200°K. The mechanism of the illumination effect is not known. This ion should have its unpaired electron in a $(2z^2 - x^2 - y^2)$ wavefunction with $g_\perp = 2(1 - (3\lambda/\Delta^*))$ and $g_\parallel = 2$ for the terms of first order in g. Observed is $g_\perp = 2.25$ and $g_\parallel = 2.05$ in good agreement.

Optical work would be quite difficult on these ions for two reasons namely because of the presence of about five times as much Ni^{2+} (which could possibly be eliminated to some extent by heating under very high O_2 pressure near 600°C) and by the strong lattice absorption in the violet, where some of the interesting absorptions would be located.

$3d^8$, Ni^{2+}

The majority of the nickel in ordinary treated TiO_2 is in this valence state. It has $S_{eff} = 1$ as is expected and in the one crystal studied at 77°K and below rather broad lines (150 mc). This is in contrast with all the ions which have an S_{eff} of a multiple of 1/2. In those cases the line width at very large dilution became 5 mc. The large zero field splitting of 250 kmc may make Ni^{2+} useful for sub mm wave amplifiers. The reason why Ni^{2+} occupies an interstitial site rather than a substitutional one is not clear. The $(2z^2 - x^2 - y^2)$ function must certainly have quite a high energy, otherwise Cu^{2+} would also go interstitially. It could perhaps be traced back to the growing process where Ni may initially go in as Ni^{3+} and later on reduced to Ni^{2+} under the reducing conditions in the flame.

$3d^9$, Cu^{2+}

This ion occupies the substitutional position for reasons discussed above. Analysis of the hyperfine splitting in the EPR data [15; 11] indicate an amount of configurational interaction appreciably larger than is observed in other, hydrated, copper salts.

A similar large charge transfer was observed in Co^{2+} in TiO_2 [13]. It appears that $\lambda = -700$ cm^{-1} is still a good value for Cu^{2+} in TiO_2 and optical absorptions near 13000 cm^{-1} indicate a value of about 13000 cm^{-1} for the splitting between doublet and triplet. Though optical absorption of Cu^{2+} surrounded by six O^{2-} have not been reported previously, this value is in good agreement with measurements on hydrated salts containing Cu^{2+} and the fact that for other ions in which both H_2O and O^{2-} surroundings were studied, the splittings were about equal. More work on the optical spectrum is in progress.

$4d^1$, Nb^{4+} and $5d^1$, Ta^{4+}

These spectra were first investigated by P. Chester [7]. The g-values are quite close to those of interstitial Ti^{3+}, and very different from V^{4+} (both $3d^1$). The hf-splitting is quite anisotropic. Since the g-values are so close to those of interstitial Ti^{3+}, we decided to try to determine the lattice site for Nb^{4+}. Since the g (110)-values are not so different it is necessary to work at high frequency. The hyperfine structure and appearance of many "forbidden" transitions close to the axes complicate the experiment, but we are almost certain that Nb^{4+} occupies the substitutional site and not the interstitial one [11]. This is surprising to us, since one would expect in that case a resemblance to V^{4+}, with which it has site and charge in common. If, however, the Ti^{3+} center of substitutional character and g-values similar to those of the interstitial site would be more firmly established, the situation would become more acceptable. The reason as to why Ti^{3+} prefers the interstitial site is not clear but the mechanism of the reduction process should elucidate this point. In connection with the chemical equilibria in the crystal it is interesting to note that TiO_2 seems to have a great tolerance as to valence state of the impurity ion. Mn goes in as Mn^{4+} and Mn^{3+} and Ni as Ni^{2+} and Ni^{3+} both.

Finally I want to make a remark about the peculiar fact that the limiting line width (line width at infinite dilution) in so many Kramers doublet type ions was about 5 mc as compared to 60 mc for ruby [19]. This could be explained by assuming that the limiting line width is partly due to imperfections but to a large part also to nuclear spins. There should be more contact with far away nuclei than is usually assumed, if this explanation is true, since the dipole effect would give far too small a contribution. In ruby one has 100% nuclear spin on the Al nuclei and in TiO_2 only 13% of Ti with nuclear spins. The fairly large amount of charge transfer mentioned, E. Yamaka's results on super hfs and several experiments of effects of Al nuclei in ruby [20; 21] point in this direction.

We performed an experiment on TiO_2 free from isotopes with nuclear spins [11]. Unfortunately the starting powder of the tiny crystal, grown for us by Dr. D. Beals from National Lead Corp., contained some impurity which prevented growth of a good single crystal. The iron lines observed appeared in the average narrower than in ordinary rutile. A more decisive study is desirable.

The author is indebted to several persons of RCA Labs for stimulating discussions and cooperation in particular to H. R. Lewis who participated in much of the earlier work, and kindly lend me the TiO_2 : Cu for optical work, E. S. Sabisky for his stimulating and continued cooperation in many of the investigations, D. S. McClure (now at Chicago University) and Sol Harrison for discussions and M. E. Heller for his excellent technical assistance. Also discussions and correspondence with H. G. Andresen (U.S. Signal Corps), P. F. Chester (now at Central Electricity Res. Labs, Leatherhead, Surrey, England), H. P. R. Frederikse (National Bureau of Standards, Washington D.C.), S. Geschwind (Bell Telephone Labs, Murray Hill), N. V. Karlov (Lebedev Institute, Moscow) and Dr. E. Yamaka (Electr. Commun. Lab., Tokyo) are gratefully acknowledged. In the initial stages of selecting crystals of possible interest for maser and EPR studies thanks are due to K. A. Müller (now at Battelle Memorial Institute, Geneva, Switzerland) for informing me on the low loss for microwaves and good mechanical properties of single crystal rutile.

REFERENCES

[1]   F. A. GRANT, Rev. Mod. Physics 31, 646 (1959); D. C. CRONEMEYER, Phys. Rev. 87, 876 (1952).

[2]   H. J. GERRITSEN AND H. R. LEWIS, Quantum Electronics, Columbia Press, 1960, p. 385.

[3]   D. L. CARTER AND A. OKAYA, Phys. Rev. 118, 1485 (1960).

[4]   S. FONER, L. R. MOMO, J. B. THAXTER, G. S. HELLER AND R. M. WHITE, Quantum Electronics, Columbia Univ. Press, 1961, p. 553.

[5]   E. S. SABISKY AND H. J. GERRITSEN, Journ. Appl. Phys. 33, 1450 (1962).

[6]   H. J. GERRITSEN, Journ. Appl. Opt. 1, 37 (1962).

[7]   P. F. CHESTER, Journ. Appl. Phys. 32, 866 (1961).

[8]   H. J. GERRITSEN AND H. R. LEWIS, Phys. Rev. 119, 1010 (1960); G. M. ZVEREV AND A. M. PROKHOROV, JETP 39, 222 (1960).

[9]   C. B. P. FINN, R. ORBACH AND W. P. WOLF, 7th International Conf. on Low Temp. Physics, page 43, University of Toronto Press, Toronto, 1960.

[10]   H. J. GERRITSEN, S. E. HARRISON, H. R. LEWIS AND J. P. WITTKE, Phys. Rev. Letters 2, 153 (1959); I. SIERRO, K. A. MÜLLER AND R. LACROIX, Arch. Sci. (Geneva) 12, 122 (1959).

[11]   H. J. GERRITSEN AND E. S. SABISKY, unpublished data.

[12]   H. G. ANDRESEN, Phys. Rev. 120, 1606 (1960).

[13]   E. YAMAKA AND R. G. BARNES, Phys. Rev. 125, 1568 (1962).

[14]   M. TINKHAM, Proc. Royal Soc. (London) A236, 549 (1956).

[15]   H. J. GERRITSEN AND E. S. SABISKY, Phys. Rev. 125, 1853 (1962).

[16]   S. GESCHWIND AND J. P. REMEIKA, Intern. Conf. of Chem. and Phys. of Ionic Solids 1961. To be published in J.A.P.

[17]   K. D. BOWERS AND J. OWEN, Rep. of Progr. in Phys. 18, 304 (1955).

[18]   M. H. L. PRYCE, Suppl. Vol. 6, Nuovo Cimento 817 (1957). Note: Pryce's notation is different from the more usual one, which is followed in this article. Pryce labels the energy levels such as would hold for a single hole.

[19]   T. MAIMAN, Quantum Electronics, Columbia Press, 1960, p. 324; A. A. MANENKOV AND A. M. PROKHOROV, JETP, (Engl. transl.) 11, 527 (1960).

[20]   J. A. COWEN, W. R. SCHAFER AND R. D. SPENCE, Phys. Rev. Letters 3, 13 (1959).

[21]   J. LAMBE, N. LAWRENCE, E. C. MACIRVINE AND R. W. TERHUNE, Phys. Rev. 122, 1161 (1961).

[22]   R. TACKYI, Phys. Rev. 128, 151 (1962).

Electron Spin Resonance of Rutile with Cobalt

G. M. ZVEREV AND A. M. PROKHOROV

Institute of Nuclear Physics, Moscow State University

ABSTRACT

Some paramagnetic ions, included as impurities in rutile (TiO_2) have been studied extensively. The electron spin resonance (ESR) of Cr^{3+}, Fe^{3+}, V^{4+} in this crystal was investigated recently. In this paper the discussion will be confined to the experimental results for rutile with cobalt.

I. ESR spectrum for cobalt

An ESR spectrum in a rutile monocrystal with a small admixture (0.05%) of cobalt has been detected at a temperature of 4.2°K. The spectrum consists of two distinct groups of lines. Each group consists of eight well resolved hyperfine structure components due to Co^{59} nuclear spin $I = 7/2$. These groups arise from two magnetically inequivalent systems of cobalt ions, replacing the titanium in the rutile crystal lattice. In rutile there are two types of Ti^{4+} ions with a different displacement of the neighboring ions. One type can be obtained from the other one by rotation about the tetragonal axis (*C*-axis) at the angle 90°.

It follows from the crystallographic and ESR data that the local crystal field at the site of the paramagnetic ion possesses rhombic symmetry. For the external magnetic field **H** directed along the *C*-axis, the spectrum shows one group of eight hyperfine structure lines, attributed to both inequivalent systems simultaneously. For the case $\mathbf{H} \perp C$, two sets of lines are observed and the spectra have the same form after the crystal has been rotated through 90° about the *C*-axis.

The positions of the absorption lines can be described by the spin-Hamiltonian of the form

$$\hat{\mathcal{H}} = g_x \beta H_x \hat{S}'_x + g_y \beta H_y \hat{S}'_y + g_z \beta H_z \hat{S}'_z +$$
$$+ A_x \hat{I}_x \hat{S}'_x + A_y \hat{I}_y \hat{S}'_y + A_z \hat{I}_z \hat{S}'_z \ , \tag{1}$$

with effective electron spin $S = 1/2$ and nuclear spin $I = 7/2$. The spin-Hamiltonian (1) describes the energy level spacings for two magnetically inequivalent systems only when the x,y,z-axes coincide with the (110), (001), $1\bar{1}0$) directions for the first system, and with the ($1\bar{1}0$), (001), ($\bar{1}\bar{1}0$) direc-

13

tions for the second one. The tetragonal axis of the crystal coincides with the y-axis.

The spin-Hamiltonian constants were calculated from the absorption line positions at the frequency of 9400 Mc/sec and at a temperature of 4.2°K. The desirable crystal orientations were achieved by rotating the crystal about two mutually perpendicular axes.

The obtained values of constants are presented in the Table*. The ESR

$g_x = 2.090 \pm 0.001$	$A_x = (3.91 \pm 0.04) \cdot 10^{-3} \text{cm}^{-1}$
$g_y = 3.725 \pm 0.002$	$A_y = (2.50 \pm 0.03) \cdot 10^{-3} \text{cm}^{-1}$
$g_z = 5.860 \pm 0.001$	$A_z = (14.28 \pm 0.06) \cdot 10^{-3} \text{cm}^{-1}$

*   The constants for Co^{2+} in TiO_2 were published recently [5] and the results coincide closely with those presented here.

spectrum shows that cobalt replaces titanium in rutile as divalent Co^{2+} ions. In addition to these strong lines several weak lines characteristic of cobalt hyperfine structure were obtained at 4.2°K. The latter lines were not investigated in detail but presumably they may be interpreted as due to Co^{2+} ions displacing near crystal imperfections. The imperfections could stem from the fact that Ti^{4+} ions are replaced by divalent Co^{2+} ions.

II. Spin-lattice relaxation. Line widths

Spin-lattice relaxation time τ_1 for Co^{2+} in rutile in the temperature range 4.2–11°K at the frequency 9400 Mc/sec was measured by the pulse saturation method. To obtain the intermediate temperature points, a cavity with heater was used. The measurements were made with the magnetic field **H** parallel to the x-axis where the absorption line intensities achieve their maximum values. At temperatures 16–23°K τ_1 was calculated from the resonance line broadening. For temperatures below 16°K the line width is independent of temperature and $\Delta H_0 \cong 5$ G for **H** $\parallel x$. The line width ΔH_0 may result from the dipole–dipole interaction between paramagnetic ions. The lines have a Lorentzian shape and this means that the broadening is homogeneous. At temperatures above 16°K the lines broaden, and the relaxation time was calculated supposing that the overall width ΔH is

$$\Delta H = \Delta H_0 + \Delta H_{s-1} \tag{2}$$

where ΔH_{s-1} is due to spin-lattice interaction.

Temperature dependence of $\tau_1(T)$ is shown in Figure 1. At temperatures 7–23°K (the linear part of the curve) τ_1 may be given by the expression

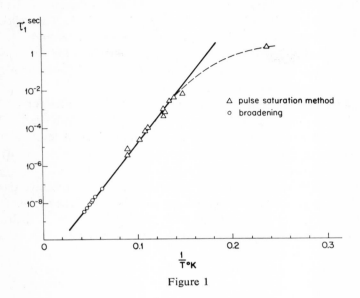

Figure 1

$$\tau_1 = 5.9 \cdot 10^{-12} \exp{(\delta/kT)} \text{ sec,} \tag{3}$$

where $\delta = (102 \pm 5)$ cm^{-1}.

At a temperature below 7°K temperature dependence gradually transforms to the low $\tau_1 \sim 1/T$.

III.   Discussion

The exponential variation $\tau_1(T)$ for Co^{2+} ions has been observed earlier in corundum [1]. That dependence occurred when relaxation processes ran through the upper level [2; 3; 4]. The quantity δ which we determined from the temperature behavior of τ_1 represents the splitting of the first excited Kramers doublet above the ground state. Its value can be compared with that calculated from the experimental data for g-factors. The calculation can be carried out using the theory developed by Abragam and Pryce for Co^{2+} ions in crystalline fields possessing cubic symmetry with small tetragonal or trigonal distortion. The rutile crystal field near the cobalt ion has rhombic symmetry. But for the evaluation of the splitting it can be considered roughly as tetragonal. With this assumption we get $\delta = 150$ cm^{-1} for the splitting value.

The factor $5.9 \cdot 10^{-12}$ sec in (3) represents the lifetime of the excited state due to a relaxation process to the ground state. This yields a level width of ~ 1.8 cm^{-1}.

The direct relaxation processes between two levels of the ground Kramers doublet are important only at temperatures below 7°K. The relaxation probability for this process is proportional to the temperature.

It is to be noted that the lifetime of the excited states for Co^{2+} ions in corundum were found to be $1.6 \cdot 10^{-11}$ and $1 \cdot 10^{-12}$ sec [1] and these values are very close to those obtained for rutile.

The splitting between the ground state and excited states for Co^{2+} in TiO_2 fall in the submillimeter range (~ 0.1 mm). It seems to be very difficult to accumulate a considerable number of ions in the excited levels of Co^{2+} in order to have maser action, since its lifetime is too short and cannot be increased by decreasing the temperature.

Therefore we have, that for the case described above, the investigation of ESR lines gives information on spacing and lifetime of the excited states.

The authors would like to thank R. P. Bushook and A. S. Bebchook for preparing the samples and N. G. Petelina for assistance with measurements.

REFERENCES

[1]   G. M. ZVEREV AND N. G. PETELINA, *JETP* **42**, 1186 (1962).
[2]   C. B. P. FINN, R. ORBACH AND W. P. WOLF, *Proc. Phys. Soc.* **77**, 261 (1961).
[3]   A. A. MANENKOV AND A. M. PROKHOROV, *Solid State Physics* **4**, 388 (1962).
[4]   A. A. MANENKOV AND A. M. PROKHOROV, *JETP* **42**, 1371 (1962).
[5]   E. YAMAKA AND R. G. BARNES, *Phys. Rev.* **125**, 1568 (1962)

Paramagnetic Resonance and Optical Absorption of Transition Element Ions in SrTiO$_3$ and LaAlO$_3$

K. A. Müller

Battelle Memorial Institute, Geneva

ABSTRACT

The paramagnetic resonance and optical absorption work, on SrTiO$_3$ doped with chromium, manganese and cobalt as well as the PMR data on LaAlO$_3$ containing Gd^{3+} and Pr^{3+} are reviewed.

The resonance data of the stable $3d^3$ Cr^{3+} and Mn^{4+} ions in SrTiO$_3$ are compared with the ones found in other oxide crystals. One sees that with increasing covalent character, i.e. by going from Cr^{3+} to Mn^{4+} the g-value and hyperfine constant become more independent of the particular oxide crystal in which the ion is incorporated. This proves to be true as well for the optical absorption transitions which have also been obtained for Cr^{3+} and Mn^{4+} in TiO$_2$. The correlation of the PMR and optical data is briefly discussed in the light of the present theoretical knowledge.

For Mn^{4+} the line width becomes broader and orientation dependent compared to that of Cr^{3+} and is ascribed to the difference between the atomic radii of the Mn^{4+} and the Ti^{4+} it replaces in the lattice. The splitting of the PMR lines of Cr^{3+} in SrTiO$_3$ due to the tetragonal domains below the phase transition is discussed.

It is pointed out that by observing the forbidden $\Delta(M + m) = 0$ transitions of an ion having a nuclear spin $I \geqq 1/2$ in a pure cubic field one is able to verify analytically the electronic spin S even for a powdered sample, as in second order a constant term proportional to $S(S + 1)$ appears in the formula for the resonance magnetic fields.

From paramagnetic resonance and optical absorption data on cobalt doped SrTiO$_3$ as well as susceptibility measurements on cobalt doped LaAlO$_3$, it is concluded that the cobalt usually enters the lattice substitutionally at a Ti^{4+} or Al^{3+} site in the diamagnetic Co^{3+} $d\varepsilon^6$ state.

Deductions drawn from early resonance and roentgenographic data obtained on (Gd — La)AlO$_3$ ceramics prove to be correct in the light of recent resonance data of others with single crystals. These are: a) There is no phase transition between 300°K and 4.2°K. b) The main splitting of the $^6S_{7/2}$ state is due to the trigonal field. c) It is approximately proportional to $\Delta\beta$ where $\Delta\beta = 90° - \beta$, β being the rhombic angle of the perovskite unit cell compressed along the cube diagonal. $\Delta\beta$ increases on cooling. The small cubic field splitting parameter b_4^0 found in Gd^{3+}: SrTiO$_3$ is in good agreement with the present knowledge on the dielectric properties of the perovskite structure.

The paramagnetic resonance of Pr^{3+} in LaAlO$_3$ at 4.2°K has been analyzed giving $g_{\parallel} = 2.67 \pm 0.02$, $g_{\perp} = 0$, $A = 0.119 \pm 0.03$ cm^{-1}, i.e. $(A/g_{\parallel}) = 954 \pm 13$ gauss or 10% lower than found in the ethyl sulfate and double nitrate salts. This is ascribed to the higher A_2^0 coefficient in the electrical crystalline field of the trigonal LaAlO$_3$.

I. Introduction

Among the oxide crystals having the ABO$_3$ perovskite structure [1; 2] several show exceptional properties. The best known is the *ferroelectric*

BaTiO$_3$ [3] but there is an appreciable number of others which exhibit this property [4]. SrTiO$_3$ is remarkable because of its *paraelectric* behavior [5; 6]. The mixed crystals of LaMnO$_3$–SrMnO$_3$ and others are *ferromagnetic* [7], while LaMnO$_3$ itself is *antiferromagnetic* [8]. The mixed crystals mentioned above [7] are *semiconductors* [9] as well as other mixed crystals like SrTiO$_3$–CeTiO$_3$ [10] which also have interesting thermo-electric properties. Further, those diamagnetic crystals having this structure and showing no phase transition as LaAlO$_3$ [12] are suitableas host lattices for *Masers* as has been recently proposed [11]. In fact in the ABO$_3$ structure the B ion is surrounded octahedrally by 6 oxygen atoms. Between the oxygen octahedra are situated the larger A ions which have 12 nearest oxygen neighbors (see Figure 1). Were the ions hard spheres

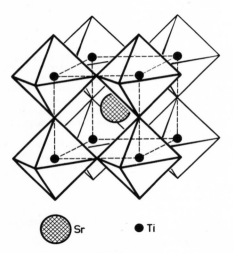

○ Sr   ● Ti

Figure 1

The perovskite structure of SrTiO$_3$. The oxygen atoms are at the corners of the octahedra and are omitted for better clarity.

they would have, when touching, radii such that the distances $\overline{AO}$ and $\overline{BO}$ between the lattice positions A–O and B–O are given by $\overline{AO} = \sqrt{2}\,\overline{BO}$. In reality the tolerance factor introduced by Goldschmidt $t = \overline{AO}\sqrt{2}\,\overline{BO}$ can vary between $t = 0.77$ to 0.92. With the known radius for oxygen of 1.32Å [13] it follows that ion A has approximately the same radius as the oxygens and twice that of ion B. Therefore most of the transition metal ions can be substituted in these structures at the B sites and others like Pb^{4+}, Sn^{4+} etc. and practically all rare earth ions can enter these lattices at the A sites as well as many others like Ba^{++}, Sr^{++} [2].

The paramagnetic resonance of transition and rare earth ions incorporated into the diamagnetic crystals of ABO_3 perovskite structure offers the possibility of getting a better understanding of the various phenomena mentioned above:

a) for electric properties these are the internal electric field gradients, their symmetry, the occurrence and kind of phase transitions, the presence and orientation of domains [14; 15; 16].

b) for the magnetic properties in conjunction with optical absorption data EPR can yield information on the magnitude of the covalent bonding of the diluted paramagnetic ion e.g. $SrTiO_3$: Mn^{4+} [17].

Further by doping a diamagnetic crystal with about 1 % of a paramagnetic ion, lines due to exchange coupled pairs will appear [19; 20]. In the perovskite structure, only exchange via oxygen atoms is possible and there can be no direct M–M interaction between the paramagnetic ions M, as in MgO [19]. From such experiments the exchange energy M–O–M might be obtained.

Apart from these possibilities which regard the bulk properties of the various crystals, there is interest in comparing the EPR and optical data found for the ions incorporated in this structure with those in other oxide crystals having octahedral coordination and fitting the data with the existing theories. Here $SrTiO_3$ seems to be of special interest since, above its phase transition at 110°K [14; 21], i.e., at room temperature, it is at the moment the only oxide crystal apart from MgO, CaO and isomorphs for which all of its ions see a cubic point symmetry. Further, below 110°K where the structure becomes tetragonal, the axial field at a B-site remains small compared to that in the cubic one [14] and it can therefore be treated by perturbation methods in contrast to the case of $BaTiO_3$ [16]. One disadvantage is that $SrTiO_3$ has a smaller optical band gap of only 3.2 eV compared to MgO and therefore higher lying levels are not observable. Nevertheless by comparing the EPR and optical absorption data of MgO and $SrTiO_3$ doped with the same metal atoms useful information can be obtained.

In this paper we intend to review briefly the paramagnetic resonance and optical absorption work done so far in Switzerland with doped diamagnetic $SrTiO_3$ and $LaAlO_3$ with the exception of Fe^{3+} in $SrTiO_3$. The latter work has been already described in detail in an earlier paper [14] and some new aspects of this work, such as the sign of the stark splitting constant a, its variation with temperature and the shift of the lines due to covalent binding (Koster + Statz term) [23] will be submitted elsewhere [24]. Also they may be mentioned in part at the conference. We would like to add that

LaAlO$_3$ shows a slight and increasing deformation to trigonal symmetry from 300°K down to 4.2°K [12] but has the advantage of a higher band gap [11].

II. Cr^{3+} and Mn^{4+} in SrTiO$_3$

1. *Paramagnetic resonance of Cr^{3+}*

SrTiO$_3$ doped with 0.005% Cr$_2$O$_3$ shows at 300°K, where it has a cubic structure, an intense isotropic line with $g = 1.9780 \pm 0.0007$ due to the even isotopes of Cr^{3+} $((3d^3)S = 3/2)$ and the 4 resolved hyperfine structure lines for the 9.5% abundant Cr^{53} $(I = 3/2)$ isotope yielding a hyperfine interaction constant of $(16.2 \pm 0.3) \times 10^{-4}$ cm^{-1} [15]*. The isotropy and the narrowness of the lines, only 1.9 gauss, proves that the environment is cubic to a high degree. This can be anticipated as the ionic radius of Cr^{3+} is 0.64 Å, i.e. practically the same as that of the Ti^{4+} ion it replaces [13]. In contrast to this we will see in paragraph 3 that the width of the resonance of the isoelectronic Mn^{4+} $(3d^3)$ is larger in agreement with the smaller ionic radius of the fourvalent manganese [17].

The hyperfine coupling constant A is slightly higher but falls within that found for MgO, i.e. $(16.0 \pm 0.3) \times 10^{-4}$ cm^{-1} [25]. It is slightly smaller than those found for Cr^{3+} substituted on to octahedral oxygen lattice sites in Al$_2$O$_3$ and rutile (TiO$_2$) (see Table I). This might be taken as an indication that the covalent binding is slightly higher in the cubic oxide crystals of MgO and SrTiO$_3$ compared to the ones having axial symmetry. The reduction of the hyperfine constant in the presence of covalent binding has first been discussed for the case of Mn^{2+} $(3d^5)$ in various crystals [26]. Table I includes the hyperfine interaction constants and the g-values of a typical ionic crystal as KAl(SeO$_4$)$_2$ · 12D$_2$O as well as those of a covalent crystal K$_3$[Co(CN)$_6$] for comparison with the present results. One sees from Table I that with the exception of Al$_2$O$_3$ the g-values increase with decreasing hyperfine interaction constant, i.e. increasing amount of covalent character of the host crystal.

The g-value in SrTiO$_3$ is slightly smaller than that in MgO. The g-values of Cr^{3+} incorporated in other oxide crystals have been determined with less precision due to the large fields, having axial or lower symmetry, which are present, for all of these crystals. These include Y$_2$O$_3$ [32], YGa- and YAl-garnet [33; 34], and Beryl [35], for which values of $g_\parallel$ and $g_\perp$ of 1.97 to 1.98 (with an accuracy of 0.01) were found. It seems therefore that the g-value is to a certain extent determined by the binding of the Cr^{3+} to the

---

* We think that the values of g and A given here are more precise than those reported earlier.

surrounding oxygens. However, we shall leave this point here and take it up again in §5 of this section where we shall discuss it together with the optical absorption data including those of the isoelectronic Mn^{4+}.

At the temperature of liquid nitrogen one observes the main line and the 4 hyperfine lines of the Cr^{53} isotope if the external magnetic field H is

TABLE I

Substance	g-value	A in $10^{-4}cm^{-1}$	Reference
$KAl(SeO_4)_2 \cdot 12\,D_2O$	1.976 $\pm$ 0.002	18.5 $\pm$ 1.0	[27]
TiO_2	1.97 $\pm$ 0.01	17.0 $\pm$ 0.5	[28]
	1.98 $\pm$ 0.01		
Al_2O_3	1.9894 $\pm$ 0.0006	17.0 $\pm$ 0.5	[29]
	1.9867 $\pm$ 0.0006		
$SrTiO_3$	1.9780 $\pm$ 0.0007	16.2 $\pm$ 0.3	This paper
MgO	1.9797 $\pm$ 0.0006	16.0 $\pm$ 0.3	[25; 30]
$K_3[Co(CN)_6]$	1.992 $\pm$ 0.002	14.7 $\pm$ 1.0	[31]

directed parallel to a [111] direction (see Figure 2). But if H is parallel to a [100] direction the main line splits into 5 equidistant lines. This is in agreement with the evidence that $SrTiO_3$ is composed of tetragonal domains below the phase change [14]. For H parallel to a [100] direction one obtains 3 fine structure lines with a separation of $2D$ from those domains parallel to H while the domains perpendicular to H, i.e. parallel to [010] and [001], also yield 3 fine structure lines but with a separation D. The central lines of the two triplets coincide giving 5 lines separated by D (Hamiltonian $\mathcal{H} = gSH + D[S_z^2 - (1/3)S(S+1)]$), the central line being the most intense. We find $|D| = (4.0 \pm 0.3) \times 10^{-4}cm^{-1}$ $T \sim 80°K$. For H parallel to [111] no fine structure is predicted with the above Hamiltonian as $D(3\cos\theta^2 - 1)$ vanishes, θ being the angle between the external magnetic field and the axis of a tetragonal domain.

Due to the splitting of the main line the inner two of the four hyperfine lines of Cr^{3+}, which also split, are not observable. Further, there appear at this temperature two anisotropic lines labelled x and y of unknown origin which are not observed at room temperature. The line y for $H_{\parallel}$ [100] is slightly superimposed on the hyperfine line at the outer right. In Figure 1 one also sees the $\pm 1/2$ line of the Fe^{3+} impurity present whose position depends in second order on the angle between H and the crystal axes [14].

2. *Optical absorption of Cr^{3+} in $SrTiO_3$ and TiO_2*

The optical spectrum of a polished plate of $SrTiO_3 : Cr^{3+}$ was scanned on a Beckman DK spectrophotometer from 2000 mμ to 350 mμ, the latter

K. A. MÜLLER

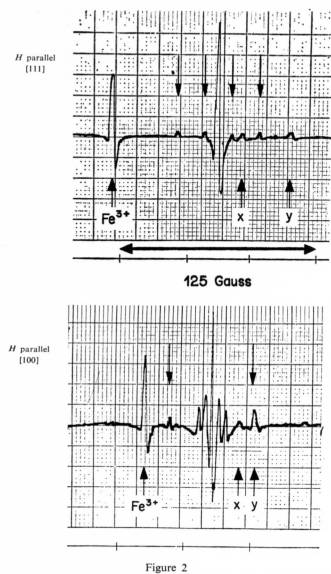

H parallel [111]

125 Gauss

H parallel [100]

Figure 2

Electron paramagnetic resonance spectrum of Cr^{3+} in $SrTiO_3$ at liquid air temperature for $H_\parallel$ [111] and $H_\parallel$ [100]. The $\pm 1/2$ line of the impurity present Fe^{3+} is also seen.

figure being slightly above the band gap of $SrTiO_3$. The Cr^{3+} doped sample was placed in the test beam of the spectrophotometer and a pure $SrTiO_3$ crystal was placed in the reference beam allowing partial compensation of the changing reflectivity due to the dependence (on the wavelength) of the refractive index of $SrTiO_3$. Records were taken at 300°K, 77°K, and approximately 30°K. No absorption was found in the infrared as expected from Cr^{3+}. In the visible region, a peak was observed at 517 mμ. In addition, a shoulder near the absorption edge indicating a second absorption at about 375 mμ was seen. Both lines narrowed slightly on cooling and Figure 3 shows a record taken at $\sim$30°K. Using the known [36] energy

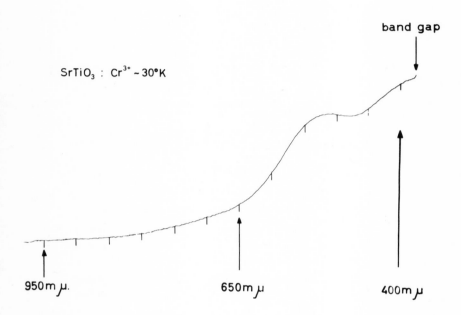

Figure 3
Optical absorption spectrum of Cr^{3+} in $SrTiO_3$ at about 30°K.

level scheme of Cr^{3+} $(d\varepsilon)^3$ in a cubic octahedral field, one easily identifies the first line as due to the allowed transition from the $^4\Gamma_2$ ground state to the $^4\Gamma_5$ excited state and the second as the transition from the $^4\Gamma_2$ to the $^4\Gamma_4$ excited state. For comparison in Figure 4 the absorption at $\sim$30°K of TiO_2 doped with 0.002% Cr_2O_3 is shown. No pure TiO_2 was placed in the reference beam. It is apparent that the absorptions definitely occur at longer wavelength in rutile, i.e. at 570 mμ and at about 410 mμ. In Table II the absorptions are also given for ruby [36] and MgO as observed by Low [37] and interpreted by McClure [36].

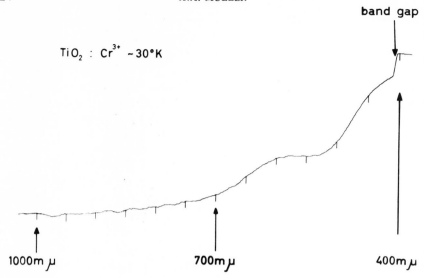

Figure 4
Optical absorption spectrum of Cr^{3+} in TiO_2 (rutile) at about 30°K.

TABLE II

Spectrum of Cr^{3+} in 4 oxide crystals

Oxide crystal	$^4\Gamma_2 \to {}^4\Gamma_5$ (cm^{-1})	$^4\Gamma_2 \to {}^4\Gamma_4$ (cm^{-1})
MgO	16,200	22,700
TiO_2	17,500	~24,400
Al_2O_3 (ruby)	18,150	25,730
$SrTiO_3$	19,300	~27,000

Knowing that the $^4\Gamma_2$ level lies at $-12\ Dq$, the $^4\Gamma_5$ level at $-2\ Dq$, and the $^4\Gamma_4$ for a pure ionic environment [57] at

$$\frac{6\ Dq\ +\ E(P)}{2}\ -\ \left[\left(\frac{E(P)-6\ Dq}{2}\right)^2 + (4\ Dq)^2\right]^{1/2},$$

we obtain values of 1930 cm^{-1} and 1750 cm^{-1} for the apparent Dq of $SrTiO_3$ and TiO_2 respectively and values of about 12,400 cm^{-1} and 11,600 cm^{-1} for the energy of the $E(P)$ level. These latter values are somewhat high compared to the ones found for Al_2O_3 [37b]. In view of the uncertainty found for the $^4\Gamma_2 \to {}^4\Gamma_4$ transitions and of the fact that the binding is not purely ionic and can shift the levels to a certain extent [38] not too much importance should be attached to these last two values. (The absorption to the next higher level is impossible to observe due to the band edge in $SrTiO_3$ but this transition is now being studied in $LaAlO_3 : Cr^{3+}$.) The higher Dq values found in Al_2O_3 as compared to those in MgO have been ascribed [36; 39] to a compression of the Cr^{3+} ion, in the Al_2O_3 lattice whereas in MgO, Cr^{3+} has a radius which is too small as compared to Mg^{2+}. The radius for Cr^{3+} is practically the same as that of Ti^{4+}, i.e. the Cr^{3+} can fit into this lattice well, thus the Dq parameter should lie between those of Al_2O_3 and MgO, assuming a similar amount of covalency. This is found to be true for TiO_2. The value for $SrTiO_3$ lies higher than that in TiO_2. The amount of covalency will probably be similar to that in TiO_2. Also, in $SrTiO_3$, the Cr^{3+} is incorporated between the nearest neighbor oxygen atoms whose mean separation is much the same as that in TiO_2. Now if an ionic model is considered, the crystal field gradient is by no means determined only by the immediate neighbors, but is rather a slowly converging function of the more distant neighbors. Calculations show that one has to consider up to 2000 neighbors [40]. It seems therefore that the higher Dq parameter in $SrTiO_3$ is due to the more distant ions which have positions different from those in TiO_2.

3. *Paramagnetic resonance of Mn^{4+} in $SrTiO_3$*

The PMR spectrum found in $SrTiO_3$ doped with MnO_2 shows six main hyperfine line groups with $g = 1.994 \pm 0.001$ and $A = 69.4 \pm 1.0 \times 10^{-4}$ cm^{-1}, $S = 3/2$.

The spectrum was assigned to Mn^{4+} ($I = 5/2$), $3d^3 = (d\varepsilon^3)(d\gamma^0)$ ion at a Ti^{4+} position [17]. The reasons for doing this was the low g-value and hyperfine splitting constant A, its detectability at room temperature and the known ionic radius of Mn^{4+}.

To remove all remaining doubts*, this assignment was verified analytically shortly afterwards. The line positions of the also observed forbidden $\Delta(M + m) = 0$ lines [41] were compared with those of the main lines. These weak lines occur for the $M = \pm 1/2$ transition about midway between the strong allowed ones. As this method of determining the total spin of an ion having a nuclear spin $I \geqq 1/2$ is applicable for ions seeing

---

* These were caused by the fact that no red fluorescence was observed as expected from the well known R lines [36] (the fluorescence has also not been observed for Cr^{3+}: $SrTiO_3$).

a cubic field even when only the pure magnetic $\pm 1/2$ transitions in a powder are observed [42], we will describe it in some detail.

Let us assume an isotropic Hamiltonian of the form

$$\mathscr{H} = g\beta \mathbf{H}S + ASI - g_N\beta_N\mathbf{H}I \qquad (1)$$

where the symbols have their usual meaning, i.e. g and g_N, S and I being the electronic and nuclear g factors and spins, respectively, A their hyperfine coupling constant, β and β_N the Bohr and proton magneton and $\mathscr{H}$ the external magnetic field. For a radio frequency field perpendicular to $\mathscr{H}$ the allowed $M = \pm 1$, $m = 0$ magnetic resonance levels $H_{M,m}^{M+1,\,m}$ are given to second order by the well known formula of Bleaney [43]

$$H_{M,m}^{M+1,m} = H_0 - A'm - \frac{A'^2}{2H_0}\left\{ I(I+1) - m^2 + m(2M+1) \right\} \qquad (2)$$

M being the electronic and m the nuclear quantum numbers, $H_0 = h\nu/g\beta$ is the resonance field in absence of hyperfine interaction and $A' = A/g\beta$ the hyperfine splitting constant in gauss.

Now for a high frequency field parallel to the constant field H, forbidden lines $M \leftrightarrow M+1$, $m \leftrightarrow m-1$ are induced [44]. The relative intensity $J_{M,m}^{M+1,\,m-1}$ of these to the allowed ones with intensity $J_{M,m}^{M+1,m}$ is

$$J_{M,m}^{M+1,m-1}\Big/ J_{M,m}^{M+1,m} = (I+m)(I-m+1)\left(\frac{A'}{H_0}\right)^2 \qquad (3)$$

and m runs from I to $-I+1$.

The resonance magnetic fields $H_{M,m}^{M+1,m-1}$ of the forbidden lines computed to second order are:

$$H_{M,m}^{M+1,m-1} = H_0 - A'm + A'(M+1) - \frac{A'^2}{2H_0}\left\{ I(I+1) + S(S+1) \right.$$

$$\left. - M^2 - m^2 + 4Mm - 3M + 3m - 2 \right\} - \frac{g_N\beta_N}{g\beta}H_0 \qquad (4)$$

M runs as for formula (2) from $S-1$ to $-S$ but m from I to $-I+1$ and not to $-I$.

From Eq. (4) one sees that the electronic quantum number has already entered in first order and that in contrast to the formula of Bleaney a constant summand $S(S+1)$ appears in second order. The observation of the forbidden transitions allows one therefore to determine S even if only the $M = \pm 1/2$ lines are observed. For this case (4) reduces to

$$H_{-1/2,m}^{+1/2,m-1} = H_0 - A'm + \frac{A'}{2} - \frac{A'^2}{2H_0}\left\{ I(I+1) + S(S+1) - m^2 \right.$$
$$\left. + m - 3/4 \right\} - \frac{g_N \beta_N}{g\beta} H_0 \qquad (5)$$

i.e. the lines are located approximately midway between the allowed ones. Figure 5 shows a record taken at 80°K in the [111] direction. The positions of the forbidden lines calculated with Eq. (4) and using $S = 3/2$ are indicated at the bottom and fit with those observed within the experimental accuracy of 1 gauss in contrast to the ones obtained taking $S = 5/2$ which yielded an average misfit of 4 gauss per line. The relative amplitudes among the forbidden lines are in agreement with formula (2), which gives a ratio of 5: 8: 9: 8: 5. Also, the relative intensities of the most intense forbidden line to the allowed ones agrees with $9(A'/H_0)^2 = 4.2 \times 10^{-3}$ (for $\lambda = 3.2$ cm wavelength). In Figure 5 the other forbidden lines due to the $M = \pm 3/2$

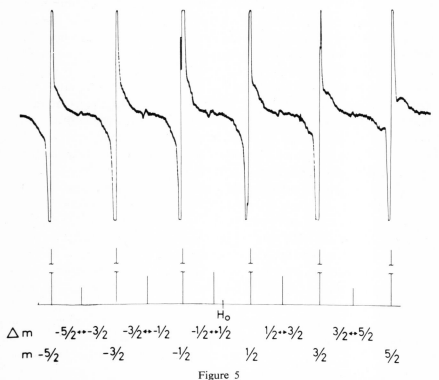

Figure 5
PMR spectrum of Mn^{4+} in $SrTiO_3$ for $H_{\parallel}$ to a [111]-direction at liquid air temperature and 3.2 cm wavelength. The theoretical lines of the $\Delta m = 0$ and $\Delta(M + m) = 0$ transitions have been calculated for the case $M = -1/2 \leftrightarrow +1/2$ with $|A| = 75$ gauss and $g = 1.994$.

$\leftrightarrow \pm 1/2$ lines, some of which should lie to first order $A'/2$ above or below the highest and lowest of the strong lines, were not seen. This is due to a certain extent to the lower intensity of the $m = \pm 3/2 \leftrightarrow \pm 1/2$ lines but to a greater extent to their larger line width even for the [111] direction. We shall therefore discuss the line widths next.

The question of the origin of the line width in oxide crystals has found considerable interest recently and it was shown that for Gd^{3+} in ThO_2 [45] and Ni^{++} in α-Al_2O_3 [46], their mosaic structure essentially determines the anisotropic broadening. Other origins have been discussed for the Fe^+, Ni^{++}, Cu^{++} and Ni^+ ions in MgO [47]. They are: a) the Jahn-Teller effect for Cu^{++} which can be excluded for our case of a $3d^3$ ion having a singlet ground state and   b) for Fe^+ and Ni^{++} small distortions in the cubic crystalline lattice (such as dislocations) giving rise to fields of tetragonal or even rhombic symmetry. In this study the difficulty of explaining the occurrence of distortions close to the [100] directions in cubic crystals was mentioned. We think that the difference of ionic radius of the paramagnetic ion and the substituted ion in the host crystal is also important. We have already mentioned in paragraph 2 that, if one substitutes Cr^{3+} for Ti^{4+} which has practically the same radius, an isotropic line of 1.9 gauss is observed in spite of the missing electronic charge. On the other hand, Ti^{4+} has a radius of 0.64 Å [13] which is 0.10Å larger than that of the Mn^{4+} [13]. Therefore the Mn does not lie exactly in the center of the octahedron or the octahedron is distorted. Due to the symmetry properties of the $SrTiO_3$ crystal lattice, distortions will first be caused along the [100], [010] and [001] directions. Thus the Mn^{4+} will see an additional field of at least tetragonal symmetry. A characteristic line broadening or splitting for $H_{\parallel}$ [100] was found but not if the external magnetic field is directed parallel to the [111] direction (see Figure 6). In the earlier paper this splitting was explained by discrete axial fields along the [100], [010] and [001] directions with terms DS_z^2 in the Hamiltonian and with $D = -1.4$ gauss. We think now that it is probably more realistic to imagine a certain variation of these axial fields D with, in addition, a distribution of weaker fields of rhombic symmetry being present. In Figure 5 otherwise the shoulders at the main transitions as well as the absence of the $\pm 3/2 \leftrightarrow \pm 1/2$ forbidden transitions in the [111] direction would be difficult to explain.

Upon cooling below the phase transition, additional splitting due to the tetragonal domains is observed as reported earlier [17]. However, we will not discuss this further here but rather will compare the g-value and the splitting constant A with the more recent work on this ion incorporated into other oxide crystals.

H ‖ [111]

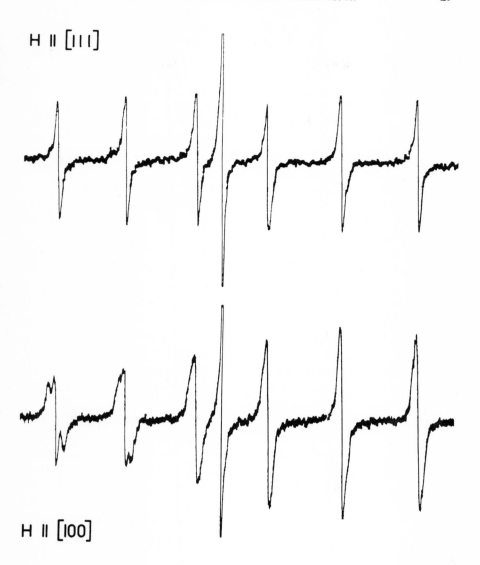

H ‖ [100]

Figure 6
Paramagnetic resonance spectrum of Mn^{4+} in $SrTiO_3$ at 300°K and 3.2 cm wavelength
for H‖ to a [100] and [111] direction.

In TiO_2 doped with MnO_2 the manganese atoms replace the Ti^{4+} atoms
and exist as Mn^{4+} as expected. The spin of $S = 3/2$ could be inferred here
from the angular line dependence as the ion does not see a cubic field [48].

The forbidden $\Delta(M + m) = 1$ transitions were also reported [49]; however, these are due to the fact that the axial DS_z and rhombic $E(S_x^2 - S_y^2)$ terms in the Hamiltonian are comparable to the Zeeman energy $g\beta HS$. This case was first observed and theoretically analyzed for the isotope 53 of Cr^{3+} in TiO_2 [50]. This contrasts with the cubic case that we have just described where the hyperfine interaction ASI alone causes admixtures in the wave functions and the transition probabilities are therefore smaller. The accurate analysis of Mn^{4+} in TiO_2 yielded slightly anisotropic g-values and hyperfine constants [49]. The mean values, which are of interest for comparison, are $g = 1.993$, $A = (71.8 \pm 0.3) \times 10^{-4}$ cm^{-1}, i.e. the g-value is slightly smaller, but not outside of the experimental error, and A is greater than in $SrTiO_3$. Both values therefore indicate that the covalent binding is somewhat smaller in TiO_2 than in $SrTiO_3$ using the empirical facts outlined in paragraph 2 of this section. More recently the PMR spectrum of Mn^{4+} in Al_2O_3 has been [51] reported. Both, g and A were found to be isotropic and within the rather small experimental errors the same as in $SrTiO_3$.

It has been pointed out in paragraph 2 that for the Cr^{3+} incorporated in various oxide crystals, the g-values and the hyperfine constant A do not differ much from one to another. We see now that this tendency is still more marked for the isoelectronic Mn^{4+} where these constants become nearly independent of the host oxide crystal and must therefore be correlated to the nearest neighbor interaction. The g-values are found to be even higher than those of Cr^{3+} in the strongly covalent $K_3[Co(CN)_6]$ complex. From this it was concluded earlier that the covalency of the Mn^{4+} in oxide lattices must be appreciably greater than that of the Cr^{3+} which is in agreement with the notion that the higher ionic charge increases the covalency.

In order to be able to estimate the effect of covalency the higher lying optical levels of the ion have to be known. In the next paragraph we therefore will give some information obtained with optical absorption. We will see that for Mn^{4+} the $^4\Gamma_2 \leftrightarrow {}^4\Gamma_5$ transitions also show a smaller relative variation than those for Cr^{3+} because of their higher Dq parameter.

4. *Optical absorption of Mn^{4+} in $SrTiO_3$ and TiO_2*

$SrTiO_3$ containing Mn^{4+} is yellow indicating that at least the tail of the $^4\Gamma_2 \leftrightarrow {}^4\Gamma_5$ transition lies in the visible. The optical absorption was measured point by point for a doped and an undoped colorless plate at $300°K$, it is shown in Figure 7, together with its difference. There is a shoulder visible, before the absorption rises strongly in the neighborhood of the band edge, which indicates an absorption at about $23,000$ cm^{-1}. We ascribe this shoulder to the $^4\Gamma_2 \leftrightarrow {}^4\Gamma_5$ transition of Mn^{4+}. To verify

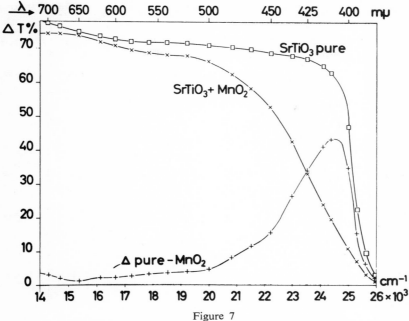

Figure 7
Optical absorption spectrum of Mn^{4+} in $SrTiO_3$ at 300°K.

that this shoulder is not due already to a charge transfer band of Mn^{4+} [39], a crystal of TiO_2 containing Mn^{4+} and yellow-green in color was examined. We have seen in section b) that, for the isoelectronic Cr^{3+}, the $^4\Gamma_2 \leftrightarrow {}^4\Gamma_5$ transition appears 1800 cm^{-1} lower than that in $SrTiO_3$. If our assignment of the shoulder is correct this should also be the case for Mn^{4+} in TiO_2. From Figure 8 we see that this is so. The shape of the tail looks as if at least another unresolved line is present*. This is possibly the higher lying $^4\Gamma_2 \leftrightarrow {}^4\Gamma_4$ transition. It has been shown that the $E(P)$ level is depressed when the apparent Dq parameter increases [37]. We estimate that if the maximum of the absorption occurs at about 360 $m\mu$, i.e. 28,000 cm^{-1}, with $E(P)$ depressed to about 9000 cm^{-1}, it would yield (see equation 1) a Dq of 2150 cm^{-1} i.e., the absorption due to the $^4\Gamma_2 (4F) \rightarrow {}^4\Gamma_5 (4F)$ transition would lie at 21,500 cm^{-1}. Assuming that the one in $SrTiO_3$ lies about 1800 cm^{-1} higher than for TiO_2, we find that the $^4\Gamma_2 \rightarrow {}^4\Gamma_5$ line of Mn^{4+} in $SrTiO_3$ is located at 23,300 cm^{-1}. This is in fair agreement with what we have deduced from Figure 7. In Al_2O_3 Geschwind et al., found this line for Mn^{4+} at 21,300

* *Note added in proof:* Some Mn^{3+} might also be present in the TiO_2 which by comparing to recent results in Al_2O_3 (D.S.McClure, *J. Chem. Phys.* **36**, 2757), should also have its first band in the observed tail.

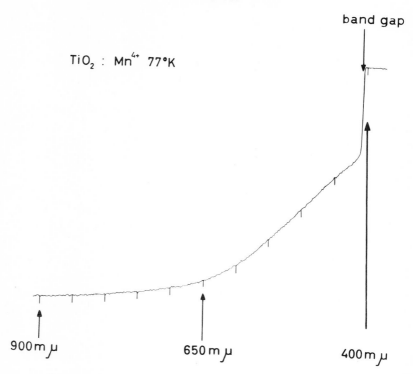

Figure 8
Optical absorption spectrum of Mn⁴⁺ in TiO₂ (rutile) at 77°K.

Figure 8
Optical absorption spectrum of Mn^{4+} in TiO_2 (rutile) at 77°K.

cm^{-1} [51], which further supports our interpretation in view of what has been said in paragraph 2 on the Dq parameters and that the Mn^{4+} with its ionic radius of 0.55 Å fits well into the A position in Al_2O_3.

5. *Discussion*

Having already compared in paragraphs 1 and 3 the g-values of Cr^{3+} and Mn^{4+} with those found in other oxide crystals and similarly having compared in paragraphs 2 and 4 the optical absorption for these two ions, it remains to discuss the correlation of the g-shifts, Δg, with the optical absorption.

From the well known theory of Pryce [52; 53] one obtains for the g-shift $\Delta g = -8\lambda/\Delta$ where λ is the spin orbit coupling constant and Δ is the separation between the $^4\Gamma_2$ and $^4\Gamma_5$ levels. In hydrated salts containing divalent ions it has already been found that with this formula Δg-values were obtained which were too large in comparison to the observed ones.

The discrepancy was found to be enhanced for the threevalent ions. Owen [54] showed that when charge transfer due to the covalent binding to the surrrounding oxygen atoms is present the ratio $8\lambda/\Delta$ is reduced. The reduction factor k is an indication of the amount of the covalency and $k = 1$ in absence of the latter. Such treatment gives in part satisfactory results for the small covalent binding present in the hydrated salts. For Cr^{3+} in $SrTiO_3$ using $\lambda = 91$ cm^{-1} we obtain $k = 0.64$ which is comparable to the values found for Cr^{3+} in other oxide crystals. For Mn^{4+} which has a higher spin orbit coupling constant $\lambda = 133.5$ cm^{-1} we obtained $k = 0.19$. Due to the small change of both Δ and Δg from crystal to crystal (see paragraphs 3 and 4) this value of k is within 10% of that for Mn^{4+} in all oxide crystals so far investigated. As k was found to be smaller than the theory of Owen predicts for complete covalent bonding this showed a serious limitation of that theory.

Another limitation is the discrepancy between the anisotropy of the g-values and the magnitude of the axial term D in the Hamiltonian (when an axial electric field is present) which is related in the theory of Pryce by $g_\parallel - g_\perp = 2D/\lambda$ and is unchanged by the Owen theory [55]. In oxide crystals $g_\parallel - g_\perp$ is often found to be smaller than the value calculated with $2D/\lambda$. For an example see the data on Cr^{3+} and Mn^{4+} in TiO_2 [28; 29]. By taking into account the interaction of the levels in the visible with those lying in the UV region and by including all of the doublets, Sugano and Peter [56] showed for the case of Cr^{3+} in Al_2O_3 that the small anisotropy in the g-values is understandable. However, they introduced the covalency in a way similar to that of Owen who, due to the relatively low value of the isotropic part of Δg, was taken as $k = 0.62$, thus the situation remained unsatisfactory in this respect. An important improvement has since come from the work of Lacroix [57]. He considered the influence of the charge transfer optical $\delta^5\varepsilon_a^4$, $\gamma_e^3\varepsilon_a^4$ and $\varepsilon_e^5\varepsilon_a^4$ levels on Δg. These levels can be depressed in the presence of covalent binding, as much as 15,000 cm^{-1} for Mn^{4+} where they lie at about 35,000 cm^{-1} [36; 51]. He showed that for the $3d^3$ configuration the action of these levels is such that they shift g to more positive values (it is in principle possible even to obtain a positive g-shift with the $3d^3$ configuration). Lacroix found that the partial covalent character for Mn^{4+} in $SrTiO_3$ is 0.35 for the σ and 0.2 for the π binding. These values will be essentially the same for Mn^{4+} in the other oxide crystals in view of what has been said earlier in this paragraph. From these values one sees that the covalent character is considerably smaller than estimated with the Owen theory. For the four-valent manganese it is therefore not necessary to use the notation Mn^{4+} as was done earlier when we interpreted our data in terms of the older theory but to use the notation Mn^{4+} as we have done in this paper. By doing so one should not forget that the Mn^{4+} has a stronger covalent binding than the Cr^{3+}.

III. Cobalt in SrTiO$_3$

1. *Paramagnetic resonance experiments*

Three samples cut from a well oxydized single crystal of $SrTiO_3$ have been investigated. The crystal was grown by the Verneuil process with addition of 0.02 percent of CoO. The measurements were made at room temperature, liquid air temperature, 4.2°K and 1.7°K. The three crystallites had a volume of about 150 mm³, 15 mm³ and 3 mm³. One of the faces was cut parallel to the (110) plane. By placing the crystallites with their oriented faces parallel at the bottom of the cavity, the external field of the rotatable magnet could be oriented parallel to the [111], [100] and [110] crystal axes. The spectrometer operated at a wavelength of 3.2 cm. It was a magic Tee reflection type but of higher sensitivity as used in previous work [14]. A superheterodyne receiver working at 60 Mc/sec was employed, followed by a lock-in detector operating at the Zeeman modulation frequency of 73 cps.

At all temperatures and orientations of the magnetic field only the spectra of the impurities present, the Fe^{3+} and Cr^{3+} ions, were observed. The concentration of the Fe^{3+} ions was estimated to be 10^{17} per cm³, by comparing their signal amplitudes at 300°K to those of a calibrated sample of ZnS powder containing Mn^{2+} ions with a concentration of 10^{-4}. Because of saturation effects the lowest signal-to-noise ratio for the iron resonance occurred at liquid helium temperature, where it amounted to 30.

The crystal should have contained about 2×10^{18} cobalt ions per cm³ (0.02 weight-percent CoO), i.e. 20 times more Co than Fe^{3+} ions. If cobalt had had a line width similar to that of the $\Delta M = \pm 1$ transitions, $M_s = \pm 3/2 \leftrightarrow \pm 1/2$ of Fe^{3+}, i.e. about 13 gauss, the signal-to-noise ratio of the spin resonance for the strongest $\Delta M = \pm 1$ transition would have been about 80. This value is obtained because cobalt has a nuclear spin of 7/2, which splits each line into eight components, and the intensity of the strongest $\Delta M = \pm 1$ line is nearly independent (to a factor of the order of unity) of the effective spin (see ref. 14, p. 183, Eq. 10). Even with a ten times larger line width, a spectrum should have been observed if cobalt had been paramagnetic. To make sure that this ratio would not be lowered by further splitting of the lines owing to the tetragonal distortion of $SrTiO_3$ at low temperatures [14; 15; 17], the decisive recordings were all taken for the [111] direction. For this direction, in first order the tetragonality should not interfere. To allow an observation, the temperature of observation should have been sufficiently low even for a very strong coupling of the magnetic system to lattice vibrations.

2. *Discussion of the EPR experiments*

Cobalt should be situated on a Ti^{4+} lattice site according to its ionic radius [13] and to the work on mixed crystals of $(La, Sr)CoO_3$ [58]. The g-factor of Co^{2+} in MgO situated at an octahedral lattice position was found to be 4.3 [59] while that of Fe^{2+} is 3.4 [60]. The latter is isoelectronic to Co^{3+} in the paramagnetic configuration $d\varepsilon^4 d\gamma^2$. The resonances of Co^{2+} and Fe^{2+} have been observed at low temperatures. We have seen no resonances between the g-values of 1.8 and 5 either at $4.2°K$ or at $1.7°K$. Therefore we can exclude Co^{2+} and Co^{3+} ($d\varepsilon^4 d\gamma^2$) as possibilities. The Co^{4+} ion isoelectronic to Fe^{3+} would have either an effective spin of 5/2 or 1/2, depending on whether its configuration is $d\varepsilon^3 d\gamma^2$ (medium covalent bonding) or $d\varepsilon^5$ (strong covalent bonding), as in $K_3[Fe(CN)_6]$. In both configurations, the resonance spectrum would be detectable at room temperature [61], but no resonance has been detected in this case either. A cobalt ion located at the site of fourvalent titanium in monovalent $d\varepsilon^6 d\gamma^2$ form should also be easily detectable at room temperature. The only remaining possibility is therefore the Co^{3+} in the diamagnetic $d\varepsilon^6$ state, as in $K_3[Co(CN)_6.]$ All other ions of cobalt with a different valency would be paramagnetic at this lattice site.

Our inerpretation is sustained by recent susceptibility measurements of a $LaAlO_3$ single crystal grown by the Verneuil process where 0.2% CoO had been added to the feed. The susceptibility measurements carried out at $300°K$ and $80°K$ gave values of -1.94×10^{-7} and -1.87×10^{-7} respectively, i.e. a paramagnetic change of only $\Delta\chi = +0.07 \times 10^{-7}$ which would correspond to paramagnetic ions present in a concentration of 0.001% [62]. This is roughly the concentration of the Fe^{3+} and Cr^{3+} ionic impurities present.

3. *Optical absorption*

The crystal was orange in color. The optical spectrum was investigated from $2000 m\mu$ to $350 m\mu$ as described for $Cr^{3+} : SrTiO_3$, with a pure $SrTiO_3$ crystal placed in the reference beam of the Beckman DK Photometer. A very broad line centered at $700 m\mu$ and a line about $60 m\mu$ broad situated

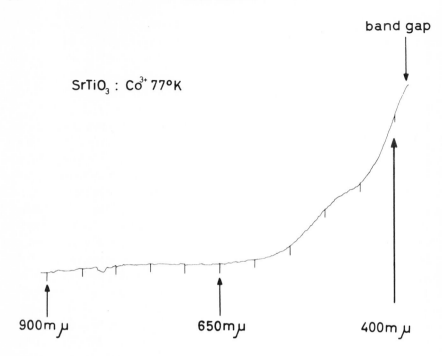

Figure 9
Optical absorption spectrum of Co^{3+} in $SrTiO_3$ at 77°K.

slightly above 500 mμ was observed at 300°K which upon cooling to 90°K did not narrow appreciably and showed no structure. This latter line has been reported earlier by Gandy [63] on Co doped $SrTiO_3$ and could be enhanced by heating it for 3 hours at 1260°C in oxygen. He ascribed this line tentatively to Co^{3+} at a Sr^{2+} site and having one of the six nearest neighbor Sr ions missing, the hole trapped at this vacancy thus giving rise to a color center. In addition to what has already been said in the discussion on the EPR experiments, there are two more reasons to believe that the cobalt is not located at a Sr^{2+} site.

a) The cubic crystalline field at a Sr^{2+} site is so small (see section V) that it would be difficult to find a Co ion in a diamagnetic state as it must be according to the EPR data on $SrTiO_3$ and susceptibility data on $LaAlO_3$.

b) In the same paper Gandy found in Fe doped $SrTiO_3$, which was heated in oxygen around 1200°C, a line which he ascribed to be due to a color center situated near a Fe^{3+} ion at a Sr^{2+} site, whereas it had already been shown earlier by EPR that the Fe^{3+} is situated at a Ti^{4+} position [14].

With a diamagnetic Co^{3+} $(d\varepsilon)^6$ state at a Ti^{4+} octahedral lattice site we can interpret the two lines easily: Sugano and Tanabe [41] found that the $3d^6$ configuration becomes diamagnetic for a crystal field to B-parameter ratio of $Dq/B = 2$ making the $^1\Gamma_1$ level the lowest. The first allowed optical absorption occurs then to the $^1\Gamma_4$ level and the next to the $^1\Gamma_5$ level. According to their graph the absorption is just 12.5% above the critical value at $Dq/B = 2.5$. The values of Dq and B obtained from the graph are: $Dq = 1560$ cm^{-1} and $B = 625$ cm^{-1}. Low investigated the paramagnetic resonance and optical absorption of Co doped MgO. In the visible he found at $300°K$ a main broad optical absorption at 500 mμ which showed structure at $77°K$. He decomposed the spectrum into a background signal plus a broad intense line at 19800 cm^{-1} and 3 less intense and narrower lines. The intense line was ascribed to the allowed $4F \to 4P(\Gamma_4)$ line of Co^{2+} the other in part to spin forbidden ones of the same ion. In the light of the present investigation we think it is possible that in MgO part of the incorporated Co was in the diamagnetic $d\varepsilon^6$ state as well and the $^1\Gamma_1 \to {}^1\Gamma_5$ line contributed to the absorption at 500 mμ. It is not so astonishing that in MgO a fraction of Co may occur in the diamagnetic state. For cubic crystalline fields sufficiently strong, i.e. Dq parameters of $1000 - 2000$ cm^{-1} as found in the oxide octahedral coordination, the ions tend to have a valency such that in the cubic field their ground state is an S state, i.e. in MgO [64]:

$$(d\varepsilon)^3 : V^{2+} \text{ and } Cr^{3+}, \qquad (d\varepsilon)^3, (d\gamma)^2 : Mn^{2+} \text{ and } Fe^{3+},$$
$$(d\varepsilon)^6 : Co^{3+}, \qquad (d\varepsilon^6 d\gamma^2) : Ni^{2+}$$

and in $SrTiO_3$ [14; 15; 17]:

$$(d\varepsilon)^3 : Cr^{3+} \text{ and } Mn^{4+}, \qquad (d\varepsilon)^3 (d\gamma)^2 : Fe^{3+}, (d\varepsilon)^6 : Co^{3+} \quad Ni^{4+}.$$

This is of course only significant for such low dilutions that a) the exchange energy between the paramagnetic ions can be neglected and b) charge compensation can be achieved non locally.

IV.   Gd^{3+} in LaAlO$_3$

More than six years ago a number of rare earth metal aluminates and scandates were prepared and their structure examined by X-rays at $294°K$, $198°K$ and $93°K$ [65]. Most aluminates studied show a deformation to

---

* See the discussion on the paper of H. J. Gerritsen, this issue.

trigonal symmetry as if the elementary cube had been compressed along the cube diagonal (see Figure 1); a measure for this deformation is the value of $\Delta\beta$ which is defined by $\beta = 90° - \Delta\beta$, where β is the rhombohedral angle. For $LaAlO_3$ $\Delta\beta$ decreases almost linearly with temperature with $\Delta\beta \cong + 8.02° - 0.96 \times 10^{-2}T$. A Debeye-Scherrer camera for measurements below 80°K was then not available. In order to obtain information concerning a phase transition possibly to a ferro-or antiferroelectric state which might occur at lower temperatures a spin resonance study on $LaAlO_3$ ceramics containing 10^{-3} and 10^{-4} mole of $GdAlO_3$ was undertaken, as at that time no single crystals were available. Due to the configurational broadening an irregular spectrum was found which had seven main peaks as one might expect for ions with an $S = 7/2$ ground state. The strongest peak was at $g = 1.992 \pm 0.002$ and did not shift with temperature. The spectra recorded at 290°K, 190°K, 85°K and 4.2°K showed that the line on the left and right side of the main line shifted away from the center line as a function of decreasing temperature in roughly linear fashion. Therefore no phase transition occurred above 4.2°K.

The main splitting was interpreted as due to the trigonal field and its increase on cooling to be roughly proportional to $\Delta\beta$. Evidence that this interpretation was correct first came from the work of J. Sierro on Gd^{3+} in $SrTiO_3$ [66]. He found at 300°K (cubic $SrTiO_3$) stark splitting constants of $b_4^0 = 5.4 \times 10^{-4} cm^{-1}$ and $b_6^0 < 10^{-5} cm^{-1}$. These constants were the smallest so far observed. Taking into account that b_4^0 and the crystalline electric field are approximately linear [67], this gives direct evidence that the cubic crystalline field at the A site is small as has often been assumed in theories of ferroelectric behavior in perovskites [68]. Data most recently obtained on single crystals of $LaAlO_3$ containing Gd^{3+} [69] have shown that the coefficient b_2^0 decreases linearly with temperature and also now confirms the linearity between the deviation of the rhombic angle $\Delta\beta$ and the trigonal splitting. From the new data one sees that the coefficient b_4^0 which is the same at 300°K as the one found in $SrTiO_3$ [66] increases on lowering the temperature. This also correlates with the reported X-ray data [65] where a decrease in lattice constant was reported on cooling. The smaller distance to the neighbor ions increases the crystalline electric field gradient the latter being proportional to the cubic splitting coefficient b_4^0 [67].

V. Pr^{3+} in $LaAlO_3$

In $LaAlO_3$ the point symmetry at the position of the La^{3+} ions at room temperature is $C_{3v} - 3m$ or possibly even $D_{3d} - 3m$ [70]. One can therefore assume that the symmetry of the field at 4.2°K is at least $C_{3v} - 3m$. Under the influence of a field of this symmetry the $3H_4$ ground level of a Pr^{3+} ion ($4f^2$) is split into 3 singlets and 3 doublets. Judd [71] showed that the lowest doublet consists of two states each of which can be described as a mixture of only three eigenstates of the total angular momentum operator J_z, where z is the direction of the trigonal axis. These states are given by

$$\phi \pm = a\,|J_z = \pm 4\rangle + b\,|J_z = \pm 1\rangle + c\,|J_z = \pm 2\rangle \qquad a^2 + b^2 + c^2 = 1,$$

where the upper signs belong to one level the lower signs to the other. This doublet is however not a Kramers doublet ($4f^2$) as J_x and J_y are not presenting the wavefunction, thus no resonance absorption can occur. However, a local distortion in the mixed crystal, due to the difference between the ionic radii of the Pr^{3+} and La^{3+} ions, can further split the two levels. In this case there exists a non vanishing transition probability for magnetic fields parallel to the constant magnetic field. The g-factor for the Pr^{3+} ion is

$$g_{\parallel} = \frac{8}{5}\left(4a^2 + b^2 - 2c^2\right), \qquad g_{\perp} = 0$$

Taking into account the coupling of the electron to the nuclear spin of the Pr^{141} nucleus ($I = 5/2$) Bleaney et al. [72] have given the following Hamiltonian:

$$\mathcal{H} = g_{\parallel}\beta H_z S_z + A S_z I_z + \Delta_x S_x + \Delta_y S_y, \quad S = 1/2, \quad I = 5/2 \tag{1}$$

This operator has eigen values:

$$h\nu = [(g_{\parallel}\beta H_z + Am)^2 + \Delta^2]^{1/2}, \text{ where } \Delta^2 = \Delta_x^2 + \Delta_y^2 \tag{2}$$

is a measure of the local distortion of the lattice which may obey a Gaussian distribution.

As only the three constants $g_{\parallel}$, $A_{\parallel}$ and Δ^2 appear in Eq. (2) it is possible to determine them with polycrystalline material. Therefore at the time when only ceramic $LaAlO_3$ was available, Pr^{3+} seemed worth investigating. Samples containing a concentration of 10^{-3} and 3×10^{-3} $PrAlO_3$ were used and their spectra recorded at 4.2°K at 3.2 cm wavelength. They showed six equidistant lines centered at a $g \sim 2.7$. Their separation was found to be $A_{\parallel}/g_{\parallel} = 954 \pm 13$ gauss.

For a single crystal Eq. (1) yields an intensity which increases according to a gaussian curve which because the transition probability is proportional to Δ^2 for $\Delta^2 = 0$ falls to zero. As in our samples all angles, θ, between the crystal axis, z, and the magnetic field, H, are equally probable for $A = 0$ and $\Delta = 0$ with the resonance condition $h\nu = g\beta H_z$ and $g = g_{\parallel}\cos\theta$ one would expect [73] that for the magnetic field $H_0 = h\nu/g_{\parallel}\beta$ the absorption intensity decreases as $1/H^2$. With the Δ term plus the polycrystalline smearing out one is able to account for the observed asymmetry of the lines if one assumes for the gaussian distribution a full width at half intensity of 70 gauss. Figure 10 gives the integrated derivative of the second lowest absorption peak.

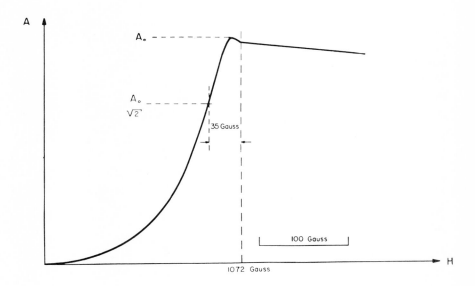

Figure 10
The integrated derivative of the second lowest line of Pr^{3+} in $LaAlO_3$ (ceramic) at 4.2°K and 3.2 cm wavelength.

From this figure it was possible to determine the magnetic field where $\Delta = 0$ and therefore to obtain $g_{\parallel}$ and the hyperfine splitting constant, A:

$$g_{\parallel} = 2.67 \pm 0.02, \qquad A = 0.119 \pm 0.03 \text{ cm}^{-1}.$$

Symmetric to the highest absorption peak two weak satellite lines were observed at a distance of 300 gauss. We can therefore not exclude completely the rather improbable case that these three lines had a different origin. The lowest line would then not have been observed (formula 1 does not give a Breit-Rabi dependence near $H \sim 0$) and both g and A would be larger by a factor of 1.62. The $g_{\parallel}$-factors observed by Bleaney and coworkers [74; 75] on La- and Y-praseodymium methyl sulphate and by Cooke and Duffus [76] on La-praseodymium manganese-double nitrate yield g-factors of 1.69, 1.53 and 1.55 respectively. It appears therefore that in our case the admixture of the state $J_z = 4$ to the lowest doublet is greater than in those salts. From this it was concluded that the crystalline field parameters $A_n^m(r^n)$ in $LaAlO_3$ differs considerably from those in these salts. Comparing the values b_2^0 of 358×10^{-4} cm^{-1} which have been recently found for gadolinium in $LaAlO_3$ [69] and the value $b_2^0 = 191 \times 10^{-4}$ cm^{-1} in the ethyl sulphate it appears that A_2^0 is higher in $LaAlO_3$. One was also led to the conclusion that the crystalline field differs considerably from that in these latter three salts by the following argument: If one assumes that the states, which describe the occupied doublets of the ions, are eigenstates of the total angular momentum operator, it can be shown [77] that the ratios $(A/g)_\parallel$ for the ions are independent of the crystal field. If alternatively for an ion in different crystal structures different ratios $(A/g)_\parallel$ are found, one can no longer assume that the crystal field splitting is small. The first excited state of the Pr^{3+} ion according to Elliott, Judd and Runciman [78] lies 2500 cm^{-1} above the ground level. If the crystal field splitting which is of the order of magnitude of 100 cm^{-1} changes by a factor of two, one expects a change of about 10% in $(A/g)_\parallel$. This is the case in the $LaAlO_3$ for which a value of 914 ± 13 gauss has been observed as compared with the value of 1050 ± 10 gauss for the ethyl sulphates and double nitrate.

VI. Acknowledgments

We would like to thank Professors U. Palma and O. Santangelo for a three weeks stay at the University of Palermo during which time the spectra at low temperature were obtained (with the aid of Mr. P. Chiricó) and using their optical spectograph.

Further we thank Professors R. Lacroix and B. Elschner for discussions, Dr. A. Linz for sending us the Co doped $SrTiO_3$ single crystal, Dr. J. Sierro for orientating and cutting it, Mr. W. Berlinger for assistance in a part of the EPR experiments and Dr. R. Kohin for reading the paper.

REFERENCES

[1] I. NARAY-SZABO, *Müegyetemi Közlemenyek* **1**, (1947).

[2] R. S. ROTH, *J. Res. Nat. Bureau of Standards* **58**, 75 (1957).

[3] B. WUL, *J. Phys. (USSR)* **10**, 95 (1946).

[4] C. KITTEL, *Introduction to Solid State Physics*, J. Wiley & Sons, New York, 1953, p. 115.

[5] J. F. YOUNGBLOOD, *Phys. Rev.* **98**, 1201 (1955).

[6] H. GRAENICHER, *Helv. Phys. Acta* **29**, 210 (1956).

[7] G. H. JONKER AND J. H. VAN SANTEN, *Physica* **16**, 337 (1950).

[8]   E. O. WOLLAN AND W. C. KOEHLER, *Phys. Rev.* **100**, 545 (1955).

[9]   G. H. JONKER, *Physica* **20**, 1118 (1954).

[10]   *Bull. Am. Phys. Soc.* **II,7**, Ba. 8, 174 (1962).

[11]   B. ELSCHNER AND K. A. MÜLLER, Proposal to the US Air Force Committee in Europe.

[12]   H. GRAENICHER AND K. A. MÜLLER, *Nuovo Cimente* **6**, 1916 (1957).

[13]   J. M. GOLDSCHMIDT, *Internat. Tabellen zur Best. von Kristallstrukturen.* Berlin, 1935, Vol. 2.

[14]   K. A. MÜLLER, *Helv. Phys. Acta* **31**, 173 (1958).

[15]   K. A. MÜLLER, *Arch. Sci. (Genève)* **11**, 150 (1958).

[16]   A. W. HORNIG, R. C. REMPEL AND H. E. WEAVER, *J. Phys. Chem. Solids* **10**, 1 (1959).

[17]   K. A. MÜLLER, *Phys. Rev. Letters* **2**, 341 (1959).

[18]   G. H. JONKER, *Physica* **22**, 707 (1956).

[19]   B. A. COLES, J. W. ORTON AND J. OWEN, *Phys. Rev. Letters* **4**, 116 (1960).

[20]   L. RIMAI, H. STATZ, M. J. WEBER AND G. A. DE MARS, *Phys. Rev. Letters* **4**, 125 (1960).

[21]   G. A. DE MARS, L. RIMAI, R. O. BELL AND G. RUPPRECHT, *Bull. Am. Phys. Soc.* **II, 7**, 7 (1962).

[22]   H. L. SUCHAN, A. S. BALCHAN AND H. G. DRICKAMER, *Phys. Chem. Solids* **10**, 343 (1959).

[23]   G. F. KOSTER AND H. STATZ, *Phys. Rev.* **113**, 445 (1959).

[24]   K. A. MÜLLER, to be published.

[25]   W. LOW, *Phys. Rev.* **105**, 801 (1957).

26]   J. S. VAN WIERINGEN, *Disc. Faraday Soc.* **19**, 118 (1955).

[27]   K. D. BOWERS AND J. OWEN, *Rep. Progr. in Phys.* **18**, 304 (1955).

[28]   a) J. SIERRO, K. A. MÜLLER AND R. LACROIX, *Arch. Sci. Genève* **12**, 122 (1959), b) H. J. GERRITSEN *et al.*, *Phys. Rev. Letters* **2**, 153 (1959).

[29]   J. W. ORTON, *Rep. Progr. in Phys.* **22**, 204 (1959).

[30]   J. E. WERTZ AND P. AUZINS, *Phys. Rev.* **106**, 484 (1957).

[31]   J. M. BAKER, B. BLEANEY AND K. D. BOWERS, *Proc. Phys. Soc.* **69**, 1205 (1956).

[32]   J. W. CARSON, D. P. DEVOR AND R. H. HOSKINS, *Phys. Rev.* **122**, 1141 (1961).

[33]   J. W. CARSON AND R. L. WHITE, *J. Appl. Phys.* **32**, 1787 (1961).

[34]   S. GESCHWIND AND J. W. NIELSEN, *Bull. Am. Phys. Soc.* **II,5**, 252 (1960).

[35]   J. E. GEUSIC, M. PETER AND E. O. SCHULZ-DUBOIS, *Bell. Syst. Techn. Journ.* **38**, 291 (1959).

[36]   D. S. MCCLURE, *Solid State Physics* **9**, 399 (1959).

[37]   W. LOW, *Phys. Rev.* **105**, 801 (1957).

[37b] R. STAHL-BRADA AND W. LOW, *Phys. Rev.* **113**, 775 (1959).

[38]   J. OWEN, *Proc. Roy. Soc.* **A227**, 183 (1955).

[39]   L. E. ORGEL, *Nature* **179**, 1348 (1957).

[40]   E. BRUN, S. HAFNER AND F. WALDNER, *Helv. Phys. Acta* **34**, 391 (1961).

[41]   K. A. MÜLLER, Conference on High Frequency Spectroscopy, Leipzig 31.3.–2.4. 1960 Akademie Verlag Berlin 1961, p. 138.

[42]   K. A. MÜLLER, *Helv. Phys. Acta* **33**, 497 (1960).

[43]   B. BLEANEY, *Physica* **17**, 175 (1951).

[44]   W. A. ANDERSON AND L. H. PIETTE, *J. Chem. Phys.* **30**, 591 (1959).

[45]   D. SHALTIEL AND W. LOW, *Phys. Rev.* **124**, 1062 (1961).

[46]   S. A. MARSHALL, T. T. RIKUCHI AND A. R. REINBERG, *Phys. Rev.* **125**, 453 (1962).

[47]   J. W. ORTON, P. AUZINS, J. H. E. GRIFFITHS AND J. E. WERTZ, *Proc. Phys. Soc.* **78**, 554 (1961).

[48] H. G. ANDRESEN, *Phys. Rev.* **120**, 1606 (1960).
[49] H. G. ANDERSEN, *J. Chem. Phys.* **35**, 1090 (1961).
[50] J. SIERRO, R. LACROIX AND K. A. MÜLLER, *Helv. Phys. Acta* **32**, 1287 (1959).
[51] S. GESCHWIND, P. KISLIUK, M. P. KLEIN, J. P. REMEIKA AND D. L. WOOD, to be published in *Phys. Rev.*
[52] M. H. L. PRYCE, *Proc. Phys. Soc.* **A63**, 25 (1950).
[53] A. ABRAGAM AND M. H. L. PRYCE, *Proc. Roy. Soc.* **A205**, 135 (1951).
[54] J. OWEN, *Proc. Roy. Soc.* **A227**, 183 (1955).
[55] G. EMCH AND R. LACROIX, *Arch. Sci., Genève* **13**, 157 (1960).
[56] S. SUGANO AND M. PETER, *Phys. Rev.* **122**, 381 (1961).
[57] R. LACROIX, *Comptes rendus* **252**, 1768 (1961).
[58] G. H. JONKER AND J. H. VAN SANTEN, *Physica* **19**, 120 (1953).
[59] W. LOW, *Phys. Rev.* **109**, 256 (1958).
[60] W. LOW AND M. WEGER *Phys. Rev.* **118**, 1131 (1960).
[61] K. D. BOWERS AND J. OWEN, *Rep. Progr. in Phys.* **18**, 304 (1955).
[62] H. SCHMID, unpublished result.
[63] H. W. GANDY, *Phys. Rev.* **113**, 795 (1959).
[64] W. LOW, *Paramagnetic Resonance in Solids*, Academic Press, N.Y., 1960.
[65] H. GRAENICHER AND K. A. MÜLLER, *Nuovo Cimento* **No. 3**, Suppl. 6, Ser. X, 1216 (1957).
[66] J. SIERRO, *Helv. Phys. Acta* **34**, 404 (1961).
[67] R. LACROIX, *Proc. Phys. Soc. London* **77**, 560 (1961).
[68] H. GRENICHER AND O. JAKITS, *Nuovo Cimento* **11**, No. 3, Suppl. 480 (1954) this issue.
[69] D. KIRO, W. LOW AND A. SUSMAN, Proc. Ist Int. Conf. Paramagnetic Resonance, Academic Press, New York. 1963, p. 44.
[70] S. GELLER AND V. B. BALA, *Acta Cryst.* **9**, 1019 (1956).
[71] B. R. JUDD, *Proc. Roy. Soc.* **A232**, 459 (1955).
[72] B. BLEANEY et al., *Phil. Mag.* **45**, 991 (1954).
[73] R. H. SANDS, *Phys. Rev.* **99**, 1222 (1955).
[74] B. BLEANEY AND H. E. D. SCOVIL, *Phil. Mag.* **43**, 999 (1952).
[75] J. M. BAKER AND B. BLEANEY, *Proc. Roy. Soc. London* **A245**, 156 (1958). *Proc. Phyps. Soc.* **A68**, 936 (1955).
[76] A. H. COOKE AND M. J. DUFFUS, *Proc. Roy. Soc.* **A229**, 407 (1955).
[77] R. J. ELLIOTT AND K. W. H. STEVENS, *Proc. Roy. Soc.* **A218**, 553 (1953).
[78] J. P. ELLIOTT, B. R. JUDD AND W. A. RUNCIMAN, *Proc. Roy. Soc.* **240**, 509 (1957).

ESR Spectra of Cr^{3+} and Gd^{3+} in Lanthanum Aluminate*

D. KIRO, W. LOW AND A. ZUSMAN

Department of Physics, The Hebrew University of Jerusalem, Israel

ABSTRACT

The crystallographic structure of $LaAlO_3$ changes gradually with temperature. At temperatures below $435° \pm 25°C$ the $LaAlO_3$ undergoes a transition from a simple cubic cell to rhombohedral structure. We have measured the spectrum of Gd^{3+} and Cr^{3+} in single crystals of $LaAlO_3$ as a function of temperature in the range of $700°K - 4°K$. The crystal field parameters change gradually and the total splitting decreases by nearly a factor of two in this temperature range.

Introduction

The crystal structure of lanthanum aluminate belongs to the class of cubic perovskite structure ABO_3. Crystals of this structure have exceptional properties. Some show ferroelectric, some paraelectric behavior, some concentrated magnetic crystals are antiferromagnetic, while other mixed crystals are ferromagnetic.

The majority crystals of the perovskite structure show one or more phase transitions at well defined temperatures. The lanthanum aluminates are the exception in that no phase transition has been detected from $700°K$ down to $4°K$. On the other hand, these crystals show a deformation from the ideal perovskite structure which is strongly temperature dependent.

This suggests the possibility of studying the paramagnetic behavior as a function of the temperature over a fairly large range of temperatures. Preliminary work has been reported by Graenicher and Müller [1] who studied the paramagnetic resonance spectrum of a powdered sample of $(Gd-La)AlO_3$. Since they had no single crystals available they were unable to determine the crystal field parameters. However, by measuring the powder spectrum at $290°K$, $190°K$, $85°K$ and $4°K$ they were able to show that there was no phase transition in this temperature range. Assuming that the main splitting is caused by a trigonal field, they concluded that the splitting increases at low temperatures and is approximately proportional to $\Delta\beta$, the deformation angle.

* The research reported in this document has been sponsored in part by the Air Force Office of Scientific Research, OAR, through the European Office, Aerospace Research, United States Air Force.

44

We have made a careful study of the paramagnetic resonance properties over a large temperature range of two types of ions: Cr^{3+} substituting for the B ion and Gd^{3+} substituting for the A ion. It is found that the crystal parameters change smoothly but very markedly from 4°K to 700°K. It is possible that such crystals may serve as a thermometer over a large temperature range and as a means for temperature stabilization.

Crystal structure and experimental details

The crystal structure of $LaAlO_3$ permits the substitution of rare earth ions for the lanthanum A site and of iron group elements for the aluminum B site. The crystal structure is a distorted perovskite lattice. The ideal perovskite structure has a cubic unit cell. In the center of the cube is the A ion and at the eight corners the B ion. Six oxygen ions surround octahedrally the B ion. Thus the A ion has 12 nearest oxygen neighbors. The distorted perovskite structure is a rhombohedron. The point symmetry is probably $D_{3d}^5 - R\bar{3}m$. Geller and Bala [2], have determined the change of the unit cell as a function of temperature. These results are given in Figure 1. This figure shows the change in the deformation angle $\Delta\beta = 90° - \beta$

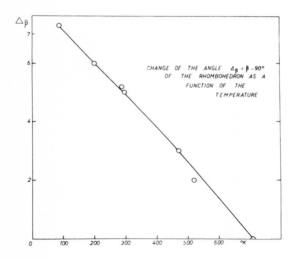

CHANGE OF THE ANGLE $\Delta_\beta = \beta - 90°$ OF THE RHOMBOHEDRON AS A FUNCTION OF THE TEMPERATURE

Figure 1

Change of the $\Delta\beta$, the angle of distortion, as a function of temperature. The results are taken from an analysis of Geller and Bala's X-ray data.

as a function of the temperature. The intercept of this curve is at 708° ± 25°K.

We have studied the spectrum of Cr^{3+} and Gd^{3+} in $LaAlO_3$ at 3 cm wavelength and at different temperatures from 4.2°K to 690°K. Since the spectrum is highly temperature dependent at elevated temperatures care has to be taken to stabilize the temperature sufficiently long so that the measurement of all the fine structure components can take place.

The crystals were obtained from Dr. E. Warekois of Lincoln Laboratory and were presumably grown by the Verneuil process. We have also obtained later crystals grown by Dr. J. P. Remeika of Bell Telephone Laboratories grown by the flux method. These crystals, however, had considerably larger line widths and were not very suitable for precise measurements.

The spectrum can be approximated by means of the simple Hamiltonian

$$\mathcal{H} = g_{\parallel}\beta H_z S_z + g_{\perp}\beta(H_x S_x + H_y S_y) + D(S_z^2 - 1/3\,S(S+1)) + A(\mathbf{S}\cdot\mathbf{I}) \quad (1)$$

with $S = 3/2$.

At room temperature (291 ± 3°K) the values of the parameters are given by

$$\begin{aligned}
g_{\parallel} &= 1.9825 \pm 0.0005 \\
g_{\perp} &= 1.985 \pm 0.001 \\
D &= 450 \pm 1 \text{ gauss} \\
A &= 19 \pm 3 \text{ gauss}
\end{aligned} \quad (2)$$

The line width of the central transition is 6–7 gauss. Figure 2 shows the

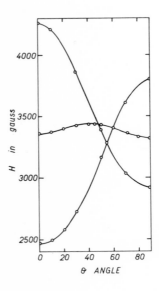

Figure 2

Angular dependence of the spectrum of Cr^{3+} in $LaAlO_3$. The spectrum is taken at room temperature.

angular dependence of the spectrum of Cr^{3+} at room temperature. Table I summarizes the temperature dependence of the initial splitting parameter D.

TABLE I

Temperature dependence of D for Cr^{3+} in $LaAlO_3$

$g_\parallel = 1.9825$

T in °K	20	80	273 ± 1	291 ± 3	257 ± 3
D in gauss	600 ± 2	587 ± 6	475.5 ± 1	450 ± 1	448 ± 2

We have not pursued the temperature dependence to higher temperatures since all these crystals contained a large number of other impurity lines, most probably iron. These lines were also very temperature dependent and with an intensity of the same order as the chromium lines. It made it difficult to sort out the chromium lines from all the other lines.

The initial splitting of Cr^{3+} is dependent according to Sugano and Tanabe [3] on three parameters:

$$D = A(\xi_\parallel^2 - \xi_\perp^2) + BK - CK \qquad (3)$$

where A, B and C depend on the separation of the ground state A_2 from the next orbital states $^4F_2$ and $^4F_1$. B and C are also dependent on $\xi_\parallel$ and $\xi_\perp$ where these constants are the effective spin-orbit parameters along the parallel and perpendicular directions. The anisotropy of the spin orbit coupling is reflected in the different g factors i.e. $g_\parallel - g_\perp \neq 0$. Sugano et al. conclude that the second term and the third term are nearly of the same order of magnitude and cancel out and that the first term may account for the initial splitting of Cr^{3+} in Al_2O_3. The first term is not strongly temperature dependent. This can be seen from the fact that there are no appreciable changes in the value of $\Delta g = \Delta g_\parallel - \Delta g_\perp$ which is proportional to $(\xi_\parallel - \xi_\perp)/E(^4F_2) - E(^4A_2)$. The first term is proportional to

$$\frac{(\xi_\parallel - \xi_\perp)(\xi_\parallel + \xi_\perp)}{E(^4F_2) - E(^4A_2)} = \Delta g(\xi_\parallel + \xi_\perp)$$

The cubic field separation of the orbital states $^4F_2$ and $^4A_2$ is not expected to change more than a few percent over the temperature change of $20°$ to $300°K$ and the anisotropy in the spin orbit coupling is also not expected to change to a large extent. Hence, the change of D as a function of temperature will depend mainly on the change in K which is proportional to the trigonal field strength. This trigonal deformation depends to a first approximation on the change in $\Delta\beta$. Hence, to a first approximation these $\Delta\beta$ and D should be proportional. At high temperatures there is an indication of a linear relationship between D and T i.e. $D \propto aT + bT^2$ with $a \gg b$ and $a \sim 0.9$ gauss/degree. Similarly, one finds $\Delta\beta \propto T$. At low temperatures the X-ray data are not sufficient for a comparison of the paramagnetic resonance. Further measurements by X-rays at temperatures below $300°K$ would be very welcome.

The spectrum of Gd³⁺

The spectrum of Gd³⁺ is considerably more complicated. The gadolinium ion takes the place of the "A" site. The relatively low symmetry is reflected by the spin-Hamiltonian.

$$\mathcal{H} = \beta H.g.S + B_2^0 O_2^0 + B_4^0 O_4^0 + B_6^0 O_6^0 + B_4^3 O_4^3 + B_6^3 O_6^3 + B_6^6 O_6^6$$

where O_n^m are operators proportional to homogenous Legendre Polynomials of the nth degree and B_n^m are crystal field parameters to be determined from the experiment. It is conventional to make the following substitution

$$b_2^0 = 3B_2^0 \; ; \; b_4^0 = 60\, B_4^0 \; ; \; b_6^0 = 1260\, B_6^0$$
$$b_4^3 = 3\, B_4^3, \; b_6^3 = 36\, B_6^3, \; b_6^6 = 1260\, B_6^6$$

A casual inspection of the spectrum shows that b_2 is the dominant term in the spectrum. A detailed analysis of the evaluation of the parameters will be given elsewhere. At $T = 293°C$ we obtain the following set of parameters: $g_\parallel = 1.9908$, $g_\perp = 1.986$, $b_2^0 = 371.2$, $b_4^0 = 6.17$, $b_6^0 = 1.0$, $b_6^6 = 7.6$, $b_4^3 \sim 5.8$, $b_6^3 \sim 0.35$, all in units of 10^{-4} cm^{-1}. The line widths at this temperature were in 7.5, 12, 14 and 17 gauss for the $1/2 \rightarrow -1/2$, $3/2 \rightarrow 1/2$, $5/2 \rightarrow 3/2$ and $7/2 \rightarrow 5/2$ transitions. The line width was temperature dependent above $300°K$, the $1/2 \rightarrow -1/2$ transition increasing from 7 gauss at $203°K$ to 21 gauss at $275°K$.

The temperature dependence of b_2^0 is given in Figure 3. It is seen that there is a very sharp change in b_2^0 between $20°K$ and $700°K$ and approximately linear at the high temperature range. The cut off for $b_2^0 = 0$ is about $720° \pm 15°K$ in very good agreement with Geller's and Baba's results. The slope indicates about $(\partial b_2^0 / \partial t) \sim 1$ gauss/degree. Hence the change of the $7/2 \rightarrow 5/2$ transition is about 6 gauss/degree. Assuming that one can stabilize the frequency of a klystron to one hundredth of the line width one could then measure or stabilize a temperature to $0.02°K$ over a temperature range of $20°K - 700°K$.

Figure 4 shows the temperature variation of b_4^0. As seen this variation is considerably smaller. Moreover b_4^0 is only of the order of 6×10^{-4} cm^{-1}. This indicates a relatively small cubic crystal field and is in agreement with

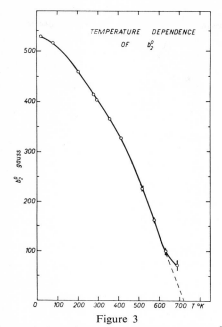

Figure 3

Temperature dependence of the axial crystal field parameter b_2^0 of the spectrum of gadolinium in LaAlO$_3$.

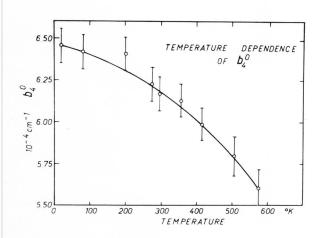

Figure 4

Temperature dependence of the cubic crystal field parameter b_4^0 of the spectrum of gadolinium in LaAlO$_3$.

the data by Sierro[4] who finds $b_4^0 = 5.4 \times 10^{-4}$ cm^{-1} in the crystal field of SrTiO$_3$.

The theory of the crystal field splitting for either parameter b_2^0 or b_4^0 for the case of gadolinium is at present not yet understood. It is, therefore, difficult to compare our results with experiments. The processes considered show that b_2^0 can be either linearly or quadratically dependent on the trigonal field. In general $b_2^0 = AK + BK^2$ where A and B are complicated constants which are not strongly temperature dependent. The rough linearity in the temperature range of 200–700°K indicates that a process proportional to the trigonal field is dominant. The cubic field variation with temperature is rather complicated since it will depend both on the fourth and sixth order potential. It is expected that the splitting should be proportional to V_{cub}^n where n may be larger than one.

Acknowledgment

We are grateful to Dr. E. Warekois of Lincoln Laboratory and to Dr. J. P. Remeika of Bell Telephone Laboratories for supplying us with some crystals of LaAlO$_3$.

REFERENCES

[1] H. GRAENICHER AND K. A. MÜLLER, *Nuovo Cimento*, Suppl. **6**, Ser. X, 1216 (1957).
[2] S. GELLER AND V. B. BALA, *Acta Cryst.* **9**, 1049 (1956).
[3] S. SUGANO AND Y. TANABE, *J. Phys. Soc. of Japan* **13**, 880 (1958).
[4] J. SIERRO, *Helv. Phys. Acta* **39**, 404 (1961).

Electron Paramagnetic Resonance of Some Rare Earth Impurities in Strontium Titanate

L. RIMAI AND G. A. DEMARS

Raytheon Research Division, Waltham, Massachusetts

ABSTRACT

In this paper we present the data obtained from paramagnetic resonance of trivalent ytterbium and neodynium, and divalent europium in the crystal field of the $SrTiO_3$ lattice. For Yb^{3+} and Nd^{3+} the resonance arises from the lowest lying Kramers doublet in the tetragonal field of the low temperature phase of the host crystal. The resonance of the $4f^7$ ^8S state of Eu^{2+} is observable also in the room temperature cubic phase. Comparison of the latter data with correspondening results on isoelectronic Gd^{3+} indicates a marked difference between the behavior of divalent and trivalent rare earth ions in this crystal. From these results it is concluded that the tetragonal distortion in the low temperature phase of $SrTiO_3$ must be exceedingly small and that the relatively large effects observed in trivalent rare earths are the result of an enhancement of this distortion by the interaction of these impurities with the host lattice.

Introduction

The electron paramagnetic resonance spectrum of Gd^{3+} in $SrTiO_3$ has been investigated in some detail [1]. These results have shown that the majority of the impurity ions entered substitutionally into the lattice The site symmetry has been found to be cubic between 300°K and 110°K. At this point the crystal undergoes a phase transition (this has been confirmed by examination of birefringence patterns of pure crystals [1]) and below this temperature the spectrum exhibits tetragonal symmetry, with a temperature dependent axial crystal field splitting term b_{20} [2]. The temperature dependence of the spectrum is indicative of a smooth transition (at least to within the spectral resolution permitted by the line widths). The tetragonality in the low temperature phase of the crystal must be very small since to this date X-ray measurements have failed to detect it [3].

These findings clearly indicate the advisability of investigating other rare earth impurities in this crystal. Such results, and especially their comparison with iron group impurities, could conceivably give useful information about the phase transition and the structure of the low temperature phase. In addition, the crystal field spectra of some of the non S state rare earth ions in fields of almost cubic symmetry should be of interest in connection with possible millimeter and far infrared maser structures.

We wish to report here the results on the following ions: Yb^{3+}, Nd^{3+} and Eu^{2+}. They do yield some information which, although far from conclusive, is applicable to the study of the host crystal.

Trivalent ions

Yb^{3+} and Nd^{3+} doped crystals exhibit at the lower temperatures an EPR spectrum characteristic of a Kramers doublet with axially symmetric g tensor. The g axes are oriented along the (100) directions of the crystal as determined by X-rays at room temperature. We observe, for an arbitrary orientation of the magnetic field, three spectra that are directionally inequivalent corresponding to the three possible orientations of "tetragonal domains" in the low temperature phase of the crystal. The Nd^{3+} spectrum is observable only at the lowest temperatures (below 4°K). The Yb^{3+} spectrum, however, is still observable at 77°K and indicates a decrease in the asymmetry of the g tensor as the temperature increases, qualitatively following the decrease in the axial splitting b_{20} of Gd^{3+} in the same temperature range as the transition to the cubic phase is approached. We feel, therefore, with reasonable certitude, that Yb^{3+} is a substitutional impurity.

The crystals studied had nominal doping of the order of 0.1% [4]. The intensity of the spectra indicated that the actual concentration of the ions in the observed valance state was much smaller. We were able to observe and measure, however, the hyperfine structure of the odd Yb isotopes. The very weak lines due to the odd Nd isotopes were observable only in the perpendicular direction (where the lines are narrower) and with very poor signal-to-noise ratio. Nevertheless, these observations served to positively identify the ion under study.

The line widths in the parallel direction were appreciably broader than in the perpendicular plane, as expected from mosaic spread in the crystal. The increase in line width of the Yb^{3+} lines as the temperature increases is a measure of the corresponding decrease in relaxation times. The relatively narrow lines that make the spectrum in this case still observable at 77°K are indicative of a large cubic field splitting. The resultant experimental data are given in Table I.

It is not possible to obtain a complete description of the crystal field at the ion site just from the Zeeman splitting of the ground state. Some useful information is made available, however, which will enable one to eventually describe this crystal field with less than complete optical data. These are hard to get with such small impurity concentrations [5]. In the following paragraphs a short discussion is given of these results in terms of crystal field theory.

TABLE I

Ion & Isotope	Frequency (kMc)	T (°K)	$g_\parallel$	$g_\perp$	$1/3(g_\parallel+g_\perp)$	$\|A\|$ (10^{-4}cm^{-1})	$\|B\|$ (10^{-4}cm^{-1})
Yb^{3+}		16	2	2.11± .01	2.780±.005	2.55		
Yb^{3+}		16	50	2.18± .01	2.720±.005	2.54		
Yb^{3+}	171 173	35	2	2.10± .01	2.785±.005	2.54	530±20	720±5 211±5
Yb^{3+}		35	50	2.17±.005	2.720±.005	2.55		
Yb^{3+}		35	65	(2.25)	2.70±.01			
Yb^{3+}		35	77		2.67±.01			
Nd^{3+}		16	2	2.61± .01	2.470±.005	2.56		
Nd^{3+}		35	2	2.62± .01	2.740±.005	2.57		

From X-ray data and also from the small anisotropy in the g tensor we know we are dealing with a dominantely cubic crystal field.

For the Yb^{3+} $4f^{13}$: $^2F_{7/2}$ ground multiplet we may write down directly the energy levels of the various doublets in a field of tetragonal (cubic plus axial) symmetry.

$$E_6 = 8b_4 - 2b_6 + b_2 + (6b_4 - 18b_6)\left[1 - \frac{1}{6}\left(\frac{b_2}{b_4 - 3b_6}\right) + \left(\frac{b_2}{b_4 - 3b_6}\right)^2\right]^{1/2}$$

$$E'_6 = 8b_4 - 2b_6 + b_2 - (6b_4 - 18b_6)\left[1 - \frac{1}{6}\left(\frac{b_2}{b_4 - 3b_6}\right) + \left(\frac{b_2}{b_4 - 3b_6}\right)^2\right]^{1/2}$$

$$\tag{1}$$

$$E'_7 = - 8b_4 + 2b_6 - b_2 + (10b_4 + 14b_6)\left[1 - \frac{b_2}{5b_4 + 7b_6} + \left(\frac{b_2}{5b_4 + 7b_6}\right)^2\right]^{1/2}$$

$$E_7 = - 8b_4 + 2b_6 - b_2 - (10b_4 + 14b_6)\left[1 - \frac{b_2}{5b_4 + 7b_6} + \left(\frac{b_2}{5b_4 + 7b_6}\right)^2\right]^{1/2}$$

The E'_6 and E'_7 are the doublets arising from the splitting by the axial field b_2 of the cubic field Γ_8 quartet. The cubic field energy levels are linear functions of the cubic field parameters b_4 and b_6 (usual convention [1]), since there are no repeated representations. The cubic field state vectors are independent of the ratio of the parameters, as are the cubic field Zeeman splittings and g-values for the doublets. We have for the two doublets $g_6 = 8/3$, $g_7 = 24/7$. For the quartet Γ_8, the angular dependence of the two main transitions should contain a fourth order spherical harmonic. In the presence of b_2 the Γ_8 splits into doublets. For the small b_2 however, some of this fourth order angular dependence should remain. This is especially true as we approach the phase transition. No detectable perturbation from the usual second order spherical harmonic angular dependence for the Zeeman splitting of an axial doublet was present. We conclude, therefore, that the resonance is due to one of the two original doublets Γ_6 or Γ_7. Furthermore, from the experimental average $g = 1/3 \, (g_\parallel + 2g_\perp)$ we are led to the conclusion that in the cubic phase the Γ_6 doublet is lowest. Eq. (1) shows that this may indeed be the case if the values of b_4 and $\delta = b_6/b_4$ are within the following domains: $(b_4 > 0, \, \delta > 4)$ or $(b_4 < 0, \, \delta < + 1/3)$.

We see from the data that the average g-value deviates measurably from the cubic field value for the Γ_6. This deviation is of the same order as the difference between the ratios $(g_\parallel/g_\perp - | A/B |) \cong .05$. It, therefore, could be attributed to the admixture of the $J = 5/2$, Γ_6 doublet and the ground doublet by the crystal field. This effect may be calculated from second order perturbation theory if the spin-orbit splitting Δ between $J = 7/2$ and $J = 5/2$ is known. It yields a linear relation between b_4 and b_6. Another relation involving these parameters may be obtained from a measurement of the dependence of the average g-value on frequency. This dependence unfortunately was found to fall within experimental error, and enabled us only to set a limit: $E_7 - E_6 > 60$ cm^{-1}. Detailed calculations [7] using the g shift due to crystal field multiplet mixing, $\Delta = 10,500$ cm^{-1}, (as indicated by preliminary optical studies) [5] and the above limit yield the following limits for the cubic field parameters: $b_4 < - 230$ cm^{-1} and $b_6 > - 70$ cm^{-1}. These inequalities, if not of any value in describing the crystal field, indicate, nevertheless, that the more subtle aspects of the experimental results are not in contradiction with a Γ_6 ground state in the cubic phase.

Calculations of the point charge potential in the $SrTiO_3$ [7] ionic lattice give for the Sr^{2+} site (including the appropriate reduced matrix elements for the Yb^{3+} ground state) $b_4 > 0$, $b_6 < 0$ in disagreement with the above conditions. Inclusion of the dipoles induced by the extra charge of the trivalent impurity on the O^{--} ions due to their electronic polarizability makes the disagreement even stronger. The point charge potentials at the Ti^{4+} site, on the other hand, give for Yb^{3+}, $b_4 < 0$ and $b_6 > 0$ which, independently of the absolute values, satisfy the conditions for a Γ_6 ground state. This result cannot be taken, however, as proof that the substitution of trivalent rare earths takes place at the Ti^{4+} site, as is shown by the following argument. The value of b_4 in the point charge potential at the divalent site has two contributions of opposite sign that differ in magnitude by less than 20% — the positive contribution from the 12 divalent oxygens and the negative contribution from the 8 tetravalent titaniums. Since we are dealing with a lattice of extremely high ionic polarizability, it could easily happen that the extra charge due to the impurity induces large enough displacements of the neighboring charges to cause a change in the sign of b_4. This would be especially plausible if the high polarizability of the lattice could be ascribed to an easily movable Ti^{4+} ion within the oxygen octahedra. Incidentally, this "quasi cancellation" does not appear either for the contributions to (b_6 at the Sr^{2+}) site or for either parameter at the Ti^{4+} site.

From the anisotropy of the g tensor one may obtain the ratio of the axial field to a certain linear combination of the cubic field parameters, namely $b_{20}/(b_4 - 3b_6) = 0.027$ at $2°K$, 0.02 at $50°K$ and 0.016 at $65°K$. This clearly indicates that the deviation from cubic symmetry even at the lowest temperatures is indeed small. If we assume that b_4 and b_6 are proportional respectively to the fourth and sixth order crystal field parameters of the Gd^{3+} spin-Hamiltonian [1] (in absolute value), these data are not in contradiction to the assumption of a perturbation mechanism for the axial term in the Gd spin-Hamiltonian, dominantely linear in the axial crystal field [1]. This, however, should be taken with reservation since this range of temperature corresponds to a relitavely small range of values of the Gd^{3+} axial splitting.

Let us now turn to the Nd^{3+} data. Here the situation is more complicated since repeated representations occur among the cubic field eigenstates. The cubic field levels are more complicated functions of the parameters:

$$E_6 = 28b_4 - 32b_6$$

$$E_8, E_8' = -7b_4 + 8b_6 \pm \frac{1}{2}\left(\frac{10300}{7}b_4^2 + 1360b_6^2 + 2240b_4b_6\right)^{1/2}. \tag{2}$$

Again the Γ_6 level yields a cubic field $g = 8/3$ independent of the parameters which is reasonably close to the measured average g- value. From a plot of the energy levels given by Eq. (2) as a function of $\delta = b_6/b_4$, one obtains as conditions for a Γ_6 ground state in the cubic field, ($b_4 > 0$, $\delta < 2.5$) or ($b_4 < 0$, $\delta < +0.3$). Consideration of the reduced matrix elements and of the change of sign in the potential when we go from electrons to holes gives for both $4f^3: {}^4I_{9/2}$ of Nd^{3+} and $4f^{13}: {}^2F_{7/2}$ of Yb^{3+} the same sign for b_4 and b_6. It, therefore, is not impossible to have a Γ_6 as a lowest level for Nd^{3+}. This is as far as we can argue, however. In this case we cannot observe the resonance except at the lowest temperatures, where the tetragonal distortion is largest. Therefore, we have no further argument to show that the doublet we observe comes from the Γ_6 cubic field doublet rather than from one of the Γ_8 quartets. Incidentally, the experimental average g-

value may be fitted for at least three different values of $\delta = b_6/b_4$, using Γ_6' doublets which originate in one or the other Γ_8, as detailed calculations indicate [7]. We cannot in this case either neglect crystal field admixing from the higher J multiplets or mixing with other terms due to breakdown of the Russell Saunders coupling scheme. [This latter effect is absent for Yb^{3+} since it is a one particle (hole) case.] In any event, one may say that the crystal field again corresponds to a small tetragonal distortion, comparable to that observed with Yb^{3+}.

We investigated the spectrum of uranium doped $SrTiO_3$ in an attempt to detect resonance from U^{3+} which has the same f^3 configuration and ground multiplet as Nd^{3+}. We were able to detect only a relatively broad resonance, with an almost isotropic g ($g_{\parallel} = 2.06$, $g_{\perp} = 2.04$). Due to the very small abundance of the odd isotopes we had no hyperfine structure evidence that this resonance is indeed due to uranium. Even if it were due to uranium one should have to prove that it was in the lattice as a trivalent ion. If all these requisites were satisfied we should take the large difference in g-values between the two ions as an indication that the cubic field ground state is one of the Γ_8's since then the g-values could vary appreciably due to variations in δ.

Europium

The main interest in the study of this impurity is that in the divalent state it is isoelectronic with Gd^{3+}. It should substitute at the Sr^{2+} site without necessity for charge compensation and without polarization effects. Due to the latter circumstance, large differences between the two spectra could be expected. This has indeed been borne out by the experimental results.

The form of the spin-Hamiltonian of Eu^{2+} is the same as that for Gd^{3+}, [1] with the same parameters present. Table II lists these parameters at three

TABLE II

Data taken at 16 kMc/sec. – Units – $10^{-4}cm^{-1}$

Ion	Isotope	T($^{\circ}$K)	g	b_{20}	b_{40}	b_{60}	$\lvert A \rvert$
Eu^{2+}		300	$1.990 \pm .001$	0	105.9 ± 2	1.1 ± 2	
Eu^{2+}	151	2	$1.990 \pm .001$	-10 ± 4	106.6 ± 2	6.7 ± 2	36.2
Eu^{2+}	153	2	$1.990 \pm .001$	-10 ± 4	106.6 ± 2	6.7 ± 2	17.6
Gd^{3+}		300	$1.992 \pm .002$	0	$-5.7 \pm .2$	$.5 \pm .3$	
Gd^{3+}		2	$1.992 \pm .002$	$-362.5 \pm .5$	$-3.2 \pm .5$	$1.4 \pm .5$	

temperatures, and includes for comparison some of the corresponding data for Gd^{3+}. At room temperature there was sufficient relaxation broadening to forbid observation of the hyperfine structure. It was resolved in the lower temperatures and the hyperfine constants for the two isotopes are also listed.

The first interesting feature of the data appears when the cubic field (room temperature) parameters b_{40} are compared for the two ions. For Eu^{2+} we find a value 20 times larger and opposite in sign to that of Gd^{3+}. The values of b_6, on the other hand, are comparable. At this point we note that spectra in other crystals yield values of b_{40} that differ by not more than 50% between the two ions. This fact supports the conclusion that the cause for this large difference in b_{40} resides in a difference of crystal field around the two ions, when they are substituted in $SrTiO_3$. The most obvious explanation that arises is that the two ions substitute at different sites, with Gd^{3+} replacing a Ti^{4+} ion. Again, however, as in the discussion of the Yb^{3+} results, one can invoke the effect on the highly polarizable lattice of the extra charge that would be present if Gd^{3+} were at a Sr^{2+} site. This latter argument seems somewhat more plausible if one considers the large size discrepancy between Ti^{4+} and the rare earths in contrast to the very nice fit that these would make at the Sr^{2+} site.

The second striking feature that appears in Table II is the values for b_{20} in the tetragonal phase, with Eu^{2+} indicating an exceedingly small distortion, comparable to that observed in the iron group spectra [8; 9], in violent contrast to the case of Gd^{3+}. This effect again could be ascribed to the lattice polarization by an additional charge provided we assume that the displacements induced by this extra charge are anisotropic in the low temperature phase.

The value of the hyperfine structure constant A is somewhat larger than observed in CaF_2 [10] and indicates that the binding of the Eu^{++} ion to the $SrTiO_3$ lattice is of dominantly ionic nature. This, of course, does not mean necessarily that the binding forces in the host are ionic to the same degree.

Conclusion

It is appropriate at this point to summarize the singular features of the resonance results in both iron group and rare earth impurities.

The cubic phase — In the iron group one finds a relatively small difference in the cubic fields between the di- and trivalent ions. (At most, a factor of 2 between Mn^{IV} and Cr^{3+}, even neglecting difference in covalent bonding.) The rare earths show a very large such difference—about a factor of 20.

The tetragonal phase — Both di- and trivalent iron group ions show extremely small tetragonality. The divalent rare earth behaves the same way.

The trivalent rare earths, however, show a much more marked tetragonality.

From the resonance data alone, it is not possible to reach a final conclusion about the sites at which the various impurities substitute. If the size effect is assumed to be the dominant factor in this consideration, one may draw an interesting conclusion: The polarization of the surroundings of the Sr^{2+} site, by the insertion of an extra electronic charge, is much larger than the polarization of the Ti^{4+} environment. A highly mobile (polarizable) Ti^{4+} ion within the framework of rigid oxygen and strontium sublattices would give just this effect. This is, however, too simple a picture especially in view of the long range of the electrostatic interactions. We have included this argument for the sake of its interest rather than its conclusiveness. It points a direction in which comparison of spectra from ions with different charges could yield information about microscopic polarization effects. For instance, this same argument could presumably be strengthened by further EPR results on different ions in this same crystal, in particular, on a non S state divalent rare earth. One qualitative result, however, is patent in these studies, independently from the microscopic model that is adopted. The deviation from cubic symmetry in the crystal below the phase transition must be exceedingly small, and the relatively large effects observable with the trivalent rare earth ions are due to some enhancement mechanism peculiar to their interaction with the host crystal. The interest of spin resonance investigations in this crystal in search for better understanding of the phase transition is thereby stressed.

REFERENCES

[1] L. RIMAI AND G. A. DEMARS, *Phys. Rev.* (to appear August 1, 1962).

[2] The existence of this phase transition has been inferred from previous EPR data on iron group impurities—K. A. MÜLLER, *Phys. Rev. Letters* **2**, 341 (1959)—however this work has not determined the temperature at which it takes place.

[3] O. GUENTERT (private communication).

[4] These were Verneuill grown crystals purchased from the National Lead Co.

[5] Preliminary optical data have displayed one $J = 7/2 \rightarrow J = 5/2$ transition for Yb^{3+} indicating a spin orbit splitting of 10,500 cm^{-1} (P. B. NUTTER, private communication).

[6] B. R. JUDD, *Proc. Phys. Soc.* **B70**, 880 (1957).

[7] L. RIMAI (to be published).

[8] K. A. MÜLLER, 7ème Colloque Ampere (Geneve) *Arch. Sci.* **11**, 150 (1958).

[9] DOBROV, VIETH, BROWNE, *Phys. Rev.* **115**, 79 (1959).

[10] W. LOW, *Paramagnetic Resonance in Solids*, Academic Press, 1960.

On the Paramagnetic Resonance Spectra of some Rare Earth and Iron Group Impurities in Strontium Titanate*

R. S. RUBINS AND W. LOW

Department of Physics, The Hebrew University of Jerusalem, Israel

ABSTRACT

The spectra of nickel, cerium, and neodymium have been observed in single crystals of $SrTiO_3$. The nickel spectra may be classified as follows:

(a) Broad($g = 2.21 \pm 0.01$) and narrow ($g = 2.204 \pm 0.001$) isotropic lines are attributed respectively to the normal and double quantum transitions of Ni^{2+} occupying a Ti^{4+} site. The narrow line is phase inverted at low microwave powers.

(b) A narrow line ($g = 2.180 \pm 0.002$), isotropic at 200°K, is probably due to Ni^{3+} occupying a Ti^{4+} site. The observed g-value may be explained if the crystalline field is large enough to make ^2E the ground level.

(c) Axial spectra, observed at 200°K, with principal g-values ($g_{||} = 2.030 \pm 0.001$, $g_\perp = 2.352 \pm 0.001$) similar to those for Cu^{2+} in a tetragonal field can possibly be attributed to Ni^{1+} occupying a Ti^{4+} site.

Below 100°K $SrTiO_3$ becomes tetragonal and the unit cell possibly loses its center of symmetry. The effects of domain formation are observed as a splitting of the spectral lines.

At 4.2°K axial spectra due to Ce^{3+} ($g_{||} = 3.005 \pm 0.005$, $g_\perp = 1.118 \pm 0.002$) and Nd^{3+} ($g_{||} = 2.609 \pm 0.003$, $g_\perp = 2.472 \pm 0.003$) have been observed.

Introduction

In recent years impurity ions of both the iron group [1;2;3;4] and the rare earth [5;6] transition elements have been investigated in single crystals of strontium titanate. The structure of $SrTiO_3$ at room temperature is cubic Perowskite [7], each Ti^{4+} ion lying at the centre of a cubic array of six O^{2-} and eight Sr^{2+} ions, and each Sr^{2+} ion at the center of a cubic array of twelve O^{2-} and eight Ti^{4+} ions. From considerations of ionic size, trivalent rare earth ions would be expected to replace Sr^{2+} ions in the lattice, and divalent and trivalent iron group ions to replace Ti^{4+} ions. The interpretations of the resonance results have generally been in agreement with this hypothesis.

At 100°K, a phase transition takes place [6], and below this temperature tetragonal domains are formed [1]. The dielectric constant at 1 kc/s varies

* The research reported in this document has been sponsored in part by the Air Force Office of Scientific Research, O. A. R., through the European Office, Aerospace Research, U. S. A. F.

59

from 370 at room temperature to a maximum of about 18,000 at 1.4°K, and ferroelectric effects have been reported below 45°K [8].

In this paper we discuss the ESR spectra at 3 cm wavelength observed in single crystals of $SrTiO_3$ containing nominally Ce^{3+} and Ni^{3+}. The crystals were provided by the National Lead Company, New-York. In the nickel-doped samples four sets of spectra were observed: these have been attributed to Nd^{3+}, and to different valence states of nickel. The results for $3d$ and $4f$ ions are set out in Tables I and II respectively, and analyzed in the following sections.

TABLE I

Resonance results(*) for nickel in strontium titanate at 3 cm

Ion	Temp. (°K)	$g_{\parallel}$	$g_{\perp}$	Notes
	203	g (isotropic) $=$	2.180 ± 0.002	**
A (Ni^{3+} : $3d^7$)	80	2.172 ± 0.001	2.184 ± 0.001	**
	20	2.136 ± 0.001	2.202 ± 0.001	**
	4.2	2.110 ± 0.002	2.213 ± 0.002	**
B (Ni^{2+} : $3d^8$)	80	g (isotropic) $=$	2.204 ± 0.001	***
C (Ni^{1+} : $3d^9$)	203			**
or	80	2.029 ± 0.001	2.352 ± 0.001	****
(Ni^{3+} : $3d^7$)	20			****

*   Some of these results have been obtained independently by Dr. K. A. Müller (private communication).

**   Three inequivalent tetragonal spectra are observed with axes parallel to the cubic [100], [010] and [001] directions.

***   The measurement was made on the double quantum transition (see text).

****   At least fifteen inequivalent sites are observed (see text).

The nickel spectra

$Ni^{3+} 3d^7$ is isoelectronic with Co^{2+}, for which the ground state in an octahedral field is a $^4T_1$ level. According to the d^7 diagram of Tanabe and Sugano [9], the "cross-over" of the $^4T_1$ and ^2E levels takes place at a crystalline field strength Δ of about 20,000 cm^{-1}, above which the ^2E level lies lowest. The size of Δ for Ni^{3+} should be sufficient to make the strong field ^2E level ($d\varepsilon^6 d\gamma^1 : S' = 1/2$) the ground level. As there are non-zero matrix elements of the spin-orbit coupling connecting the ^2E and

TABLE II

Resonance results for rare earth ions in $SrTiO_3$ at 3 cm

Ion	Temp. (°K).	$g_\parallel$	$g_\perp$	Notes
Ce^{3+} $4f^1$	4.2	3.005 ± 0.005	1.118 ± 0.003	*
Nd^{3+} $4f^3$	4.2	2.609 ± 0.003	2.472 ± 0.003	* **

*   Three inequivalent tetragonal spectra are observed with axes parallel to the cubic [100], [010], and [001] directions.
** These values agree with those obtained at 2°K by Rimai and de Mars.[5]

$^4T_1$ levels [10], the g-value of the ground level is sensitive to their separation.

In the region of the cross-over, the g-value of the ^2E level can vary appreciably from the value of 2.0 associated with the unperturbed level. In such a strong crystalline electric field, the reduction of the orbital moment due to covalent bonding is likely to be considerable. Spectrum A of Table I has been attributed to Ni^{3+} $3d^7$. The g-value in the cubic phase of 2.18*** indicates that the splitting of the ^2E and T_1 levels is probably not much greater than the magnitude of the spin-orbit coupling. At 200°K, this spectrum consists of a single isotropic line whose width (measured between points of half maximum intensity) is approximately 6 gauss.

At 80°K, which is below the temperature of the phase transition from cubic to tetragonal symmetry, three inequivalent axial spectra replace the single cubic line observed at 203°K (the sublimation temperature of CO_2). The steady divergence of $g_\perp$ and $g_\parallel$ as the temperature is further lowered to 20°K and 4.2°K is indicative of a steadily increasing tetragonal polarization. The mean g-value, given by $g = 1/3(g_\parallel + 2g_\perp)$, remains steady at $g = 2.18$ indicating that there is no noticeable change in the cubic field strength as the temperature is lowered.

Ni^{2+} $3d^8$ ($S' = 1$) has been observed as a broad isotropic line, whose width varies from about 120 gauss at room temperature to 90 gauss at 80°K. In addition, a narrow isotropic line, B in Table I, is observed at its center. At 80°K, this line is approximately 6 gauss wide and inverted at low microwave powers, and 3 gauss wide and of normal phase at high microwave powers. The narrower high-power line, belonging to the double quantum transition [12; 13], and the low power inversion, which is not yet understood, have both been observed from Ni^{2+} in MgO [12] and CaO [14]. The g-value of 2.204 in $SrTiO_3$ may be compared with that of

---

*** The value of 2.18 is consistent with the values reported for Ni^{3+} in TiO_2[11], in which a mean g-value of 2.18 is associated with the substitutional site: the cubic field strengths in TiO_2 and $SrTiO_3$ should be very similar.

2.2145 in MgO, where the respective anion-cation separations are 1.95 Å and 2.10 Å. The deviation of the g-value of Ni^{2+} from the free electron value is given approximately by

$$\Delta g = g - g_E \propto \lambda'/\Delta$$

where λ' is the reduced value of the spin-orbit coupling, and Δ is proportional to the cubic field strength. The ratio, $\Delta g(SrTiO_3)/\Delta g(MgO) = 1.05$, is a little smaller than might be expected on the basis of a simple point charge model, but the discrepancy might well be explained by the fact, that in the titanate, a divalent nickel ion replaces a quadrivalent titanium ion. The reduction of the central charge may cause the surrounding oxygen ions to be displaced outwards slightly, thus reducing the ratio of the Δg's.

It is interesting to note that the Ni^{2+} spectra are completely isotropic, even below the temperature of the phase transition. The average splitting giving the broad line-shape (due to random deviations from cubic symmetry [15]) must therefore be much greater than the tetragonal splitting due to domain formation.

A further spectrum, C in Table I, observed at 203°K, has axial symmetry even above 100°K, and consists of three axial lines with mutually perpendicular tetragonal axes. The principal g-values

$$g_{\parallel} = 2.03, \qquad g_{\perp} = 2.35$$

are similar to those which could be found for $Cu^{2+}\ 3d^9$ in a tetragonal field: i.e.

$$g_{\parallel} \simeq 2, \qquad g_{\perp} \simeq 2\left(1 - \frac{3\lambda}{\Delta}\right)$$

where Δ is the cubic field splitting of the $d\varepsilon$ and $d\gamma$ orbitals [16]. This spectrum is therefore probably due to $Ni^{1+}\ 3d^9$, although similar g-values found in rutile have been attributed to $Ni^{3+}\ 3d^7$ [11]. The deviation from cubic symmetry at high temperatures may be due to charge compensation, or to a Jahn-Taller distortion of the type observed in Cu^{2+} [16]. Further distortion of each tetragonal site takes place at the temperature of the phase transition, where the six possible directions of domain formation split each tetragonal line into at least five new lines(*). These almost coincide in the principal crystal orientations, and they show a maximum splitting close to the [111] direction of about 13 gauss at 80°K, and 18

---

* Five, and not six, lines are observed, because the extra tetragonal fields produced by domain formation parallel and anti-parallel to the high-temperature tetragonal axis should produce no change in the g-values: for $3d^9$, the magnitude of the tetragonal splitting does not enter the second-order expressions for $g_{\parallel}$ and $g_{\perp}$.

gauss at 20°K. Thus the splittings due to domain formation appear to be only a small perturbation of the initial tetragonal splitting. The line width at 80°K is narrow ($\simeq 3$ gauss), and attempts to observe the hfs of Ni^{61} have revealed the presence of small satellite lines, which are under investigation.

Experiments have also been carried out on a sample of strontium titanate cut in the form of a thin plate parallel to the (110) plane, and about 1 mm thick. In this sample, domain formation was limited to one direction. The single tetragonal axis was parallel to the [001] direction, and the low temperature spectra were accordingly simplified: below 100°K, only one ion in unit cell was observed in spectrum A (Table I), and two only of the the three high temperature lines of spectrum C showed further splittings.

The rare earth spectra

The ESR spectra of both $Ce^{3+} 4f^1$ and $Nd^{3+} 4f^3$ were not observed above 4.2°K. At liquid helium temperatures, three sets of axial spectra, with mutually perpendicular tetragonal axes were observed. At 4.2°K, the Ce^{3+} line width varied from about 20 gauss at $H \simeq 5.0$ kgauss (parallel orientation) to 5 gauss at $H \simeq 2.2$ kgauss (perpendicular orientation). The measured line widths for Nd^{3+} were 5 gauss in both the principal orientations, but the lines broadened rapidly on rotation, and were not observed at intermediate orientations. These results indicate that there might be further unresolved splittings of the tetragonal spectra, due possibly to the rare earth being in a site of tetragonal symmetry at high temperature—a situation similar to that observed in spectrum C of Table I.

The results for Nd^{3+} have been discussed in detail by Rimai and de Mars [6] in the preceding paper. In this paper we shall confine our discussion to the results for Ce^{3+}.

The experimental g-values for Ce^{3+}, which are $g_{\parallel} = 3.00_5$, $g_{\perp} = 1.12$, cannot be fitted to a tetragonal wave function made solely from the $J = 5/2$ level. The closest fit would be from a wavefunction of the form

$$\psi_{\pm} = 0.93 \left| J = \frac{5}{2}, \quad J_z = \pm \ \frac{5}{2} \right\rangle \pm 0.37 \left| J = \frac{5}{2}, \quad J_z = \mp \frac{3}{2} \right\rangle$$

leading to $g_{\parallel} = 3.36$ and $g_{\perp} = 1.32$. The admixture of the $J = 7/2$ level must therefore be appreciable.

If the admixture of the $J = 7/2$ is neglected, the tetragonal field may be represented by $V = V_c + V_t = C_4 V_4^{\text{cubic}} + A_2^0 V_2^0 + A_4^0 V_4$, where the various V's are defined as in the Appendix. Values for $g_{\parallel}$ and $g_{\perp}$, which are of the correct order of magnitude, can be obtained from a crystalline field which is basically cubic, provided that C_4 is negative*, and the Γ_8 quartet lies lowest. A small axial term, dominated by either a positive A_2^0 or a positive A_4^0 component, would then give a ground state whose wavefunction is given approximately by

$$\psi_{\pm} = \sqrt{\frac{5}{6}}\left|\frac{5}{2}, \pm\frac{5}{2}\right\rangle + \sqrt{\frac{1}{6}}\left|\frac{5}{2}, \pm\frac{3}{2}\right\rangle,$$

with $g_{\parallel} = 22/7$ and $g_{\perp} = 10/7$. Alternatively the g-values could be fitted to a ground state produced by a dominant, positive A_2^0 term. The ground level would then be a basically $J_z = \pm 5/2$ doublet, and the g-values could be explained by a smaller cubic component of either sign.

The interpretation of the experimental results in strontium titanate is complicated by the fact that the nature of the tetragonal distortion at 4.2°K is not known with certainty. If there is a polarization of the molecule at 4.2°K, similar to that observed in the tetragonal phase of barium titanate, and if the small Ti^{4+} ions are the most mobile in the crystal, then A_2^0 will be positive as required: proof of this is given in the Appendix. This theory is invalid, however, if the local symmetry of the Ce^{3+} site is not cubic above 100°K, and also, if the tetragonal distortion at 4.2°K is other than that of a simple molecular polarization**.

Discussion

The major unresolved problems arising from ESR work on strontium titanate are those relating to the low temperature crystal structure, the nature of the phase transition at 100°K, and the problems of how the impurity ions are incorporated in the lattice. Of the last mentioned type of problem, it is important to know whether the impurity replaces Sr^{2+} or Ti^{4+}, how charge compensation is effected, and details of the crystalline field potentials. The resonance results although extremely sensitive to all these factors, in general do not give unambiguous answers. Possibly, if more resonance results were available, some of these problems might be resolved with certainty.

Of the work discussed in this paper, uncertainty exists about the assignment of spectra A and C of Table I to the trivalent and monovalent states of

---

* C_4 would be negative if the negative contribution of the twelve surrounding O^{2-} ions is greater than the positive contribution of the eight surrounding Ti^{4+} ions (see Appendix).
** An alternative model has been proposed by Silverman [17].

nickel, and further auxiliary evidence is required. In this respect, the optical absorption measurements being carried out here, and also by Dr. K.A. Müller [4], should be of use. Attempts to change the Ni valence states by means of varied heat treatment in oxidising and reducing atmospheres has been unsuccessful; so has been γ-irradiation at room temperature.

Some of the strontium titanate crystals showed a deep blue coloration, and were semi-conducting at room temperature. In these crystals a strong optical absorption was observed at 19,400 cm^{-1}—an indication of the presence of Ti^{3+}. All attempts to remove the blue coloration by heat treatment have been unsuccessful and we have been unable to observe the ESR spectra of the various impurities which should have been present in these crystals.

Interest in the crystal structure is centred on the phase transition. Observation of the resonance spectra of nickel, as the system was allowed to warm slowly from 70°K to room temperature, indicated that there is no sudden change, but a gradual decrease in the tetragonal field as the transition temperature was approached, similar to that found in lanthanum aluminate [18]. It should be possible to obtain further information about the crystal structure by means of the application of strong electric fields to the sample. If the phase transition is accompanied by a polarisation of the molecule then splittings of the resonance lines should be observed.

Appendix

The crystalline field which would be experienced by a rare earth ion in site of cubic symmetry may be written

$$V_c = C_4 V_4{}^{\text{cubic}} + D_6 V_6{}^{\text{cubic}} \tag{1}$$

where
$$V_4{}^{\text{cubic}} = \Sigma[(x^4 + y^4 + z^4) - 3r^4/5],$$

$$V_6{}^{\text{cubic}} = \Sigma\left[(x^6 + y^6 + z^6) + \frac{15}{4}(x^4y^2 + x^2y^4 + y^4z^2 + y^2z^4 + z^4x^2 + z^2x^4 - \frac{15}{14}r^6\right],$$

and $r = x^2 + y^2 + z^2$.

If the tetragonal distortion is due to a simple polarization of the molecule (i.e. the surrounding O^{2-} and Ti^{4+} cubes are displaced by small amounts k_1 and k_2 respectively, along one of the three fourfold axes of the cube), the new potential may be written

$$V = V_c + V_t = C_4' V_4{}^{\text{cubic}} + C_6' V_6{}^{\text{cubic}} + A_2^0 V_2^0 + A_4^0 V_4^0 + A_6^0 V_6^0 \tag{2}$$

where
$$V_2^0 = \Sigma(3z^2 - r^2),$$
$$V_4^0 = \Sigma(35z^4 - 30r^2z^2 + 3r^4), \text{ and}$$
$$V_6^0 = \Sigma(231z^6 - 315r^2z^4 + 105r^4z^2 - 5r^6)$$

If a surrounding cube is displaced by a distance k in the z-direction with respect to a central Sr^{2+} ion, the parameters in Eq. (2) may be calculated from those in Eq. (1) by substituting $z + k$ in place of z in the latter equation. Thus we obtain

$$C_4' = C_4 + \frac{15}{4}k^2D_6 + ..., \quad D'_6 = D_6 + ...,$$
$$A_2^0 = \frac{6}{5}k^2C_4 - \frac{15}{28}k^4D_6 + ..., \tag{3}$$
$$A_4^0 = -\frac{9}{28}k^2D_6 + ..., \quad A_6^0 = 0 + ...$$

The results quoted above are not complete as the terms in the cubic potential of the eighth and higher orders, which were not included in Eq. (1), will all contribute to the parameters of Eqs. (3). For example the largest term contributing to A_6^0 will be proportional to k^2E_8, where E_8 is the eighth order cubic potential. Since the tetragonal displacement is probably much smaller than the side of the cube ($k^2 \ll a^2$), only the first term in the expression for each parameter need be considered.

In determining the signs of the contributions in $SrTiO_3$, both surrounding Ti^{4+} and O^{2-} cubes must be considered. Values of C_4 and D_6 calculated by the point charge method for 6-, 8- and 12-fold coordinations are given in Table III. The contribution to C_4 of the surrounding Ti^{4+} ions is found

TABLE III

Values gf C_4 and D_6 for 6-, 8-, and 12-fold cubic coordinations

	C_4(Units of e/R^5) *	D_6(Units of e/R^7) *
6-fold	$+ 35/4$	$- 21/2$
8-fold	$- 70/9$	$- 224/9$
12-fold	$- 35/8$	$+ 273/8$

* e is the charge on the electron and R the cation-anion separation.

to be of opposite sign and slightly greater than that of the nearest neighbor O^{2-} ions. However, because of overlap of the rare earth ions with the nearer O^{2-} ions, and the shielding effect of the latter, this conclusion is likely to be false. What does seem probable, however, is that the Sr^{2+} ions experience a relatively small fourth-order cubic field.

In order to determine the energy level schemes for rare earth ions substituted at Sr^{2+} sites in the tetragonal phase, it is necessary to know the $C_4\langle r^4 \rangle$ and $D_6\langle r^6 \rangle$ for the O^{2-} and Ti^{4+} arrays, as well as k_1^2 and k_2^2. From Eq. (3) and Table III, it is possible to find the signs of the most important contributions to the parameters of Eq. (2). The most important conclusions are that D_6' is positive and A_4^0 negative; C_4' is negative only if the fourth-order contribution of the surrounding O^{2-} ions is dominant, and A_2^0 is positive, only if the term $(6/5) k_2^2 C_4$ due to the surrounding Ti^{4+} is largest; i.e., $k_2^2 \gg k_1^2$. As the Ti^{4+} ions are probably the most mobile in the lattice, the inequality may well hold true, leaving a positive A_2^0 as the dominant contribution to the axial field.

REFERENCES

[1] K. A. MÜLLER, *Helv. Phys. Acta* **31**, 173, (1958).

[2] K. A. MÜLLER, *7ème Colloque Ampère, Arch. Sci. (Genève)* **11**, 150 (1958).

[3] K. A. MÜLLER, *Phys. Rev. Letters* **2**, 341 (1959).

[4] K. A. MÜLLER, Proc. Ist Int. Conf. Paramagnetic Resonance, Academic Press, New York, 1963, p. 17.

[5] J. SIERRO, *Helv. Phys. Acta* **34**, 404 (1961).

[6] L. RIMAI, AND G. A. DE MARS, Proc. Ist Int. Conf. Paramagnetic Resonance, Academic Press, New York, 1963, p. 51.

[7] R. W. G. WYCKOFF, *Crystal Structures*, Vol. I, Interscience Publishers, New York, 1951.

[8] H. E. WEAVER, *J. Phys. Chem. Solids* **11**, 274 (1959).

[9] Y. TANABE AND S. SUGANO, *J. Phys. Soc. Japan* **9**, 753 (1954).

[10] J. S. GRIFFITH, *The Theory of Transition Metal Ions*, Cambridge University Press, 1961, p. 423.

[11] H. J. GERRITSEN, Proc. Ist. Int. Conf. Paramagnetic Resonance, Academic Press, New York, 1963, p. 3.

[12] J. W. ORTON, P. AUZINS AND J. E. WERTZ, *Phys. Rev. Letters* **4**, 128, (1960).

[13] Z. SROUBECK, *Czech. J. Physics* **B11**, 634 (1961).

[14] W. LOW AND R. S. RUBINS, Proc. Ist Int. Conf. Paramagnetic Resonance, Academic Press, New York, 1963, p. 79.

[15] J. W. ORTON, P. AUZINS, J. H. E. GRIFFITHS AND J. E. WERTZ, *Proc. Phys. Soc. (London)* **78**, 554 (1961).

[16] A. ABRAGAM AND M. H. L. PRYCE, *Proc. Roy. Soc.* **A63**, 409 (1950).

[17] B. D. SILVERMAN, *Phys. Rev.* **125**, 1921 (1962).

[18] D. KIRO, W. LOW AND A. SUSSMAN, Proc. Ist. Int. Conf. Paramagnetic Resonance, Academic Press, New York, 1963, p. 44.

Paramagnetic Resonance of Fe^{3+} in Spinel-type Single Crystals

V. J. FOLEN

U. S. Naval Research Laboratory, Washington 25, D. C., U. S. A.

ABSTRACT

Measurements of the ESR spectra are reported for Fe^{3+} in single crystals of "ordered" and "disordered" lithium aluminate ($Li_{0.5}Al_{2.5}O_4$) and "ordered" lithium gallate ($Li_{0.5}Ga_{2.5}O_4$). Both of these compounds are isomorphous with the spinel lithium ferrite ($Li_{0.5}Fe_{2.5}O_4$). For the tetrahedral sites, the values $|D| = 0.104$ cm⁻¹, $|a - F| = 0.0166$ cm⁻¹, and $g_{\parallel} = 2.006 \pm 0.002$ were obtained in the "ordered" aluminate and the values $|D| = 0.080$ cm⁻¹ and $g_{\parallel} = 2.008 \pm 0.003$ were obtained in the gallate. The broad line widths in the spectrum of the "disordered" aluminate prevented quantitative determination of the crystal field parameters in this state. A discussion is given of: (1) the influence of the distribution of nearest neighbor cations on ESR line width; (2) the variation of D with lattice constant in isomorphous crystals and (3) the interpretation of the magnetocrystalline anisotropy of $Li_{0.5}Fe_{2.5}O_4$ on the basis of the crystalline field parameters in the aluminate and the gallate.

Introduction

Trivalent iron possesses a $3d^5 - {}^6S_{5/2}$ ground state configuration which splits into a quartet and doublet under the influence of a cubic crystal field [1] alone, and into three Kramers doublets under the influence of an additional axial or rhombic crystal field [2]. In principle, these splittings may arise [1; 2] from the combination action of the crystal field and the spin-orbit interaction or the crystal field and the intra-spin interaction, but the specific mechanisms responsible for these splittings and thus the origins of the various terms in the ferric ion spin-Hamiltonian have not been determined. Considerable attention has been given to experimental (ESR) and theoretical studies of these spin-Hamiltonian terms for the purpose of understanding the mechanisms responsible for the S-state splittings. In addition, there has been considerable interest in the application of ESR studies in diamagnetic crystals to the interpretation of properties of ferrimagnetic materials that are structurally related to these crystals. The reason for the latter interest is due to the success of the "one-ion" model in the interpretation of magnetocrystalline anisotropy [3–6] and other properties of ferrimagnetic compounds. Since the magnetic properties that are predictable by this model depend only on the kind of magnetic ion under consideration and on the crystal structure of the ferrimagnetic compound, rather than on the interactions between the magnetic ions, one can interpret these properties with the use of the crystalline electric field parameters obtained from ESR measurements on doped diamagnetic single crystals which are isomorphous with the ferrimagnetic compound. In the important class of ferrimagnets having the spinel structure, i.e., the ferrites, the only previous studies of the ferric ion (the major cation constituent in ferrites) have been in polycrystals [7]. In this work Sugiura [7] determined the cubic crystalline electric field parameter, a, by interpreting the line widths in polycrystalline $MgAl_2O_4$ and $ZnAl_2O_4$. Attempts [7] to determine the crystalline field parameters in single crystals of these spinels were unsuccessful because of the broadness of the Fe^{3+} ESR lines in the single crystals of $MgAl_2O_4$ and because of the difficulty in obtaining single crystals of $ZnAl_2O_4$.

The present paper contains a review of our studies [8] of the ESR spectra for Fe^{3+} in both long range "ordered" and "disordered" single crystals of lithium aluminate $(Li_{0.5}Al_{2.5}O_4)$ which is isomorphous with lithium ferrite $(Li_{0.5}Fe_{2.5}O_4)$. In addition, experimental results on the ESR spectra for Fe^{3+} in lithium gallate $(Li_{0.5}Ga_{2.5}O_4)$ are presented. These results are then discussed in relation to: (1) the influence of the distribution of nearest neighbor cations on ESR line width; (2) the variation of D with lattice constant in isomorphous crystals; and (3) the interpretation of the magnetocrystalline anisotropy in $Li_{0.5}Fe_{2.5}O_4$ on the basis of the crystalline field parameters in the aluminate and the gallate.

Crystallography and experimental methods

In the spinel structure, the cations reside in two types of sites, the tetrahedral (A) sites and octahedral (B) sites which have four and six nearest neighbor oxygen ions, respectively. The space groups [9] for the long range "disordered" and "ordered" $Li_{0.5}M_{2.5}^{3+}O_4$ are $O_h(7)$-$Fd3m$ and $O(6)$-$P4_3 3$ or $P4_1 3$, respectively. Here M^{3+} can be Fe^{3+}, Ga^{3+} or Al^{3+}. In the case of $Li_{0.5}Ga_{2.5}O_4$ there is evidence [10] that only the "ordered" structure occurs. The symmetries of the various trivalent cation sites in the "ordered" and "disordered" structures are shown in Table I. In the "ordered structure

TABLE I

Symmetries at trivalent cation sites in "ordered" and "disordered" structures

State	Tetrahedral (A) site symmetry	Octahedral (B) site symmetry
"Ordered"	3	2
"Disordered"	$\bar{4}$ 3 m	$\bar{3}$ m

the three-fold and two-fold axes are in the [111] and [110] directions, respectively and in the "disordered" structure the three-fold axes are in the [111] directions.

The $Li_{0.5}Al_{2.5}O_4$ and $Li_{0.5}Ga_{2.5}O_4$ single crystals were synthesized using flux [11; 12] techniques. The aluminate was grown in a combined flux of PbO and PbF_2, and the gallate was grown in a pure PbO flux. In the synthesis of both types of crystals a lowering rate of 1°C per hour from 1300°C was used. The "disordering" of the aluminate was produced by quenching from 1350°C in water, and the "ordered" state was produced by cooling at the rate of 10°C per hour from 1300°C. Measurements of the intensities of the superstructure lines in the X-ray patterns obtained from single crystals which had been powdered enabled us to determine the degree of long range order. The lattice parameters of the single crystals of $Li_{0.5}Al_{2.5}O_4$, $Li_{0.5}Ga_{2.5}O_4$, and $Li_{0.5}Fe_{2.5}O_4$ were found to be 7.92Å, 8.23Å, and 8.33Å, respectively.

The measurements of the ESR spectra were made at 24 kMc using a stabilized microwave oscillator (Laboratory for Electronics, Model 817–K–24 and a cylindrical TE_{011} transmission cavity. A silicon diode was used to detect the cavity output which was then amplified in a narrow band 1000-cps amplifier, phase detected, and finally displayed as the first derivative of an absorption curve on an X-Y recorder. The magnetic field was sinusoidally modulated at 1000cps and was measured using proton and lithium nuclear resonance.

Theory

The ESR spectra of the aluminate and gallate were analyzed using the spin-Hamiltonian [2; 13]

$$\mathcal{H} = g\beta\mathbf{H}\cdot\mathbf{S} + (a/6)(S_\xi^4 + S_\eta^4 + S_\zeta^4 - 707/16)$$
$$+ D(S_z^2 - 35/12) + E(S_x^2 - S_y^2) \tag{1}$$
$$+ (7/36)F[S_z^4 - (95/14)S_z^2 + 81/16]$$

where the z axis is in the direction of the axial crystalline field. For a magnetic field at an angle θ with respect to this axis, the value of H (to third order in D) corresponding to the $1/2 \leftrightarrow -1/2$ transition is obtained from

$$H = H_0 + 8D^2\sin^2\theta\cos^2\theta[(H+q)^{-1} + (H-q)^{-1}] - \tfrac{1}{2}D^2\sin^4\theta[9(2H-q)^{-1}$$
$$+ 9(2H+q)^{-1} - 5(2H-3q)^{-1} - 5(2H+3q)^{-1}] \tag{2}$$
$$- 40D^3\cos^2\theta\sin^4\theta\{[(H+q)(2H+3q)]^{-1} - [(H-q)(2H-3q)]^{-1}\}$$

where $H_0 = h\nu/g\beta$, $q = D(3\cos^2\theta - 1)$, and $D/(g\beta)$ is written as D.

Assuming $E = 0$, the magnetic fields of the ESR transitions for H along a trigonal axis ($\theta = 0$) are obtained from [14]

$$\pm\frac{3}{2} \leftrightarrow \pm\frac{5}{2}: H_{1,5} = H_0 \mp 4D \pm \frac{4}{3}(a - F) - (20/27)a^2(H_{1,5} \pm 2D)^{-1}$$

$$\pm\frac{1}{2} \leftrightarrow \pm\frac{3}{2}: H_{2,4} = H_0 \mp 2D \mp \frac{5}{3}(a - F) + (20/27)a^2(H_{2,4} \mp 2D)^{-1} \quad (3)$$

$$-\frac{1}{2} \leftrightarrow +\frac{1}{2}: H_3 = H_0 - (20/27)a^2\left[(H_3 + 2D)^{-1} + (H_3 - 2D)^{-1}\right]$$

where all the crystalline field parameters have now been divided by $g\beta$.

Spectra of Fe^{3+} in $Li_{0.5}Al_{2.5}O_4$

Measurements of the Fe^{3+} ESR spectra were made on the "disordered" aluminate with H in the ($\bar{1}10$) plane. From observations with H in the [111], [110] and [001] directions in this plane, it was found that the ESR spectra were very broad in these directions except for one $1/2 \leftrightarrow -1/2$ transition in the [111] spectrum (which had a line width of 40 gauss as determined by the separation between points of maximum slope in an absorption curve). As a result of the observed broadness in line width, quantitative measurements of the crystalline field parameters in the "disordered" crystals could not be made. The spectrum for H parallel to the [111] direction consisted of a broad $1/2 \rightarrow -1/2$ transition, corresponding to Fe^{3+} in trigonal fields directed along the [$\bar{1}11$], [$1\bar{1}1$] and [$11\bar{1}$] directions for which $\theta = 70.5°$. Superimposed on the transition was the 40-gauss line width $1/2 \leftrightarrow -1/2$ transition whose trigonal axis coincided with the [111] direction. In addition, $\Delta M = \pm 2$ transitions were also observed in this spectrum. From measurements of the angular variations of the resonance field and line width of the 40-gauss $1/2 \leftrightarrow -1/2$ transition, it was found that the resonance field for this transition varied in a manner described by Eq. (2) (where $\theta = 0$ when H is parallel to [111]), and that its line width was a minimum in the [111] direction. In view of the fact that the D contribution to the line width which arises from crystalline field inhomogeneities is also a minimum at $\theta = 0$, it is seen that the angular variation of the resonance field and line width are consistent with trigonal symmetry. Since the B sites possess this symmetry, it appears that a substantial number of Fe^{3+} ions are located on B sites in the "disordered" aluminate. However, the possible presence of short range order in the aluminate may influence the site allocation of the Fe^{3+} ion. The magnitude of D on the B sites was estimated (by using Eq. (2) and the measurements of the angular variation of the $1/2 \leftrightarrow -1/2$ transitions) to be approximately 0.13cm^{-1}.

In the long range "ordered" aluminate, the ESR spectrum was measured with H in the (110) plane. In this spectrum, the line widths of all the Fe^{3+} transitions were considerably smaller than in the spectrum of the "disordered" aluminate and thus the transitions were easily measurable. The angular variation of the spectrum in the (110) plane showed that there are four types of sites per unit cell and that their (trigonal) symmetry axes are along the [111], [$\bar{1}$11], [1$\bar{1}$1] and [11$\bar{1}$] directions, respectively. Except for some transitions $\Delta M = \pm 2$, all of the observed lines could be attributed to $\Delta M = \pm 1$ transitions for Fe^{3+} in these four types of sites. For example, the spectrum for H in the [111] direction consisted of $\pm 5/2 \leftrightarrow \pm 3/2$, $\pm 3/2 \leftrightarrow \pm 1/2$ and $1/2 \leftrightarrow -1/2$ transitions, as expected for one ion with $\theta = 0°$ and 3 ions with $\theta = 70.5°$. Using Eq. (3), the results of the measurements of the transitions with H parallel to [111] yielded the following values: $|D| = 0.104$ cm^{-1}, $|a - F| = 0.0166$ cm^{-1} and $g_{\parallel} = 2.006 \pm 0.002$. The sign of D was found to be the same as that $a - F$. Also, measurements of the magnetic fields occurring in Eq. (3) yielded 0.01 cm^{-1} as a preliminary value of the magnitude of a in the "ordered" aluminate. Since the symmetry of this spectrum is in accord with the symmetry of the A sites, it appears that a substantial number of Fe^{3+} ions are located on A sites in the "ordered" aluminate.

Spectra of Fe^{3+} in $Li_{0.5}Ga_{2.5}O_4$

Since it has been reported [10] that $Li_{0.5}Ga_{2.5}O_4$ exists only in the "ordered" state, no attempt was made to observe the "disordered" spectrum in this material. The ESR measurements were made on an X-ray oriented crystal which was oriented so that H was always parallel to the (110) plane. The spectrum consists of lines having trigonal symmetry along the [111] directions in accord with the A site symmetry similar to that observed in the "ordered" aluminate and, in addition, a number of lines which are presumably due to Fe^{3+} in the octahedral sites. The analysis of this latter set of lines was not completed in time for this Conference. For the set of lines which are in accord with the A site symmetry, the $\pm 5/2 \leftrightarrow \pm 3/2$ and $\pm 3/2 \leftrightarrow \pm 1/2$ lines were not sufficiently intense and narrow to be measured quantitatively. Therefore, D was evaluated with the help of Eq. (2) by measuring the angular dependence of the four $1/2 \leftrightarrow -1/2$ transitions. In particular, for $\theta = 54°44'$ the third-order term in Eq. (2) vanishes so that D was calculated from the second-order terms only by using the measured field for H at an angle of $54°44'$ with respect to the [111] axis. From these measurements we obtained the values $|D| = 0.080$ cm^{-1} and $g_{\parallel} = 2.008 \pm 0.003$. In addition to the previously mentioned $\Delta M = \pm 1$ transitions, $\Delta M = \pm 2$ transitions having intensities as large as the most intense $\Delta M = \pm 1$ transitions were observed for H in the (110) plane.

Discussion

From a comparison of the ESR line widths in "ordered" and "disordered" $Li_{0.5}Al_{2.5}O_4$, it appears that there are large inhomogeneities in the crystal line electric fields in "disordered" spinels. Such inhomogeneities may be responsible for the broadness of the Fe^{3+} ESR lines in $MgAl_2O_4$ [7] (which is a disordered spinel) as well as in "disordered" $Li_{0.5}Al_{2.5}O_4$. Additional evidence for the large crystalline field inhomogeneities in "disordered" spinels is provided by the absence of fine structure in the spectra of Mn^{2+} in single crystals of $ZnAl_2O_4$ [15] and "disordered" $Li_{0.5}Al_{2.5}O_4$ [16]. In view of the fact that the "ordering" primarily involves a rearrangement of cations, it appears that the cation distribution strongly influences the inhomogeneous broadening of the ESR lines in spinels. In addition, the magnitude of this crystalline field inhomogeneity is relevant to the Callen-Pittelli theory [17] of ferromagnetic resonance line width which is based on spin wave scattering by spatial fluctuations of the crystalline fields associated with the D term in "disordered" ferrimagnetic materials.

In comparing the measured D parameter in the "ordered" aluminate with that in the gallate, one sees that the value of D is smaller in the gallate, as one would expect on the basis of point charge calculations. Within the limitations of the point charge approximation, the ratio of the D's of these two materials may be calculated from the ratio of their axial potentials by using the fact that these potentials are proportional to the inverse cubes of the lattice constants. Using the lattice constants given earlier, the ratio of the aluminate axial potential to the gallate axial potential is 1.12, and the square of this ratio is 1.26. Comparing these numbers with the measured D ratio of 1.30, it is seen that it is most likely that the D term for the Fe^{3+} ion in these spinels arises from processes that are quadratic in the axial potential. One such process has been proposed by Watanabe [18] whose mechanism is quadratic in both the axial potential and the spin orbit interaction. It should be emphasized here that the above conclusion (based on the point charge approximation) is valid only if one neglects covalency effects.

On the basis of the "one-ion" model of magnetocrystalline anisotropy in ferrimagnetics, one can calculate the D contribution to the first order cubic anisotropy constant of the A site in "ordered" $Li_{0.5}Fe_{2.5}O_4$ by using the D value obtained for the isomorphous compound "ordered" $Li_{0.5}Fe_{2.5}O_4$. This contribution can be obtained from [5]

$$k_1 = \gamma(D^2/kT)t(y)$$

where k_1 is the first order anisotropy constant per ion, t is a certain function [5] of y, and $y = \exp(-g\beta H_m/kT)$, where H_m is the molecular field. The constant γ is 4/9 when the axial fields are along the four [111] directions. Using the molecular fields that have been evaluated [19] from saturation magnetization measurements on $Li_{0.5}Fe_{2.5}O_4$ and the D value for "ordered" lithium aluminate, one obtains $k_1 = 1.3 \times 10^{-4}$ cm^{-1} for $T = 126°K$. At this temperature the measured [20] value of k_1 for the tetrahedral sites in $Li_{0.5}Fe_{2.5}O_4$ is about 65 times larger than the value calculated from the D measured in the aluminate. Since the D value in the gallate is even smaller than that in the aluminate, the discrepancy would be even larger than the above factor if the D value of the gallate were used in this calculation. Although the D value obtained from EPR measurements on the aluminate or gallate may be different from that in the isomorphous ferrite, extrapolation (based on the ratio of the cubes of the lattice constants) of the D values in the aluminate and gallate to that in the ferrite indicates that the D in the ferrite is even smaller than in the aluminate or gallate. Thus it appears that the D contribution to k_1 is small, in agreement with the conclusion [20] based on the observed temperature dependence of the anisotropy in lithium ferrite.

From a comparison of the a value and the value of $a - F$ measured in "ordered" lithium aluminate, it is seen that the F term is comparable in magnitude with the a term. This is in accord with the conclusion [20] obtained from the effects of the "order-disorder" transition on the magneto-crystalline anisotropy in $Li_{0.5}Fe_{2.5}O_4$. Thus it is reasonable to attribute [20] a part of the anisotropy of the tetrahedral sublattice in "ordered" $Li_{0.5}Fe_{2.5}O_4$ to the F term in the spin-Hamiltonian.

Acknowledgments

The author wishes to express his gratitude to Dr. G. T. Rado for many useful discussions and R. A. Becker for assistance in the single crystal synthesis and X-ray analysis.

REFERENCES

[1] J. H. VAN VLECK AND W. G. PENNEY, *Phil. Mag.* **17**, 961 (1934).

[2] A. ABRAGAM AND M. PRYCE, *Proc. Roy. Soc.* (London) , **A205**, 135 (1951).

[3] G. T. RADO AND V. J. FOLEN, *Bull. Am. Phys. Soc.* **1**, 132 (1956); G. T. RADO. V. J. FOLEN AND W. H. EMERSON, *Proc. Inst. Elec. Engr.* (London) **104B**, Suppl. No. 5, 198 (1957); V. J. FOLEN AND G. T. RADO, *J. Appl. Phys.* **29**, 438 (1958).

[4] K. YOSIDA AND M. TACHIKI, *Progr. theoret. Phys.* (Kyoto) **17**, 331 (1957).

[5] W. P. WOLF, *Phys. Rev.* **108**, 1152 (1957).

[6] J. C. SLONCZEWSKI, *Phys. Rev.* **110**, 1341 (1958).

[7] Y. SUGIURA, *J. Phys. Soc. Japan* **15**, 1217 (1960).

[8] V. J. FOLEN, *J. Appl. Phys.* **33**, 1084 (1962).

[9] P. B. BRAUN, *Nature* **170**, 1123 (1952).

[10] R. K. DATTA, *Order-Disorder in Spinels*, The Pennsylvania State University, Ph. D Thesis (1961).

[11] J. W. NIELSON AND E. F. DEARBORN, *J. Phys. Chem. Solids* **5**, 202 (1958).

[12] J. W. NIELSON, *J. Appl. Phys.* **29**, 390 (1958).

[13] B. BLEANEY AND R. S. TRENAM, *Proc. Roy. Soc.* (London) **A223**, 1 (1954).

[14] S. GESCHWIND, *Phys. Rev.* **121**, 363 (1961).

[15] R. STAHL-BRADA AND W. LOW, *Phys. Rev.* **116**, 561 (1959).

[16] W. H. KELLY, V. J. FOLEN, M. HASS, W. N. SCHREINER AND W. G. BEARD, *Phys. Rev.* **124**, 80 (1961).

[17] H. B. CALLEN AND E. PITTELLI, *Phys. Rev.* **119**, 1523 (1960).

[18] H. WATANABE. *Progr. theoret. Phys.* (Kyoto) **18**, 405 (1957).

[19] G. T. RADO AND V. J. FOLEN, *J. Appl. Phys.* **31**, 62 (1960)

[20] V. J. FOLEN, *J. Appl. Phys.* **31**, 166S (1960).

PART I

ESR SPECTRA OF IRON GROUP ELEMENTS

B.

Paramagnetic Resonance of Iron Group and Rare Earth Impurities in Calcium Oxide*

W. LOW AND R. S. RUBINS

Department of Physics, The Hebrew University of Jerusalem, Israel

ABSTRACT

A systematic study of the magnetic properties of $3d$ and $4f$ transition ions in cubic crystalline fields is being carried out in single crystals of CaO. The results for the iron group indicate that the crystalline field in CaO is smaller than that in isomorphous MgO. Rare earth ions can also enter the larger CaO lattice, and the spectra of Eu^{2+} and Gd^{3+} have been observed for the first time in surroundings of octahedral symmetry. The sign of the initial splitting parameter c for $4f^7$ in CaO is found to be the same as that recorded for eight -fold co-ordinated CaF_2. The magnitude of the initial splitting of the $^8S_{7/2}$ (f^7) level is smaller in CaO than in CaF_2, but the reverse appears to be true for $^6S_{5/2}$ ($3d^5$). Other striking results are:
a) Large hyperfine splittings measured for Cr^{3+} and Co^{2+} in CaO, the latter being more than 30% greater than in MgO.
b) An increase in the hfs of Mn^{2+} and V^{2+} as the temperature is decreased.
c) Unusually short relaxation times in Cr^{3+}, Fe^{3+} and Ni^{2+}—a result, probably of the weaker crystalline field strength in CaO.

Introduction

Both calcium oxide and magnesium oxide form cubic crystals of the NaCl type [1], in which the divalent cation lies at the center of an octahedron of six O^{2-} ions. The anion-cation separation in CaO is 2.40 Å, compared to that of 2.10 Å in MgO. As the only difference between the two lattices is in the strength of the crystalline field interaction, a comparison of the resonance results should provide a good means of testing the applicability of the conventional crystalline field theory. In addition, rare earth ions can enter substitutionally into the larger CaO lattice, thus allowing a direct comparison to be made between the strength and sign of the crystalline field in an octahedral arrangement, and that in an eight-fold cubic coordination, such as calcium fluoride.

In this paper we describe the results of preliminary investigations of the paramagnetic resonance spectra of the iron group impurities: V^{2+}, Cr^{3+},

* The research reported in this document has been sponsored in part by the Air Force Office of Scientific Research, O.A.R., through the European Office, Aerospace Research, U.S.A.F.

Mn^{2+}, Fe^{3+}, Co^{2+} and Ni^{2+}, and the rare earth impurities: Eu^{2+} and Gd^{3+} in single crystals of CaO. The measurements were made at 3 cm wavelength in the temperature range between room and helium temperatures. The recorded spectra all showed cubic or almost-cubic symmetry, indicating that both divalent and trivalent ions replace Ca^{2+} cations without disturbing the local cubic symmetry (although weak spectra of lower than cubic symmetry have been observed in the Gd^{3+} sample).

In the following sections the results are presented in detail, ion by ion, and wherever possible comparison is made with the corresponding data for MgO or CaF_2.

The resonance results

(a) $3d^3$: V^{2+} and Cr^{3+}

Cubic spectra of V^{2+} and Cr^{3+} have been observed at room temperature with line widths (between points of half-maximum intensity) of approximately 1 gauss and 5 gauss respectively. At 77°K the Cr^{3+} line width is 1.5 gauss, and the hfs of Cr^{53} ($I = 3/2$) clearly observed.

In Table I the resonance results in CaO have been compared with those in MgO. The deviations of the measured g-values from the free electron value are considerably greater in CaO for both ions. As the relation between the g-factor and the cubic field splitting Δ is of the form $(g - g_e) \propto \lambda'/\Delta$ (where λ' is the appropriate value of the spin-orbit coupling and g_e is the free electron g-value), the deviation should be greater in CaO. If the measured g-values are inserted in the above expression, the ratio x (CaO)/ x (MgO), where $x = \lambda'/\Delta$, is found to be 1.55 for V^{2+} and 1.30 for Cr^{3+}. The ratio

TABLE I

Resonance results for $3d^3$: V^{2+} and Cr^{3+}

Ion	Lattice	Temp. (°K)	g	A(cm^{-1} × 10^4)	Reference
V^{2+}	CaO	290		76.04 ± 0.05	
		77	1.9683 ± 0.0005	76.15 ± 0.05	This paper
		20		76.22 ± 0.05	
Cr^{3+}	MgO	290	1.9803 ± 0.0005	74.3 ± 0.2	[3]
	CaO	77	1.9732 ± 0.0005	17.0 ± 0.1	This paper
	MgO	290	1.9800 ± 0.0005	16.2 ± 0.3	[4]

---

* We assume in our discussion in this paper that the deviation of the g-factor is proportional to λ'/Δ, and that all other contributions are small in comparison. However, as pointed out by Lacroix[2], there may be a non-negligible contribution from matrix elements connecting the ground state with the charge transfer states. Unfortunately, these states are not well known, and it has not been possible to estimate this contribution for MgO and CaO.

$\Delta(MgO)/\Delta(CaO)$ calculated from a point charge model is 1.95. The very small ratio deduced for Cr^{3+} may be due to a contraction of the surrounding oxygen octahedron produced by the extra positive charge of the trivalent ion, and a corresponding increase in the strength of the crystalline field*.

The ratio of hyperfine splittings $A(CaO)/A(MgO)$ of 1.02 for V^{2+} and 1.05 for Cr^{3+} is probably associated with a decrease in covalent bonding as the lattice spacing is increased, although it is surprising that the ratio is so much larger for Cr^{3+} than for V^{2+}. On the other hand, the increase of A in V^{2+}, observed as the temperature was lowered, cannot be due to covalent bonding, which would decrease A as the lattice contracts.

(b) $3d^5$: Mn^{2+} and Fe^{3+}

The experimental results for Mn^{2+} and Fe^{3+} have been fitted to the spin-Hamiltonian.

$$\mathscr{H} = g\beta H \cdot S + A S \cdot I + (1/6) a [S_x^4 + S_y^4 + S_z^4 - (1/5) S(S+1)(3S^2 + 3S - 1)]$$

The measured parameters have been given in Table II.

TABLE II

Resonance results for $3d^5$: Mn^{2+} and Fe^{3+}*

Ion	Lattice	Temp (°K)	g	A(cm^{-1} × 10^9)	a(cm^{-1} × 10^4)	Reference
Mn^{2+}	CaO	290		80.7 ± 0.1		
		77	2.0011 ± 0.0005	81.6 ± 0.1		This paper
		20		81.7 ± 0.1	6.0 ± 0.3**	
	MgO	290	2.0014 ± 0.0005	-81.0 ± 0.1	$+ 18.65 \pm 0.3$	[8]
	CaF$_2$	90	1.998 ± 0.003	97.8 ± 1.0	$\leqq 4$	[9;10]
Fe^{3+}	CaO	77			$+ 64.3 \pm 0.3$***	This paper
		20	2.0059 ± 0.0006	10.5 ± 0.5	$+ 65.1 \pm 0.3$***	This paper
	MgO	77	2.0037 ± 0.0007	10.1 ± 0.2	$+ 205$	[11;12]

* Similar results have been reported independently by A. J. Shuskus [21].
** A and a are of opposite sign.
*** a was determined positive by means of a separate measurement made at 4.2°K

---

* A more tightly bound lattice, besides producing a stronger crystalline field, will also increase the degree of covalent bonding, thus decreasing the effective value of the spin-orbit coupling constant.

The g-and A-factors for Mn^{2+} in CaO agree closely with those measured in MgO, but the fine structure splitting is about three times smaller than that in MgO. A reduction of about 30% in the strength of the crystalline field is sufficient to explain this difference, as the initial splitting is expected to vary as $\lambda^4 \Delta^n$, with $3 \leq n \leq 6$ in this range of field strengths [5; 6]. The Mn^{2+} line widths are quite narrow at room temperature, varying from about 2.5 gauss for $(|S_z = 1/2\rangle \leftrightarrow |S_z = -1/2\rangle)$ transitions to 4 gauss for $(|\pm 5/2\rangle \leftrightarrow |\pm 3/2\rangle)$ transitions.

The fine structure splitting in Fe^{3+} is again three times smaller in CaO than in MgO. The Fe^{3+} g-values are somewhat greater than the free electron value, possibly as a result of charge transfer [2] or of covalent bonding [7]. The deviation is, however, considerably greater in CaO, where the degree of covalent bonding should be smaller. The Fe^{3+} lines are considerably broadened at room temperature. At 77°K, the measured line widths are approximately 13 gauss for the central $(|1/2\rangle \leftrightarrow |-1/2\rangle)$ transition and 16 gauss for the $(|\pm 3/2\rangle \leftrightarrow |\pm 1/2\rangle)$ transitions: at 20°K, the corresponding values are 2 gauss and 8 gauss, and it is possible to observe the hfs of Fe^{57} $(I = 1/2)$. In both Mn^{2+} and Fe^{3+}, a is observed to increase slightly as the temperature is decreased, indicating that the lattice contracts slightly. An "anomalous" increase in the hfs with decreasing temperature is also observed in Mn^{2+}.

(c) $3d^7$: Co^{2+}

The resonance results for Co^{2+} in CaO and MgO are compared in Table III: the g-factor is about 2% greater and the A-factor over 30% greater in CaO. The g-and A-factors of Co^{2+} in an octahedral field [13;14] are given theoretically by

$$g = \frac{10}{3} + \frac{2}{3}k\alpha - \frac{15}{2}\frac{\lambda'}{\Delta}, \tag{1}$$

$$A = N^2 P \left[\frac{2}{3}\alpha - \frac{5}{3}\kappa + \frac{2}{63}(1 - 15\tau^2) - \frac{15}{2}\frac{\lambda'}{\Delta} \right] \tag{2}$$

where $-\alpha$ is the effective orbital momentum of the Γ_4 triplet, τ is the amplitude of the admixture of the ^4P to the ^4F state, $P = 2g_N \beta \beta_N \langle r^{-3} \rangle$, κ is the unpaired electron contribution, Δ is the separation of the Γ_4 and Γ_5 components of the ^4F state, λ' is the reduced value of the spin-orbit coupling, k is the orbital reduction factor, and N^2 is a normalization factor depending on charge transfer. The last term in the expression for A arises through matrix elements of the form

$$\sum_n \frac{\langle o | \lambda' L \cdot S | n \rangle \langle n | N^2 P(L - \kappa S) | o \rangle}{\Delta}$$

where $|o\rangle$ represents the ground doublet and the $|n\rangle$ are the Γ_5 levels. The second order contribution to the hyperfine structure may be written

$$A^{(2)} = N^2 P(g_L^{(2)} - \frac{1}{2} \kappa g_s^{(2)}),$$

where $g_L^{(2)} = -\frac{15}{2}\frac{\lambda'}{\Delta}$ and $g_S^{(2)} = 0$. An additional term in the hyperfine structure proportional to λ'/Δ arises from cross-interactions between the spin-orbit coupling and the operator $P\xi[(\mathbf{L} \cdot \mathbf{S})(\mathbf{L} \cdot \mathbf{I}) + (\mathbf{L} \cdot \mathbf{I})(\mathbf{L} \cdot \mathbf{S})]$. This term is less than a tenth of the former term and has been neglected.

In view of the large number of unknowns in Eqs. (1) and (2) many of whose magnitudes can be estimated only approximately, it is not possible to obtain exact quantitative reduction of the experimental data. It is possible, however, to postulate several effects which will combine to increase g and A in CaO relative to MgO:

(1) The second-order terms proportional to λ'/Δ (denoted by x) are of greater importance in CaO, where the crystalline field is smaller and the effective value of the spin-orbit coupling constant is probably larger. An indication of the size of this effect is given by the results for V^{2+} and Ni^{2+}, and in the following calculations the ratio $x(CaO)/x(MgO)$ has been taken as 1.55.

(2) The admixture of the ^4P to the ^4F state by the crystalline field is smaller in CaO: the magnitude of α is therefore greater, and that of τ smaller in CaO — effects which should increase both A and g. The roughly linear relationship between E_p (the separation of the ^4P and ^4F levels extrapolated to zero field) and Δ[17] may be used to estimate E_p for CaO. If E_p is taken to be 13.500 cm^{-1} and Δ is assumed to be 1.5 times smaller in CaO than in MgO, then α is found to be 1.44 for CaO and 1.385 for MgO: the corresponding values of τ^2 are 0.039 and 0.020 respectively.

(3) A reduction in the strength of the covalent bonding, and therefore an increase in magnitude of both N^2 and k, would be expected in CaO. As it is not possible to estimate these differences a priori, N^2 and k have been evaluated by fitting the theoretical expressions to the experimental results. In order to do this, it is necessary to assume values for P and κ: those of Pryce [14], $P = 0.022$ cm^{-1} and $\kappa = 0.32$, have been used. The parameter k calculated from Eq. (1) is 0.89 for both CaO and MgO, and N^2, obtained from Eq. (2), is 0.95 for CaO and 0.85 for MgO. These values, though of the expected orders of magnitude, cannot be taken too seriously, in view of the approximations used in their derivation.

The symmetry of the Co^{2+} site in CaO—like that of isoelectronic Fe^{1+} in

MgO [16]—is not perfectly cubic. In both cases, an angular variation of the line width indicates that there are three inequivalent ion sites in the unit cell, each having a small tetragonal distortion along one of the three fourfold axes of the cube. In the Co^{2+} spectrum in CaO, there is also an additional variation of the line width across the hyperfine structure, such that the extreme high field hyperfine line is narrowest, and the extreme lowfield line broadest; e.g. in the [100] orientation the variation is from 3 gauss to 4 gauss, and in the [110] orientation from 2 gauss to 3 gauss. Such a variation can be explained, qualitatively at least, by the anisotropy in the hyperfine structure which would follow anisotropy in the g-factor.

(d) $3d^8$: Ni^{2+}

The Ni^{2+} spectrum in CaO (Table III) consists of three characteristic components:

(a) a broad line (width $\simeq$ 95 gauss) with $g = 2.32 \pm 0.01$, visible at 20°K;

(b) a narrow line with $g = 2.327 \pm 0.001$, phase inverted and 3 gauss wide at 20°K, but of normal phase and 1 gauss wide at 14°K;

(c) a narrow absorption edge (width $\simeq$ 1 gauss) with $g = 4.654 \pm 0.002$. The lines (a) and (b) have been observed previously from Ni^{2+} in MgO [15] and $SrTiO_3$ [18], and are attributed to the normal $\Delta M = \pm 1$ and double quantum transition respectively. The inverted line observed at the center of the broad line (see Plate 1a) at 20°K, using small microwave power, has not yet been explained. As pointed out by Orton et al., it does not appear to be connected with the double quantum transition. As the temperature is lowered or the microwave power increased, the double quantum line is observed to develop at the center of the inverted line (see Plate 1b), until finally only the

TABLE III

The resonance results for $3d^7$: Co^{2+} and $3d^8$: Ni^{2+}

Ion	Lattice	Temp (°K)	g	A(cm^{-1} × 10^4)	Reference
Co^{2+}	CaO	20	4.372 $\pm$ 0.002	132.2 $\pm$ 0.2	This paper
	MgO	20	4.278 $\pm$ 0.001	97.8 $\pm$ 0.2	[13;14]
Ni^{2+}	CaO	20 $\rbrace$	2.327 $\pm$ 0.001*	?	This paper
		4.2			[15;16]
	MgO	77	2.2145 $\pm$ 0.0005*	8.3 $\pm$ 0.4(a)	

* These values were obtained by measurements made either on the double quantum transition or on the phase inverted line (see text).

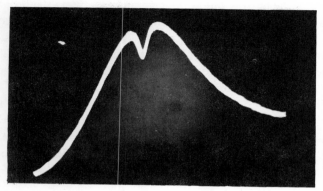

Plate 1a
The phase-inverted line at the center of the broad Ni^{2+} line in CaO at 20°K.

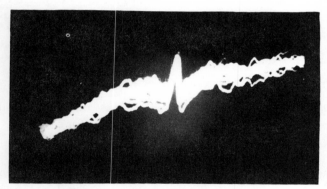

Plate 1b
The development of the double quantum jump within the phase-inverted line.

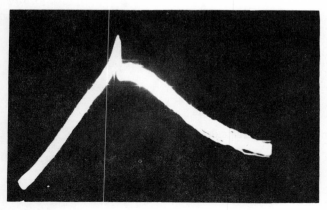

Plate 1c
Double and single quantum jumps of Ni^{2+} at about 14°K

double quantum line is observed on the broad line (Plate 1c). There is an indication that the narrow line is not centered exactly on the broad line, but lies slightly on the low-field side of it. At 4.2°K, both single and double quantum jumps show saturation effects. The low-field edge (c) has the characteristic shape and g-factor of a "forbidden" $\Delta M = \pm 2$ transition [19].

The relation between g-factor and cubic field is again of the form $(g - g_E) \propto \lambda'/\Delta$. A calculation identical to that carried out for V^{2+} leads to $x(CaO)/x(MgO) = 1.53$ — a value in excellent agreement with the ratio of 1.55 obtained for V^{2+}. The Ni^{2+} spectrum is not observed above 20°K — an unusually low temperature for this ion—probably as a result of the short relaxation time associated with the small crystalline field splitting in CaO.

(e) $4f^7$: Eu^{2+} and Gd^{3+}

The experimental results have been fitted to the cubic spin-Hamiltonian

$$\mathcal{H} = g\beta\mathbf{H\cdot S} + A\mathbf{S\cdot I} + B_4(O_4^0 + 5\,O_4^4) + B_6(O_6^0 - 21\,O_6^6)$$

The measured parameters have been given in Table IV, where $c = 240\,B_4$ and $d = 5040\,B_6$. The Gd^{3+} line widths were broader than those previously encountered from "odd-electron" ions, varying at 77°K from 17 gauss for the central $(\left|\frac{1}{2}\right\rangle \leftrightarrow \left|-\frac{1}{2}\right\rangle)$ transition to 21 gauss for the outermost $(\left|\pm\frac{5}{2}\right\rangle \leftrightarrow \left|\pm\frac{7}{2}\right\rangle)$ transition. The central electronic lines in Eu^{2+} were approximately 4 gauss wide, but the outer sets of hyperfine lines could not be distinguished clearly, so that a rough estimate only has been given for c.

The sign of the initial splitting parameter c is negative for Gd^{3+} in CaO, negative for Eu^{2+} in CaF_2 and probably also negative for Gd^{3+} in CaF_2: this is similar to the case of the $3d^5$ ·ions in which the sign of the initial splitting is independent of that of the fourth order crystal field. A comparison of the magnitudes of the fouth order splitting terms in CaO and CaF_2 lead to some apparent contradictions, because the ground splittings for f^7—unlike those for d^5 (see Table II) — are considerably smaller in CaO than in CaF_2. If the crystalline potential be written

$$V = C_4(x^4 + y^4 + z^4 - \frac{3}{5}r^4) + D_6\left[x^6 + y^6 + z^6 + \frac{15}{4}(x^4y^2 + x^2y^4 + \right.$$
$$\left. + y^4z^2 + y^2z^4 + z^4x^2 + z^2x^4) - \frac{15}{14}r^6\right]$$

a simple point charge calculation gives:

(a) $C = +35e/4d^5$ and $D = -21e/2d^7$ for the 6-fold coordination,

TABLE IV

Resonance results for $4f^7*$: Eu^{2+} and Gd^{3+}

Ion	Lattice	Temp.	g	A(cm^{-1} × 10^4)	c(cm^{-1} × 10^4)	d(cm^{-1} × 10^4)	Reference
Eu^{2+}	CaO	77	1.9941 ± 0.0005	A^{151} = 30.1 ± 0.2 / A^{153} = 13.4 ± 0.2	≲ 115		This paper
	CaF$_2$	90	1.989 ± 0.002	A^{151} = 34.5 ± 0.2 / A^{153} = 15.4 ± 0.1	−231.6 ± 0.8	+ 2.0 ± 0.8	[9]
Gd^{3+}	CaO	290	1.9922 ± 0.0005	—	− 45.8 ± 0.4	+ 4.3 ± 0.4	This paper
		77		—	− 48.7 ± 0.2	+ 4.7 ± 0.2	
		4.2		—	− 48.8 ± 0.2**	+ 4.8 ± 0.2	
	CaF$_2$	290	1.991 ± 0.002	—	−185 ± 5***	+ 4 ± 2	[20]

* Similar results have been reported independently by A. J. Shuskus [22].

** c was determined negative by means of intensity measurements made at 4.2°K. We wish to thank A. J. Shuskus (private communication) for pointing out a mistake in the sign of c for Gd^{3+} in CaO given in error in ref. [23].

*** The positive sign given for c in [20] is probably wrong, as it appears unlikely that the sign will differ between Eu^{2+} and Gd^{3+}.

(b) $C = -70e/9d^5$ and $D = -224e/9d^7$ for the 8-fold coordination, where d is in each case the anion-cation separation. The calculated value of the fourth-order term in CaO is found to be about three times that in CaF_2 — in qualitative agreement with the results for Mn^{2+} in the two lattices. At present there is no theory giving explicit expressions for the initial splitting of f^7, but it seems apparent that the sixth-order potential plays an important role in determining the magnitude, and possibly the sign also, of the overall splitting.

Discussion

From the preceding account it can be seen that many of the resonance results in CaO may be interpreted semi-quantitatively by postulating a crystalline field smaller than that in MgO. The most important effects produced by a smaller crystalline field interaction may be summarized as follows:
(a) the g-values for F-state ions (d^3, d^7 and d^8) show greater deviations from the free electron value;
(b) certain ions—Cr^{3+}, Fe^{3+}, and Ni^{2+}—require lower temperatures than is usual for their observation, indicative of shorter than normal spin-lattice relaxation times;
(c) slightly larger hyperfine structure splittings (except for Mn^{2+}, which showed a slightly smaller splitting than in MgO, and Co^{2+}, where there was an increase of over 30% in the hfs) are probably related to a decrease in the strength of covalent bonding.

The results for rare earth ions have been discussed in the previous section. We hope shortly to carry out measurements on non S-state rare earth ions in CaO. It will be interesting to see if such ions appear in sites of cubic symmetry, or whether lower symmetry positions are more favorable. In either case interesting comparisons between the 6-fold and 8-fold coordinations should be possible. Work on the effects of radiation on these crystals is also in progress.

Acknowledgment

The authors would like to thank Dr. B. Venkataraman of the Tata Institute of Fundamental Research, Bombay, for his help in carrying out some of the experiments.

REFERENCES

[1]   R.W. G.WYCKOFF, *Crystal Structures*, New York Interscience Publishers, Vol. I, 1951.
[2]   R. LACROIX, *Comptes Rendus* **252**, 1768 (1961).
[3]   W. Low, *Phys. Rev.* **101**, 1827 (1956).
[4]   W. Low, *Phys Rev.* **105**, 801 (1957).

[5]   J. R. GABRIEL, D. F. JOHNSTON AND M. J. D. POWELL, *Proc. Roy. Soc.* **A264,** 503 (1961).
[6]   W. LOW AND G. ROSENGARTEN, Proc. Ist. Int. Conf. Paramagnetic Resonance, Academic Press, New York, 1963 p. 314.
[7]   I. FIDONE AND K. W. H. STEVENS, *Proc. Phys. Soc.* (London), **73,** 116 (1959).
[8]   W. LOW, *Phys. Rev.* **105,** 793 (1957).
[9]   J. M. BAKER, B. BLEANEY AND W. HAYES, *Proc. Roy. Soc.* **A247,** 141 (1958). 883 (1961).
[10] T. P. P. HALL, W. HAYES AND F. I. B. WILLIAMS, *Proc. Phys. Soc.* (London) **78,** 883 (1961).
[11] W. LOW, *Proc. Phys. Soc.* (London) **B69,** 1169 (1956).
[12] E. S. ROSENVASSER AND G. FEHER, *Bull. Am. Phys. Soc.* **II 6,** 117 (1961).
[13] W. LOW, *Phys. Rev.* **109,** 256 (1958).
[14] D. J. I. FRY AND P. M. LLEWELLYN, *Proc. Roy. Soc.* **A266,** 84 (1962). (Appendix by M. H. L. PRYCE)
[15] J. W. ORTON, P. AUZINS AND J. E. WERTZ, *Phys. Rev. Letters* **4,** 128 (1960).
[16] J. W. ORTON, P. AUZINS, J. H. E. GRIFFITHS AND J. E. WERTZ, *Proc. Phys. Soc.* (London), **78,** 554 (1961).
[17] R. STAHL-BRADA AND W. LOW, *Phys. Rev.* **113,** 775 (1959).
[18] R. S. RUBINS AND W. LOW, Proc. Ist. Int. Conf. Paragmagnetic Resonance, Academic Press, New York, 1963 p. 59.
[19] W. LOW AND M. WEGER, *Phys. Rev.* **118,** 1130 (1960).
[20] W. LOW, *Phys. Rev.* **109,** 265 (1958).
[21] A. J. SHUSKUS, *Phys. Rev.* **127,** 1529 (1962).
[22] A. J. SHUSKUS, *Phys. Rev.* **127,** 2022 (1962).
[23] W. LOW AND R. S. RUBINS, *Physics Letters* **1,** 316 (1962).

Electron Spin Resonance Studies of Impurities in II-VI Compounds

P. Auzins, J. W. Orton and J. E. Wertz

*Department of Chemistry, University of Minnesota,
Mullard Laboratories, Salfords, Surrey, England*

ABSTRACT

Magnesium oxide serves as a nearly ideal host for electron spin resonance observations of transition metal ions. Other oxides, sulfides and selenides of the alkaline earth metals have also been used as hosts. For most ions, it is readily possible to change the valence state by irradiation or other treatment. The impurity which is usually present in MgO without doping is iron, which may be observed in single crystals in its mono-, di- and trivalent forms. Other ions which have been observed are those of vanadium, chromium, manganese, cobalt, nickel, copper, ruthenium, rhodium, palladium and gadolinium. Hosts other than MgO were in the form of powders, and hence our observations were limited to isotropic spectra or those having a very small zero-field splitting. Strontium sulfide is outstanding for the number of spectra seen, giving sharper lines than any of the other powdered hosts. As the radius of the host cation increases relative to that of a substitutional cation, one comes to a host in which the spectrum of this impurity ion is not observed. However, the ESR spectra of larger impurity ions may be seen. It is possible that factors other than size alone are involved.

When the size of the substitutional ion is smaller than that of the vacancy and no isotropic spectrum is seen, there are two possibilities. If the ion is only very slightly smaller than the vacancy, it may "rattle" in random fashion. If it is much smaller, the substitutional ion will tend to be bound close to one of its neighbors and show an axial component of symmetry.

For every two trivalent impurity ions incorporated into a II-VI compound, one positive ion vacancy is also incorporated. Positive holes, created by irradiation of crystalline MgO are trapped on oxygen atoms adjacent to such positive ion vacancies, forming V_1 centers. These centers have now been detected in powders of MgO, CaO and SrO. Although their ESR spectrum is anisotropic, one sees an asymmetric line at its turning point, corresponding to centers with axes oriented nearly perpendicular to the magnetic field. Two kinds of trapped electron centers (F and F_2) are also observed in nearly all the II-VI compounds.

Introduction

In recent years a number of papers have dealt with the ESR spectra of iron group ions in MgO. It provides a very useful host lattice largely for two reasons; the crystal structure is simple cubic (NaCl-type) and the ionic radius of Mg^{2+} (0.65Å) is close to that of the iron group (Table IA). The stable ions measured so far in single crystals include V^{2+}, Cr^{3+},

90

Mn^{2+}, Fe^{3+}, Fe^{2+}, Co^{2+}, Ni^{2+} and Cu^{2+} [1–7]. Also, following X-irradiation, Fe^{1+}, Co^{1+} and Ni^{1+} have been detected [6]. The results on all these ions indicate that they substitute for Mg^{2+} in the MgO lattice and that the local symmetry is accurately cubic. (An "anomalous" spectrum of Mn^{2+} in MgO, CaO and CaSe described later may be evidence for inclusion of ions at other than substitutional sites.) Cr^{3+} and Fe^{3+} also show spectra arising from ions in non-cubic sites where the symmetry is thought to be altered by associated positive ion vacancies.

It is of some interest to extend this work to other, similar lattices. The oxides, sulphides, selenides and tellurides of magnesium, calcium, strontium and barium form an ideal series for such a study as they all (with the single exception of MgTe) crystallize in the same cubic form. Measured inter-atomic spacings are given in Table IB. The chief drawback at the moment

TABLE IA

"Crystal" radii of ions in Å [8]

O^{2-}	S^{2-}	Se^{2-}	Te^{2-}	F^-		
1.40	1.84	1.98	2.21	1.36		
Mg^{2+}	Ca^{2+}	Sr^{2+}	Ba^{2+}	Zn^{2+}		
0.65	0.99	1.13	1.35	0.74		
V^{2+}	Cr^{2+}	Mn^{2+}	Fe^{2+}	Co^{2+}	Ni^{2+}	
0.88	0.84	0.80	0.76	0.74	0.72	
Rh^{3+}[15]	Pd^{2+}	V^{3+}	Cr^{3+}	Mn^{3+}	Fe^{3+}	Gd^{3+}
0.69	0.86	0.74	0.69	0.66	0.64	1.02

TABLE IB

Observed interatomic distances in crystals [8]

	Mg^{2+}	Ca^{2+}	Sr^{2+}	Ba^{2+}
O^{2-}	2.10	2.40	2.54	2.75
S^{2-}	2.54	2.83	3.00	3.18
Se^{2-}	2.72	2.96	3.11	3.31
Te^{2-}	Not cubic	3.17	3.33	3.50

is the difficulty of obtaining single crystals of any of these other than MgO and CaO, though this is not so serious as might at first appear. All the above ions except Mn^{2+}, Fe^{3+} and Gd^{3+} give isotropic spectra and may therefore be investigated in powders. Even the *S*-state ions show an iso-tropic $1/2 \leftrightarrow -1/2$ transition provided the cubic field splitting is not too large. Several papers have been devoted to transition metal ions in powders [4; 5].

Any such investigation as this immediately raises the question as to what happens when one attempts to substitute impurity ions which do not "fit" the host lattice. In particular, the ionic radii of Ca^{2+}, Sr^{2+} and Ba^{2+} are progressively larger than those of any iron group ions, Ba^{2+} being roughly twice as big as many of them (Table IA). On the other hand, rare earth ions are much closer in size to Ca^{2+} and Sr^{2+}, being much larger than Mg^{2+}. It is this question with which we are concerned here.

Experimental

We have examined the ESR spectra of powder samples of the oxides, sulphides and selenides of magnesium, calcium, strontium and barium containing the ions V^{2+}, Cr^{3+}, Mn^{2+}, Fe^{3+}, Co^{2+}, Ni^{2+}, Gd^{3+} and Cu^{2+}, as well as ions from Ru, Rh and Pd. The preparation of these samples is given below. The ESR spectrometer operated at 9.2 Gc/s and employed 300 c/s modulation, balanced bolometer detection and recorder display of the first derivative of the absorption. Most of the measurements were made at room temperature and at $77°K$, but the samples containing Co^{2+}, Fe^{1+}, Ni^{2+} and Ni^{1+} were examined at $20°K$ also. The g-values were measured with the aid of a Hewlett-Packard 524D frequency counter, measuring microwave and proton resonance frequencies in the same field.

Preparation of samples

Oxides. Two different procedures were used to get doped oxides which were low in concentration of undesired impurities. The first is to suspend alkaline earth oxide or carbonate powders in dilute solutions of the chloride of the desired paramagnetic ion and heat to dryness. The powder is then heated directly with a methane-oxygen flame. The maximum ratio of impurity to intrinsic cation was 0.01.

A preferable procedure (since it is more often successful) is to start with a solution to an alkaline earth nitrate and add the chloride of the doping salt. After careful evaporation to dryness, the material was heated in a graphite crucible with a methane-oxygen or hydrogen-oxygen flame until the oxide began to sublime. For preparation of BaO, the iodate was used instead of the nitrate. In some cases strontium hydroxide was used as starting material, since its solubility in hot water is adequate.

The high rate of cooling plus the low concentrations of doping salts insures that enough impurity ions will be substitutionally distributed at isolated sites so that those listed here may readily be detected by their ESR spectrum. It is very probable that aggregations of impurities were also present, but in a powder these would not be detected by the ESR technique.

A single crystal of "pure" CaO supplied by Semi-Elements, Inc., Saxon-burg, Pa., was also examined.

Sulfides. Sulfates were generally used as starting materials, although sulfites were also used. The solid alkaline earth sulfate powder was wetted with the doping ion solution when the sulfate of the latter was soluble. In other cases, an alkaline earth chloride was mixed with the chloride of the doping ion and sodium sulfate solution added. The sulfate precipitate was dried and then heated in a quartz tube at 900°C while a stream of helium carrying CS_2 vapor was passed over it. When no more sulfur was evolved, the CS_2 was eliminated from the flowing helium and heating continued. The temperature was then increased until the sulfide began to sublime. The flow of helium was continued until the sulfide had cooled to room temperature.

Selenides. An aqueous solution of the alkaline earth chloride and the doping ion was added to aqueous sodium selenite. The resulting precipitate was filtered and repeatedly washed. In some cases it was found necessary to suspend the selenite in another portion of doping solution to achieve the desired doping level. After gentle heating in a crucible to dispose of water, the powder was heated in a quartz tube with a flow of dry NH_3 gas. When evolution of selenium ceased, the ammonia stream was replaced by helium. Heating was continued at progressively higher temperatures until sublimation began to occur.

While strontium and barium selenides are easily produced by this method, those of magnesium and calcium give some difficulty. There is a tendency toward formation of the oxide and of free selenium.

When doping of selenides was not required, these were made by allowing selenium vapor in a stream of hydrogen gas to flow over the heated alkaline earth hydride. The latter is made from the metal by heating in hydrogen and later grinding to a powder.

Tellurides. These were made by passing tellurium vapors over the hydride, as indicated in the previous paragraph. The products made in this way showed considerable microwave losses, the latter being so great with BaTe that no measurements were possible. Selenides prepared from the elements gave this difficulty in lesser measure.

Results

1. *S-state ions*

In order that resonance may be seen directly in powder samples, it is essential that the spectrum should be isotropic or at least very nearly so

In perfectly cubic symmetry, this condition is satisfied for all the ions investigated except those having S-ground states, i.e., Mn^{2+}, Fe^{3+} and Gd^{3+} where there is a zero-field splitting even in cubic field. However, the anisotropy of the $1/2 \to -1/2$ transition in all these is only of order $\delta^2/g^2\beta^2 H_0$ (where δ represents the zero-field splitting and H_0 the resonant field). At x-band this anisotropy is often of order only a few gauss. Thus, though we do not expect to observe fine structure, this central line should be detectable in all cases where $\delta \approx 10^{-2} cm^{-1}$ or less. This is apparently true for Mn^{2+} in oxides or selenides, but not always so for Fe^{3+} and Gd^{3+} (see Tables IIA–D). Measurements on single crystals [2] show that for Fe^{3+} in MgO,

TABLE IIA

Table of g-factors (maximum error 0.0005) $Gd^{3+}M$ spectra

	O^{2-}	S^{2-}	Se^{2-}
Mg^{2+}	Very anisotropic	1.9882 (14.5 gauss wide)	1.9800 (5.5 gauss wide)
Ca^{2+}	1.9904 (11 gauss wide)	1.9903	Very broad line
Sr^{2+}	1.9911	1.9909	Very broad line
Ba^{2+}	1.9895	1.9915	Very broad line

TABLE IIB

$^{55}Mn^{2+}$ *spectra*, $77°K$

		Mg^{2+}	Ca^{2+}	Sr^{2+}
O^{2-}	g	2.0012	2.0015	2.0014
	A	81.3	81.4	80.2
S^{2-}	g	2.0017	2.0018	2.0015
	A	74.8	76.8	76.8

TABLE IIC

"Anomalous" $^{55}Mn^{2+}$ *spectra*, $77°K$

		MgO	CaO	CaSe
		Room temp.		
g		1.9942	1.9931	2.0037
A		70.8	72.8	74.05

TABLE IID

$^{57}Fe^{3+}$ *spectra*, $298°K$

	MgO	CaO*	SrO*
g	2.0037[2]	2.0054	2.004 (77°K)
A	11.4	Broad line	

* Line width temperature-dependent.

δ has the value $6.15 \times 10^{-2} cm^{-1}$. In MgO one thus sees only vestiges of the $1/2 \leftrightarrow -1/2$ transition for Fe^{3+} at its turning points. The other transitions are more anisotropic and are therefore lost. In CaO and SrO where the zero-field splitting is reduced, the $1/2 \leftrightarrow -1/2$ transition is seen as a single line. We may reasonably infer that a similar argument holds for Gd^{3+} in MgO. On moving through the series towards larger lattices one expects the cubic crystal field (and thus δ) to become progressively smaller (as the neighbors are further away). There should then be no difficulty in observing resonance in the "higher" members of the series. This point is well illustrated by Gd^{3+} where we obtained spectra for the oxides of Ca, Sr and Ba, but not for MgO. In addition, some evidence of fine structure was observed in several cases. Thus, in CaO there were broad satellites symmetrically placed about the central line and separated from it by 71, 108 and 167 gauss respectively. In SrO this fine structure had shrunk close to the principal line and in BaO it was undetectable. Similarly, in MgS the satellite spacings were approximately 75, 140 and 240 gauss. In SrS they were only of order 10 gauss, while in BaS the satellites were absorbed within the central line. They were unfortunately obscured in CaS by a strong Mn^{2+} spectrum. No hyperfine structure was detected in any of the Gd^{3+} spectra on account of the rather large line widths.

Mn^{2+} (Table IIB) showed the characteristic set of six hyperfine lines from Mn^{55} nuclei which have nuclear spin 5/2. In all cases where a spectrum was observed the lines were sharp, i.e., approximately 1 gauss wide, whereas even in the best single crystals the line width is about 0.5 gauss. This confirms that the crystal field has cubic symmetry to a high order of accuracy. When accurate cubic symmetry is lost, as in MgO crystals after neutron irradiation, these Mn^{2+} lines also disappear. They may be recovered by high-temperature annealing.

An early investigation [9] of Mn-containing MgO powders gave two very different values of the hyperfine constant A. These splittings were obtained from two similar samples (with added lithium) having different thermal treatments. The unusually low value (77 gauss $\approx 72 \times 10^{-4}$ cm^{-1}) of A was published without comments. Depending upon the lithium or sodium doping and the heat treatment given, we find that it is possible to prepare samples in which both hyperfine sextets are present. Indeed, the sextet with smaller A, (70.8×10^{-4} cm^{-1}) which for brevity we refer to as the "anomalous" one, may be made to appear more intense than the normal one ($A = 81.3 \times 10^{-4}$ cm^{-1}). Additionally, the g-value for the anomalous sextet in MgO is 1.9942, while that for the normal spectrum is 2.0012 (Table IIC).

A similar situation prevails in the case of Mn^{2+} in CaO, where the normal spectrum has $g = 2.0015$ and $A = 81.4 \times 10^{-4}$ cm^{-1} and the anomalous one has $g = 1.9931$ and $A = 72.8 \times 10^{-4}$ cm^{-1}. Another method of preparation which provides the anomalous spectrum is to suspend CaO powder in dilute (5%) HF solution, with subsequent slow drying and then firing with an oxygen-hydrogen flame. The same procedure works for MgO powders, but the anomalous spectrum produced in this way is weak.

In CaSe we have only been able to observe the one Mn^{2+} spectrum, with $g = 2.0037$ and $A = 74.1 \times 10^{-4}$ cm^{-1}. The g-values and hyperfine splitting constants are given in Table IIC. Remarkably, there are fine structure satellites 5.2 gauss apart, of width only 1.7 gauss.

The rather marked changes in g and in A would make it seem likely that in the presence of alkali or of fluoride ions there is an alteration of local ordering about the Mn^{2+} ion. If we assume that in doped MgO, CaO or CaSe there may be local regions of tetrahedral electric field symmetry about the Mn^{2+} ion, the anomalous spectrum would not be unreasonable. It remains to be established that such locally altered symmetry exists in the MgO, CaO and CaSe.

Fe^{3+} has been detected without any difficulty in CaO where the line width showed a marked temperature dependence. At 77°K it was 11 gauss, at 200°K 25 gauss and at room temperature is almost too broad for detection. The Fe^{3+} line is seen in SrO powders at 77°K with a line width about 20 gauss. If one resorts to addition of univalent ions in making the doped powders, one can force the Fe^{3+} ion into many of the other II–VI compounds. However, the line widths are usually very great (~ 100 to 500 gauss). These widths were found to be independent of microwave frequency between 6.5 and 9 Gc/s, which rules out the possibility of their being due to anisotropy, as the term $\delta/g^2\beta^2H_0$ is freqnency dependent (through H_0).

2. *Other ions*

Two other ions which have given detectable spectra are V^{2+} and Cr^{3+}, both having the $3d^3$ configuration. $^{51}V^{2+}$ ($I = 7/2$), which is nearly 100% abundant, gives an eight line hyperfine spectrum which shows sharp lines in MgO and MgS (Table IIE); in all other lattices investigated no resonance has been detected*. Cr^{3+} spectra were observed in MgO, MgS, CaO and

TABLE IIE

$^{51}V^{2+}$ *spectra*, 298°K

	MgO	MgS
g	1.9800[3]	1.9896
A	74.2	70.7

* Low and Rubins (this volume) have seen the V^{2+} spectrum in single crystals of CaO.

SrO, but hyperfine structure from $^{53}Cr^{3+}$ ($I = 3/2$, 9.5% abundant) was detected only in MgO, MgS and CaO (Table IIF), where the lines were

TABLE IIF

$^{53}Cr^{3+}$ spectra, 298°K

	MgO	CaO	MgS	SrO*
g	1.9796	1.9734	1.9874	1.952 (77°K)
A	16.5	16.8	15.3	

*Line width temperature dependent.

sharp. In CaO the line width was 2 gauss while in SrO it showed a temperature dependence similar to Fe^{3+} in CaO. At 77° K the width was 8 gauss while at room temperature it was much larger (> 50 gauss) so as to make detection difficult. In fact, it was necessary to add a univalent ion such as Li^{1+} in order to incorporate a sufficiently high concentration of Cr^{3+} for measurement. Remarkably, even Cs^{1+} or Ag^{1+} could be used as univalent ions.

The other ions investigated were Co^{2+} and Ni^{2+}, but only very broad resonance lines could be detected in any lattice other than MgO. It is apparent from the results on MgO that Ni^{2+} is particularly sensitive to small departures from cubic symmetry so it seems reasonable to attribute the negative result in other lattices to this cause, the lines being too anisotropic (or too broad) to be visible. Even mild grinding of single MgO crystals showing strong ESR lines is sufficient to obliterate the Ni^{2+} spectrum. At 20°K, Co^{2+} was seen (as a broad octet) only for MgO.

Of the II–VI compounds considered here, only MgO[6] and CaO (Table IIG) show an isotropic ESR spectrum of Cu^{2+}. Both for MgO powders

TABLE IIG

Cu^{++} spectrum (^{63}Cu and ^{65}Cu) 77°K

	MgO	CaO
g	2.190	2.221
A	19 ± 1	21.5

and for single crystals, the successive amplitudes of the four hyperfine lines increase with increasing field, the line width correspondingly decreasing. This effect has been ascribed to a dependence of relaxation times upon I_z [10]. However, for Cu^{2+} in CaO, the order of line widths is inverted, that of the lowest field hyperfine component having the minimum value. Such opposite behavior might be due either to a reversal in sign of the quantity $(A-B)$, the hyperfine parameters, or of $\Delta g = g_\parallel - g_\perp$. Both the apparent g-value and the observed hyperfine coupling constant are slightly larger for CaO than for MgO.

All three members of the palladium group (Ru, Rh, Pd) were successfully incorporated into MgO powders and Pd into CaO as well. In MgO, one valence state of each was seen by electron spin resonance. Following preparation, it was necessary to X-irradiate the samples before a spectrum could be seen at 77°K. (The spectra were not observable at room temperature.) When the Rh-doped samples had been heated in pure oxygen, nothing was seen following X-irradiation. Heating in hydrogen restored the Rh line partially, and X-irradiation further enhanced it. When the Ru-doped samples had been heated in oxygen, it was necessary both to heat in hydrogen and to X-irradiate before the line was seen. For palladium in MgO, X-irradiation alone makes the line visible, regardless of oxygen or hydrogen treatment. However, following heating in oxygen, another line with $g = 2.115$ is seen immediately. Its intensity is diminished by X-irradiation. One might surmise that this line is due to Pd^{2+}, though the line width of only 5 gauss would seem to be two small from such an ion. The g-factors (Table IIH) are all near those for a $4d^9$ ion, in analogy with Ni^{1+}, which

TABLE IIH

Other spectra in MgO ($77°K$ except for Fe^{1+} and Co^{2+} at $20°K$)

	Fe^{1+}	$^{59}Co^{1+}$	$^{59}Co^{2+}$	Ni^{1+}	$^{61}Ni^{2+}$	Ru	^{103}Rh	Pd
g	4.15	2.1728	4.278	2.1693	2.2145	2.1697	2.1708	2.1698
A		54.0	97.8		8.3		12.3	

has $g = 2.1693$. We tentatively suggest the states correspond to Ru^{-1}, Rh^0 and Pd^{1+}. We had rather expected that at least some of the ions would be $3d^8$, analogous to Ni^{2+}. Two peculiarities of the latter ion were the "dip" in the center of the ESR line at low microwave powers and the strong double-quantum transition at high powers. Neither of these effects could be detected in the Ru-, Rh- or Pd-doped MgO samples. However, a line of inverted phase with $g = 2.209$ was found for Pd in CaO, along with a line of normal appearance with $g = 2.1528$. The former we would ascribe to Pd^{2+} and the latter to Pd^{1+}.

Trapped hole centers

Rather distinct from the impurity ion spectra considered up to this point is an ESR spectrum arising from positive holes trapped at positive ion vacancies [11]. Although this spectrum is not directly ascribable to impurities, it arises because positive ion vacancies are incorporated to compensate the excess charge of trivalent impurity cations. This type of center has previously been described for MgO single crystals subjected to 4.9 ev or X-irradiation. It has now been seen in MgO, CaO and SrO powders at 77°K when X-irradiated at room temperature. When a positive hole created by irradiation is trapped upon an oxygen ion adjacent to a positive ion vacancy, the hole-plus-vacancy serves to define an electric field symmetry axis. The geometry is that of the V_1 center proposed by Seitz. Since there are centers with symmetry axes along each of the three principal crystal axes, one observes three lines for general orientations of the crystal in the magnetic field. These three lines show the simple oscillation between the $g_\parallel$ and $g_\perp$ positions as predicted for pure axial symmetry One would not normally expect to see ESR lines from a powder when the spectrum shows appreciable asymmetry. However, the lines arising from centers with symmetry axes parallel or at right angles to the magnetic field direction will show the minimum rate of variation of line displacement with magnetic field orientation. In a powder one will have a significant number of centers near the perpendicular orientation, and hence this line only is seen. It is highly asymmetric, rising steeply on the low-field side and falling off more slowly towards higher fields, as expected. In single crystals of MgO at 77°K, the lifetime of the positive hole upon a particular oxygen atom must be long compared with 10^{-7} sec, for the line widths are less than 1 gauss. For CaO powders at the same temperature, the separation of the two peaks of the asymmetric derivative curve is 1 gauss, while in SrO it is 2 gauss. Here too there must be comparable localization lifetimes.

This ESR line from the V_1 center has thus far been observed with the greatest intensity in powders which had been doped with ruthenium, rhodium or palladium. It seems rather probable that after high temperature heating in a methane-oxygen flame the valence state of some impurity cations would exceed 2; hence numerous positive ion vacancies are doubtless incorporated and serve as sites for trapping positive holes. One should get the same effect in powders doped with other trivalent transition metals. Indeed, Figure 1 shows that the V_1 center can be induced in "electronic grade" (Fisher Scientific Company) MgO powder which has not been doped. Besides showing Mn^{2+} strongly, it has appreciable quantities of Fe^{3+} and

Cr^{3+}, also visible in Figure 1. This powder was heated strongly in a methane-oxygen flame and then X-rayed for three hours at 30 kV. At the end of

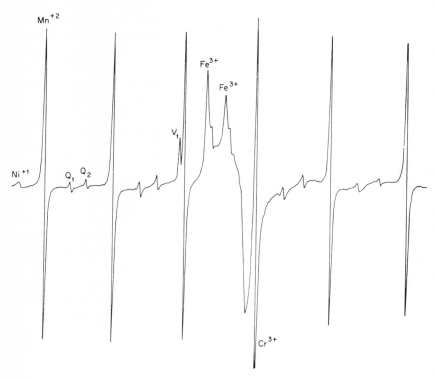

Figure 1

The ESR spectrum of "electronic grade" MgO powder (Fisher Scientific Company) after direct heating with methane-oxygen flame. The six Mn^{2+} $1/2 \rightarrow -1/2$ transitions are prominent. The intermediate pairs labelled Q are "forbidden" Mn^{2+} ($M = -\frac{1}{2} \leftrightarrow M = +\frac{1}{2}$, $\Delta m = \pm 1$) transitions described by Bleaney and Rubins [12]. The line due to Cr^{3+} in cubic electric field overlaps the fourth Mn^{2+} line on the high-field side. The Ni^{1+} ion appears on the low-field side of the Mn^{2+} spectrum. Finally, the line labelled V_1 arises from positive holes trapped on an oxygen ion adjacent to a positive ion vacancy. This line arises from those centers having the positive hole-vacancy axis nearly at right angles to the magnetic field H_0.

this time it showed a visible coloration characteristic of the V_1 center in single crystals. The ESR line of the V_1 center in Figure 1 does not show its characteristic asymmetry, since it is not fully resolved from the third Mn^{2+} hyperfine line.

We infer that the trapped hole center concentration must be very high when it is seen in powders, for one observes only a small fraction of the total ESR line intensity. Upon grinding MgO crystals which show the three-line trapped hole spectrum, one fails to see the line at the $g_\perp$ position for the powder unless the concentration of V_1 centers in the original crystal was unusually high.

Taking the value of $g_\perp = 2 - 2\lambda/\Delta$, one can calculate ratios of Δ values for the trapped hole in the MgO, CaO and SrO powders since λ is the same for all. Here Δ is the separation in energy of the singlet orbital ground state from the excited doublet level. The Δ-ratios are respectively 1:0. 54:0. 13. One may speculate about the failure to see the spectrum of trapped hole centers in the sulfides or selenides; however, such speculation is probably better deferred until single crystals have been prepared and examined.

Finally, we mention briefly the F- and F_2-centers previously found in a number of powders of II–VI compounds [13]. The F-center is a single electron trapped at a negative ion vacancy. In single crystals it is necessary to irradiate with neutrons to form negative ion vacancies in appreciable numbers; in powders, such vacancies are distributed from the surface or

TABLE III

Table of g-factors for F and F_2 centers

		O^{2-}	S^{2-}	Se^{2-}	Te^{2-}
Mg^{2+}	F	2.0023	2.0062	2.0035	Not cubic lattices
	F_2	2.0008	2.0038	1.9981	
Ca^{2+}	F	2.0001	2.0033	2.0030	2.0305
	F_2	1.9995			
Sr^{2+}	F	1.9846	2.0036*	2.0032**	2.0125
	F_2	1.9816	2.0023*	1.9890**	2.0092
Ba^{2+}	F	1.936 [14]	1.9641***	1.9670	Semiconductor
	F_2				

*   There are also strong lines at $g = 1.9964$ (F) and $g = 1.9942$ (F_2).
**   When prepared from the elements, another F line appears at $g = 1.9988$ and an F_2 line at $g = 1.9978$.
***   Another line presumably due to F-centers appears at $g = 2.0023$.

from dislocations by grinding. The ESR spectra of F-centers may be observed at room temperature, and show microwave saturation at relatively low powers. The F_2-center is believed to have an electron trapped at a vacancy pair. This center also is easy to saturate. The g-values for both types of centers are given in Table III, which lists some values not measured previously.

Discussion

Gd^{3+} (ionic radius 1.02 Å) in MgO, MgS and MgSe is a substitutional impurity which is much larger than the host cation. In this case it is obviously necessary for the lattice to distort in order to accept the larger ion, i.e., the neighbors move outwards from their normal positions. This distortion implies an increase in lattice energy and provides a measure of the difficulty of incorporating a large ion in the structure. Provided the disparity in size is not too great, one expects the distortion to be uniform, leaving the local symmetry unchanged. (This will probably apply only to cubic crystals.) The experimental results appear to bear this out.

The opposite case in which the impurity ion is too small for the site available to it is more interesting in that it is less obvious what is to be expected. Three possibilities arise: (1) The neighboring negative ions close in upon the impurity ion "holding it in place" and maintaining an accurately cubic crystal field; (2) the impurity ion "rattles" about in the hole available to it; (3) the impurity ion moves away from the center of the hole and takes up a (stable) position close to one or more of its neighbors. ESR measurements on powders should be able to distinguish between (1) and the other two, but may be unable to distinguish (2) and (3). Work with single crystals would obviously throw more light on this problem.

It is of interest to estimate the change in potential energy resulting from a non-centered position of a substitutional ion in an MgO-like lattice. Because of the cubic symmetry, when one expands in inverse powers of interatomic distances in terms of Legendre polynomials, the lowest non-zero one is P_4. We let the displacement of the substitutional ion from an exactly centered position be Δr. The latter makes direction cosines α, β and γ with the principal axes of the octahedron of surrounding ions. Letting z_1 and z_2 be the charges of central and neighboring ions, the change in potential energy due to the displacement Δr is given by:

$$\Delta U = \frac{7z_1 z_2}{2r} \left(\frac{\Delta r}{r}\right)^4 [1 - 5(\alpha^2 \beta^2 + \alpha^2 \gamma^2 + \beta^2 \gamma^2)].$$

One sums over successive shells of neighbors until contributions become negligible. If r is taken as 2.5Å as an intermediate value of interionic distance (corresponding to the SrO or MgS lattices) and Δr as 0.1Å, then $\Delta U \approx 10^{-4}$ev. Thus on this model the central ion is in a very shallow potential well in which at room temperatures it has considerable freedom of motion. A very similar argument suggests that a stable configuration of the surrounding X^{2-} ions would be achieved if they remained in their normal lattice sites rather than closing in on the impurity. Leaving the point-charge model, we expect that these conclusions will be valid for a perfect octahedron with a substitutional ion of radius only very slightly smaller than the maximum permitted by the site. Thus the ion may "rattle". However, as the substitutional ion becomes much smaller than this maximum allowed size, the former tends to be bound increasingly in an off-center position. As distortions of the octahedron take place, this "sticking" tendency increases. This implies that axial components of symmetry will be expected whenever the substitutional ion is appreciably smaller than its host.

The situation may, of course, be modified when the impurity ion is trivalent, there being a stronger tendency then for the neighboring anions to be drawn in. However, it should be added that the extent of this contraction may be limited by "contact" between the anions. Thus, if these have radius R, the largest sphere which is enclosed by them when in contact is $r = (\sqrt{2}-1)R$. For oxides, sulphides and selenides, r takes the values 0.56, 0.75 and 0.80Å respectively, so even with maximum contraction some of the iron group ions will still be "loose" in the latter two. It is perhaps significant that we observed no spectra from iron group ions in any of the selenides, except for Mn^{2+} in CaSe, where it is not certain that the manganese enters substitutionally.

In attempting an interpretation of the experimental results one must tread warily on account of the small amount of data and large number of possible explanations. It is unfortunate that we are obliged to attach considerable importance to purely negative evidence, i.e., the failure to observe resonance, as this may obviously be caused by an insufficient concentration of impurity ions or by imperfect formation of the host material. We have repeated most preparations many times with numerous modifications of preparative procedures, especially where we have had failures. The fact that we have seen spectra in most of the lattices from Gd^{3+} and from F-centers [13] supports us in believing that the various powders are really what we think they are. The hyperfine structure of Mn and Cr also supports this view. However, we have no definite evidence that an impurity ion has been incorporated into a lattice, other than that provided by the resonance spectrum. We can only argue that the doping methods used work consistently enough in "successful" cases and there appears no obvious reason why they should not work in others.

Bearing in mind these limitations in the argument, it is still possible to interpret our results along the general lines proposed earlier. There is an obvious tendency for all ions to show resonance in "small" lattices where they are either too large or fairly close fits while not doing so in "larger" lattices. As additional evidence on this point, we cite the case of ThO_2 with each cation surrounded by eight bulky oxygen ions. For the large Gd^{3+} ion one observes an ESR spectrum. For the smaller ions Mn^{2+} and Fe^{3+} one does not. This is in accord with the suggestion that a small ion may be trapped close to one (or more) of its neighboring anions so that the effective crystal field has a symmetry lower than cubic, producing an anisotropic spectrum.

Perhaps the most significant results are those of Fe^{3+} in CaO and SrO and Cr^{3+} in SrO where the line widths are markedly temperature dependent. It may be that these are "borderline" cases where the potential well is so shallow as to be only of order of thermal energies. At room temperature we suppose the ion to "rattle" within its "cage" of neighboring ions while at lower temperatures it becomes more nearly frozen in.

It is apparent that a complete understanding of the problem can only be obtained from working with single crystals; however, we feel we have obtained sufficient evidence from our powder measurements at least to discover the nature of the problem if not to answer it.

REFERENCES

[1] W. Low, *Paramagnetic Resonance in Solids*, Solid State Physics Supplement 2, Academic Press, New York, 1960. Numerous references to the author's papers are given here.

[2] W. Low, *Proc. Phys. Soc.* **B69,** 1169 (1956).

[3] W. Low, *Phys. Rev.* **101,** 1827 (1955).

[4] A. A. MANENKOV AND A. M. PROKHOROV, *Soviet Phys. JETP* **6,** 860 (1958)

[5] A. A. MANENKOV AND A. M. PROKHOROV, *Soviet Phys. JETP* **13,** 1129 (1961).

[6] J. W. ORTON, P. AUZINS, J. H. E. GRIFFITHS AND J. E. WERTZ, *Proc. Phys. Soc.* **78,** 554 (1961).

[7] J. E. WERTZ, J. W. ORTON AND P. AUZINS, *J. Appl. Phys. Supplement* **33,** 322 (1962).

[8] L. PAULING, *Nature of the Chemical Bond*, third edition, Cornell University Press, 1960.

[9] W. D. HERSHBERGER AND H. N. LEIFER, *Phys. Rev.* **88,** 714 (1952).

[10] H. M. McCONNELL, *J. Chem. Phys.* **25,** 709 (1956).

[11] J. E. WERTZ, P. AUZINS, J. H. E. GRIFFITHS AND J. W. ORTON, *Disc. Faraday Soc.* **28,** 136 (1959).

[12] B. BLEANEY AND R. S. RUBINS, *Proc. Phys. Soc. (London)* **77,** 103 (1961).

[13] J. E. WERTZ, J. W. ORTON AND P. AUZINS, *Disc. Faraday Soc.* **31,** 140 (1961).

[14] J. W. CARSON, D. F. HOLCOMB AND H. RUCHARDT, *J. Chem. Phys. Solids* **12,** 66 (1959).

[15] *Handbook of Chemistry and Physics*, 35th edition, p. 3091.

Influence of Lattice Imperfections on the Paramagnetic Resonance of V^{2+} and Cr^{3+} in MgO

J. S. VAN WIERINGEN AND J. G. RENSEN

*Philips Research Laboratories, N. V. Philips' Gloeilampenfabrieken,
Eindhoven, Netherlands*

ABSTRACT

The paramagnetic resonance spectra of V^{2+} and Cr^{3+} in MgO are described by a spin-hamiltonian $\mathscr{H} = g\beta HS + AIS + D(S_\zeta^2 - 5/4) + E(S_\xi^2 - S_\eta^2)$ with $S = 3/2$, $g = 1.9800 \pm 0.0005$; for V^{2+}: $I = 7/2$ (100%), $A = (-75.1 \pm 0.1)$ 10^{-4} cm^{-1}; whereas for Cr^{3+}: $I^{53} = 3/2$ (9.5%), $A^{53} = (\pm 16.0 \pm 0.2) 10^{-4}$ cm^{-1}. The last two terms of $\mathscr{H}$ describe the influence of weak crystalline fields superimposed on the main cubic field. The ζ-axes are along the body diagonals of the MgO cubic unit cell, D varies between $+2$ and $-2 \cdot 10^{-4}$ cm^{-1} and $|E| < 0.7 \cdot 10^{-4}$. The fields are ascribed to the presence of impurities in molar concentration of about 10^{-3}. In V^{2+} they give rise to anisotropic broadening of some of the resonance lines and in Cr^{3+} to an anisotropic line height.

Introduction

In the magnesium oxide lattice many different iron group ions can be incorporated, e.g., V^{2+}, Cr^{3+}, Mn^{2+} and Fe^{3+}. Their properties have been studied by means of paramagnetic resonance [1–10]. In the present investigation the paramagnetic resonance spectra of V^{2+} and Cr^{3+} are discussed in more detail than has been done before.

Single crystals of MgO were made in the following way. Magnesium oxide powder was melted by passing an electric current through it between two carbon electrodes. The molten MgO was cooled down so slowly that single crystals were formed during solidification. The largest crystals formed in this way were cubes of 1 to 2 cm³ volume. They were grown by Mr. Ter Vrugt who kindly put them at our disposal. The crystals contained many iron group impurities like Cr, Mn, and Fe in concentrations of the order of 10^{18}–10^{19} ions/cm³, originating, presumably, from the carbon electrodes. Some crystals contained vanadium. This can be seen from their paramagnetic resonance spectrum which shows eight characteristic hyperfine lines [1], spaced at a mutual distance of about 80 gauss (see Figure 1). Each of the eight hyperfine lines has an outer line on either side so that, in all, there are 24 lines. Another spectrum that will be discussed in the present paper is that of Cr^{3+} in a supposedly cubic environment [2]. This spectrum

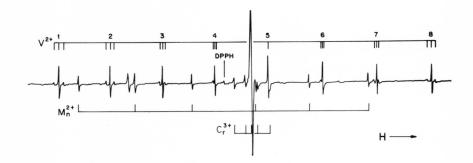

Figure 1

Typical paramagnetic resonance spectrum of MgO single crystal containing V^{2+}, Mn^{2+} and Cr^{3+}. The magnetic field H is parallel to a cubic axis. Additional lines are due to a DPPH field marker and to Cr^{3+} in non-cubic surroundings.

consists of a strong single line plus four weak lines due to the Cr^{53} isotope with nuclear spin $I = 3/2^*$. It will be shown that both V^{2+} and Cr^{3+} are in a predominantly cubic crystalline field with superimposed on it weak fields of lower symmetry. The latter fields vary from site to site and are supposed to be caused by impurities.

Determination of the spin-Hamiltonian

In four different crystals** the paramagnetic resonance spectrum was measured in a "Varian" 3 cm EPR spectrometer with 400 Hz magnetic field modulation. Most measurements were made at room temperature, but the sign of the hyperfine coupling parameter A in V^{2+} was determined by a measurement at 2°K. The line positions were determined within 0.7 gauss with the help of a proton resonance coil. The line positions were found to be independent of the orientation of the crystal in the magnetic field. The line width of the eight central lines is independent of the orientation as well. In contrast to this, the line width of the sixteen outer lines in the V^2 spectrum and the line shape of the Cr^{3+} line proved to be angular dependent; this effect will be treated in the next section.

---

* Apart from this spectrum another Cr^{3+} spectrum is found due to Cr^{3+} in an environment of lower symmetry [8]. This will not be discussed in the present paper.

** Paramagnetic impurities: Cr^{3+} $10^{18} - 10^{19}/cm^3$, V^{2+} and Mn^{2+} $10^{18}/cm^3$, Fe^{3+} from $10^{17}/cm^3$ to $10^{19}/cm^3$.

The line positions can be described by the following spin-Hamiltonian

$$\mathcal{H}_1 = g\beta HS + AIS \tag{1}$$

with $S = 3/2$, $g = 1.9800 \pm 0.0005$. In V^{2+}, $I = 7/2$ and $A = (-75.1 \pm 0.1)$ $\cdot 10^{-4}$ cm^{-1} whereas in Cr^{3+}, the isotope Cr^{53} (abundance 9.5%) has $I = 3/2$, $A = (\pm 16.0 \pm 0.2) \, 10^{-4}$cm^{-1}. Diagonalisation of (1) gives the following energy levels

$$E_{Mm} = g\beta HM + AMm + \frac{A^2}{2g\beta H}[I(I+1)M - S(S+1)m + Mm(M-m)]$$

$$+ \frac{A^3}{2g^2\beta^2 H^2}[S(S+1)m(2m-M) + I(I+1)M(2M-m) \tag{2}$$

$$+ Mm(M^2 + m^2 - 3Mm + 1) - S(S+1)I(I+1)]$$

The terms in A^2 and A^3 split the eight hyperfine lines of V^{2+} into a central and two outer lines*. Still higher terms in A can be omitted: they give corrections of less than 0.2 gauss. From E_{Mm} the resonance fields for the allowed transitions $M, m \to M - 1$, m at fixed frequency f can be derived:

$$g\beta H = hf - Am - \frac{A^2}{2hf}[I(I+1) + m(2M - m - 1)]$$

$$- \frac{A^3}{2h^2 f^2}[(4M-2)\{I(I+1)-m^2\} - m\{S(S+1)-3M(M-1)-2\}] \tag{3}$$

In Table I measured and calculated line positions are compared; the differences are within the experimental error.

The spin-Hamiltonian (1) is what one would expect for a V^{2+} or Cr^{3+} ion in a cubic octahedral field:

1) the orbital moment is almost completely quenched by the crystalline field i.e., $S = 3/2$.

2) g and A tensor are isotropic

3) terms of the types $(H_x S_x^3 + H_y S_y^3 + H_z S_z^3)$ and $(I_x S_x^3 + I_y S_y^3 + I_z S_z^3)$, although permitted by cubic symmetry [11], are absent. However, this is in accordance with the estimation of these terms which shows that, for V^{2+} and Cr^{3+}, they will be negligible.

This result supports the view that V^{2+} and Cr^{3+} in MgO are found at Mg lattice sites. In our crystals no sign was found of the deviations from (1), reported by Low [10].

---

* Theoretically and experimentally, within each of the eight groups the intensities of the three lines are in the ratio 3:4:3.

TABLE I

Paramagnetic resonance spectrum of V^{2+} in MgO at a frequency of 9144 MHz at room temperature

m	Transition M	M1	Resonance field in gauss Measured	Resonance field in gauss Calculated using (3)
−7/2	$-1/2 \rightarrow -3/2$		3008.2	3007.5
	$1/2 \rightarrow -1/2$		3015.0	3015.0
	$-3/2 \rightarrow 1/2$		3021.8	3021.9
−5/2	$1/2 \rightarrow -3/2$		3082.9	3084.1
	$1/2 \rightarrow -1/2$		3088.8	3090.1
	$-3/2 \rightarrow 1/2$		3094.4	3095.0
−3/2	$1/2 \rightarrow -3/2$		3161.4	3161.3
	$1/2 \rightarrow -1/2$		3165.6	3165.7
	$-3/2 \rightarrow 1/2$		3169.3	3169.8
−1/2	$1/2 \rightarrow -3/2$		3241.4	3241.4
	$1/2 \rightarrow -1/2$		3244.3	3243.9
	$3/2 \rightarrow 1/2$		3245.9	3246.4
+1/2	$-1/2 \rightarrow -3/2$		—	3323.8
	$1/2 \rightarrow -1/2$		—	3324.3
	$3/2 \rightarrow 1/2$		—	3324.8
+3/2	$3/2 \rightarrow 1/2$		3405.1	3404.9
	$1/2 \rightarrow -1/2$		3406.8	3406.5
	$-1/2 \rightarrow -3/2$		—	3408.2
+5/2	$3/2 \rightarrow 1/2$		3486.9	3486.1
	$1/2 \rightarrow -1/2$		3491.1	3489.9
	$-1/2 \rightarrow -3/2$		3494.6	3494.8
+7/2	$3/2 \rightarrow 1/2$		3569.3	3570.5
	$1/2 \rightarrow -1/2$		3576.1	3576.8
	$-1/2 \rightarrow -3/2$		3582.5	3583.5

The influence of lattice imperfections

As stated before, the line width of the sixteen outer lines in V^{2+} is angular dependent. It is smallest when the magnetic field H is parallel to a cubic crystal axis; in this case the width between inflexion points is

1.5 gauss, about twice as large as the width of the eight central lines. Away from these directions the line width increases; e.g., midway between two cubic axes it is about 5 gauss (see Figure 2). This effect cannot be caused by a cubic crystalline field because such a field gives an isotropic spectrum as was shown above. Neither could it be caused by cubic fields that are different for different ions (i.e., if there is a spread in the values of g and/or A) because this would not give the same effect for all eight groups of lines.

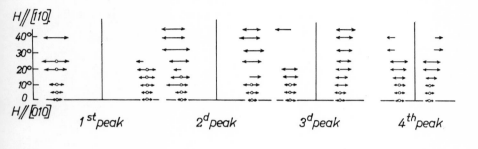

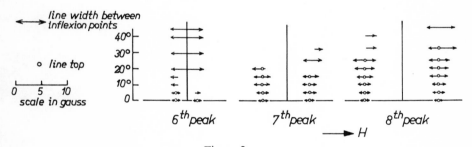

Figure 2

Angular dependence of the eight groups of three V^{2+} lines each. H is perpendicular to the cubic axis [001].

Hence one is obliged to assume the presence of crystalline fields of lower symmetry, giving rise to an extra term

$$D\left(S_\zeta^2 - \frac{5}{4}\right) + E(S_\xi^2 - S_\eta^2) \qquad (4)$$

in the spin-Hamiltonian (1). If the ζ axis is chosen along the main distortion, $|E| < 1/3|D|$. In the rock salt structure of MgO as many as 24 orientations of the ξ, η, ζ axes are possible. In spite of this large number it was found to be impossible to explain the observed line widths with the help of (4) with a single value of D and E. Instead, one has to assume that there is a spread in the value of these parameters, i.e., that the crystalline fields of low symmetry are not equal for all V^{2+} ions. From the angular dependence of the line width it follows that the main or ζ axes are in or near to the [111] directions of the crystal. In order to account for the observed line width, D should be between about plus and minus $2 \cdot 10^{-4} \text{cm}^{-1}$ and hence $|E| < 0.7 \cdot 10^{-4} \text{cm}^{-1}$.

Axial field splittings of the isoelectronic ion Cr^{3+} have been measured in three oxidic compounds, $MgAl_2O_4$ [12], Al_2O_3 [13] and TiO_2 [14]. If one assumes a point-charge lattice which is not distorted by the incor-

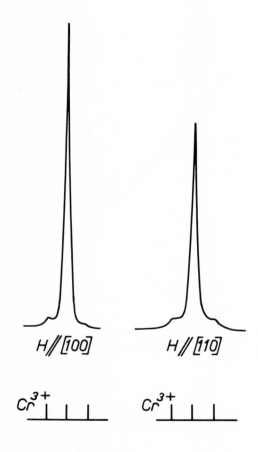

Figure 3

Integrated derivative of Cr^{3+} line in two orientations. Left: $H \parallel$ [100]. Right: $H \parallel$ [110]. (Only two of the four Cr^{53} hyperfine lines are shown.)

poration of Cr^{3+}, it is found that D is proportional to the local axial field. Using this result for V^{2+} it is found that our D value of $2\cdot10^{-4}$ cm^{-1} could be caused by the Coulomb field of one elementary charge at a distance of 30 Å. In MgO this means about 10 interatomic distances. Consequently, the observed effect could be caused by impurity centers with one excess or one missing electronic charge in a molar concentration of about 10^{-3}. The crystals we investigated contained impurities like Fe and Cr in concentrations of 10^{-4} to 10^{-3}. Hence, it is likely that the observed broadening of the outer lines of V^{2+} in MgO is caused by the electric fields of these impurities. This is not necessarily a direct influence but it could be an indirect one via lattice distortions.

One would expect that Cr^{3+} in MgO will experience the influence of these electric fields as well. One of the three coinciding transitions should have a narrow isotropic line, namely the line corresponding to the $M = \frac{1}{2} \rightarrow -\frac{1}{2}$ transition, whereas the other two should have broader lines of anisotropic width. The result would be that the single line of Cr^{3+} has its maximum height when the magnetic field H is parallel to a cubic axis and is lower with H in between the cubic axes. In the latter case the line is expected to have a broadened foot. This behavior is exactly what is found experimentally (see Figure 3). The order of magnitude of the effect is the same as in V^{2+}, as shown by comparison with the dotted line in Figure 4. This

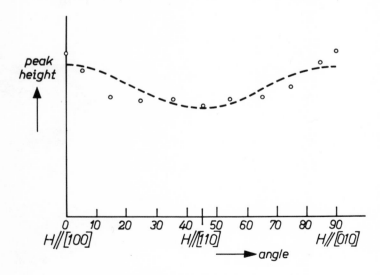

Figure 4
Height of Cr^{3+} peak as a function of orientation.

was calculated on the assumption that the lines of the $3/2 \to 1/2$ and $-1/2 \to -3/2$ transitions are twice as wide as that of the $M = 1/2 \to -1/2$ transition; with H parallel to a [110] direction they are supposed to be six times as wide, just as in V^{2+}. According to the picture proposed here, the Cr^{3+} line in MgO should be broadened inhomogeneously. This has indeed been found experimentally [15].

REFERENCES

[1] W. Low, *Phys. Rev.* **101**, 1827–1828 (1956).
[2] W. Low, *Phys. Rev.* **105**, 801–805 (1957).
[3] W. Low, *Phys. Rev.* **105**, 793–800 (1957).
[4] W. Low, *Proc. Phys. Soc.* (London) **B69**, 1169–1170 (1956).
[5] J. H. E. Griffiths and J. W. Orton, *Proc. Phys. Soc.* (London) **73**, 948–950 (1959).
[6] W. Low, *Phys. Rev.* **109**, 247–255, (1958).
[7] W. Low, *Phys. Rev.* **109**, 256–265 (1958).
[8] J. E. Wertz and P. Auzins, *Phys. Rev.* **106**, 484–488 (1957).
[9] J. E. Wertz, P. Auzins, J. H. E. Griffiths and J. W. Orton, *Disc. Faraday Soc.* **26**, 66–71 (1958).
[10] W. Low, *Ann. N. Y. Acad. Sc.* **72**, 69–126 (1958).
[11] F. S. Ham, G. W. Ludwig, G. D. Watkins and H. H. Woodbury, *Phys. Rev. Letters* **5**, 468–470 (1960).
[12] R. Stahl-Brada and W. Low, *Phys. Rev.* **116**, 561–564 (1959).
[13] L. Cross and R. W. Terhune, *Bull. Am. Phys. Soc. II.* **3**, 371 (1958).
[14] H. J. Gerritsen, S. E. Harrison, H. R. Lewis and J. P. Wittke, *Phys. Rev. Letters* **2**, 153–155 (1959).
[15] J. G. Castle and D. W. Feldman, *Phys. Rev.* **121**, 1349–1350 (1961).

Sharp Line Fluorescence, EPR and Thermoluminescence of Mn^{4+} in α-Al_2O_3

S. Geschwind, P. Kisliuk*, M. P. Klein**, J. P. Remeika

and D. L. Wood

Bell Telephone Laboratories, Murray Hill, New Jersey

ABSTRACT

Mn^{4+} is isoelectronic with Cr^{3+} (configuration $3d^3$) so that when Mn^{4+} is substituted for Al^{3+} in α-Al_2O_3 one expects it in some ways to be analogous to ruby. Indeed, sharp line fluorescence corresponding to emission from the metastable ^2E state of Mn^{4+} has been observed in single crystals of α-Al_2O_3. The R_1 and R_2 emission lines occur at 14,866 cm^{-1} and 14,786 cm^{-1} at 79°K and have lifetimes of 0.8 milliseconds independent of temperature. The ratio of the intensities of the R_1 and R_2 lines, measured as a function of temperature correspond to fast thermalization between levels 82 ± 5 cm^{-1} apart, in good agreement with the measured separation of 80 cm^{-1}. The optical absorption spectrum indicates that the cubic crystal field and covalency are greater for the Mn^{4+} as anticipated. A correlation was made between the intensity of the R_1 and R_2 emission and the intensity of the ground state paramagnetic resonance of Mn^{4+}. The ground state splitting is 0.3914 cm^{-1}. When the crystals were irradiated with uv (< 3000 Å) at 79°K more than 50% of the Mn^{4+} ground state was depopulated and long lived traps are created as observed by EPR. On warming, the crystals thermoluminesce in the R_1 and R_2 lines and return to their original state. Details of this latter process will be presented and possible applications to lasers will be discussed.

I. Introduction

Mn^{4+} is isoelectronic with Cr^{3+} (both have the configuration $3d^3$) and as such would be expected to exhibit analogous properties, such as sharp line fluorescence, when incorporated in α-Al_2O_3. This has indeed been found to be the case and we will initially emphasize this parallel between the two ions in the corundum host lattice. However, the charge compensation needed to maintain the manganese in the tetravalent state gives rise to a striking thermoluminescent phenomenon which is absent in ruby and which will be described below. While reference may be found in the phosphor literature [1 ; 2] to Mn^{4+} in Al_2O_3, the description of the optical and magnetic properties has been greatly extended and clarified in this work.

---

*Now at Aerospace Corporation, El Segundo, California.

**Now at the University of California, Lawrence Radiation Laboratory, Livermore, California.

We will initially describe the preparation of the single crystals of α-Al_2O_3 with Mn^{4+}. In Section III, will be presented a description of the optical spectrum and this will be followed by the ESR spectrum in Section IV. The thermoluminescent properties will be outlined in Section V and possible application to lasers will be cited.

II. Preparation of single crystals

The single crystals of Al_2O_3 were grown from oxide fluxes to which were added MnO_2 and MgO. Initial efforts to observe Mn^{4+} in crystals which were not intentionally charge compensated failed and only Mn^{2+} and Mn^{3+} were seen, the latter identified by its optical spectrum only as no ESR spectrum is seen in the crystal for Mn^{3+}. Mg^{2+} was selected as the charge compensator for the Mn^{4+} as we wanted a divalent ion which prefers octahedral coordination, (MgO, for example) so that it would substitute for the Al^{3+} which is found in six-fold oxygen coordination. In contrast Cd^{2+} and Zn^{2+} are more commonly found in tetrahedral coordination (ZnO, CaO). In addition, Mg^{2+} was more favorable from a size point of view. Experiment confirmed these predictions as efforts to obtain the Mn^{4+} with Zn^{2+} and Cd^{2+} were unsuccessful. The presence of Mn^{4+} was verified in all cases by correlation between the optical and paramagnetic resonance data in the same crystal.

Similar results were obtained with Mg^{2+} compensated crystals grown by the Linde Company by the flame fusion process. The final concentration of Mn^{4+} in the Linde crystals was no greater than 1 part in 10^4, while in the flux grown crystals concentrations of at least 1 part in 10^3 were achieved.

III. Optical absorption and emission spectrum

The optical spectrum of Cr^{3+} in corundum has been studied in detail by Sugano and Tanabe [3], Sugano and Tsujikawa [4] and McClure [5]. It is a well known empirical fact that the strength of the crystal field as well as covalency increase with increased ionic charge [5; 6]. Therefore, one expects the crystal field paramerer, Dq, as well as covalency to be greater in Mn^{4+} as compared to Cr^{3+} in Al_2O_3. As a result, the $^4A_2 \to {}^4T_2$ absorption band falls at 21,300 cm^{-1} for Mn^{4+} (See Figure 1a) as compared to 18,000 cm^{-1} for Cr^{3+}. This shift of the $^4A_2 \to {}^4T_2$ absorption to shorter wavelength compared to ruby gives these crystals an amber color. As the $^4A_2 \to {}^4T_2$ separation is very nearly 10 Dq, one finds $Dq = 2130$ cm^{-1} for Mn^{+4}.

The increased charge of the Mn^{4+} moves the charge transfer bands to a much longer wavelength giving an absorption edge near 35,000 cm^{-1} instead of 50,000 cm^{-1} as found for Cr^{3+}. As a result, the $^4A_2 \to {}^4T_1$ absorption band, which is observed in ruby, is obscured by the charge transfer band in Mn^{4+}.

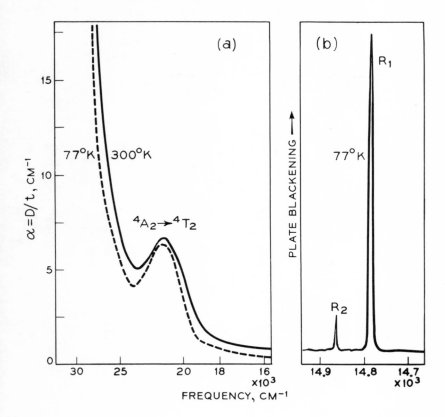

Figure 1a

Absorption spectrum of Al_2O_3 + Mn^{4+} grown from flux.

Figure 1b

R_1 and R_2 lines of fluorescence spectrum. Weaker lines may be seen under increased gain but are not discussed.

The analogous R_1 and R_2 emission lines for Mn^{4+} fall at 14,786 cm^{-1} and 14,866 cm^{-1} respectively at 79°K (Figure 1b) and from the position of this ^2E level, we determine $B \cong 700$ cm^{-1}. This represents approximately a 30% reduction in B from the free ion value and is characteristic of the reduction generally found in B for other transition metal ions in the crystal, which is ascribed to covalent effects.

In Figure 2 is plotted on a semi-log scale the intensity of the R_1 and R_2 lines as a function of the inverse temperature. Their intensity ratio R_1/R_2 follows an $e^{\Delta/kT}$ dependence and from the slope of the plot one finds $\Delta = 82 \pm 5$ cm^{-1} in good agreement with the measured separation of 80 cm^{-1}

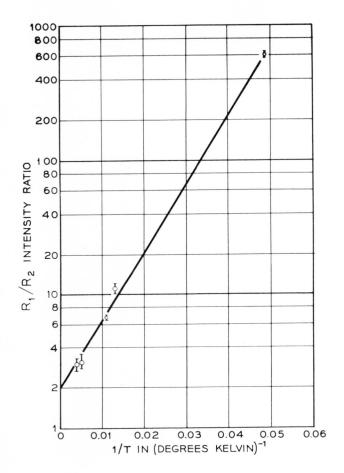

Figure 2

Temperature variation of R_1/R_2 intensity ratio in $Al_2O_3 + Mn^{4+}$.

between the R_1 and R_2 lines as cited above. The lifetime of the R_1 and R_2 lines is 0.8 ± 0.1 milliseconds and is essentially independent of temperature. The R_1 and R_2 levels are therefore seen to thermalize in a time much shorter than this decay time, just as is found in ruby.

Pursuing the analogy with ruby, we plot in Figure 3 the shift in the position of the R_1 and R_2 lines and the line width as a function of temperature. Note the similarity between these results and those for ruby [7]. There have been recent theoretical attempts to explain these results in terms of the

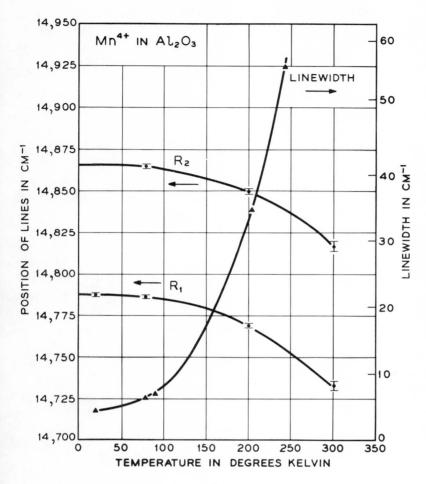

Figure 3
Line width and shift of R lines vs. temperature.

local dynamic strain produced by the lattice phonons [8;9;10]. Line widths as narrow as 2 cm^{-1} were observed at 4.2°K in the best crystals. We believe that a good part of this line width results from defects and strain in the crystal (perhaps from the Mg^{2+}) as shown by the paramagnetic resonance results described below.

IV. Paramagnetic resonance spectrum

The electron paramagnetic resonance spectrum of Mn^{4+} was studied at 24 KMc over a range of temperatures from 295°K to 1.6°K. A correlation was observed between the intensity of emission in the R_1, R_2 lines and the intensity of the paramagnetic resonance spectrum of Mn^{4+}. In Figure 4a is shown the central $m_s = -1/2 \rightarrow +1/2$ transition split into six components by the hfs interaction with the Mn^{55} whose nuclear spin, $I = 5/2$. In those crystals which showed broad emission lines, the hfs in the $\mp 1/2 \rightarrow \mp 3/2$ transitions was unresolved. This generally occurred in the more concentrated crystals and suggests increased strain with increased concentration which was also checked optically by looking at the crystals between crossed polaroids. In those crystals where the R lines were 3 cm^{-1} or less at low temperature, (which generally corresponded to a concentration of less than 1 part in 10^4 of Mn^{4+}) the hfs of the $\mp 1/2 \rightarrow \mp 3/2$ lines was resolved. The observed ESR spectrum is adequately described within the accuracy of our measurements by the following spin-Hamiltonian.

$$\mathscr{H} = \beta \mathbf{H} \cdot \tilde{g} \cdot \mathbf{S} + D[S_z^2 - 1/3\, S(S+1)] + \mathbf{I} \cdot \tilde{A} \cdot \mathbf{S} \tag{1}$$

where $S = 3/2$, $I = 5/2$ and the other experimentally determined parameters are listed in Table I. The quadrupole coupling of Mn^{55} is small and is neglected and in either case its effect does not appear in the parallel spectrum, and even in the perpendicular spectrum it has a negligible effect insofar as determining the parameters in the spin-Hamiltonian listed below.

TABLE I

Spin-Hamiltonian parameters for Mn^{4+} in α-Al_2O_3

$$D = -0.1957 \pm 0.0001 \text{ cm}^{-1}$$
$$g_{\parallel} = 1.9937 \pm 0.0010$$
$$g_{\perp} = 1.9937 \pm 0.0020$$
$$|\tilde{A}_{\parallel}| \cong |A_{\perp}| = (70.0 \pm 0.5) \times 10^{-4} \text{ cm}^{-1}$$

This value of the hfs is essentially the same as that previously observed for Mn^{4+} by Müller [11] in $SrTiO_3$ and in TiO_2 by Andresen [12], and corresponds to a field per unit electron spin at the Mn nucleus of -199 ± 3 kilogauss, i.e. $H_{hf} = -199,000\, S_z$. It is indeed striking that this field is the same to within 1% as that observed for the isoelectronic ions Cr^{3+} and V^{2+} in the same crystal. Moreover, it is not very different from Mn^{2+} ($3d^5$) for which $H_{hf} = -230,000\, S_z$ [13]. This is all in accord with the ideas of exchange polarization of the core s-electrons by the outer d-electrons, which predicted that the h. f. field per spin would be relatively constant [14].

It is interesting to note that the ground state splitting of 11,732 Mc in Mn^{4+} is only one per cent larger than that of Cr^{3+} in Al_2O_3 [15], yet the splitting of the ^2E state is almost 2.7 times as large as in Cr^{3+}. The ^2E state splitting is given in lowest order by [3]

$$^2E(\bar{E}) - {}^2E(\bar{A}_2) \sim \lambda V_{\text{trig}}/({}^2T_2 - {}^2E) \tag{2}$$

where λ is the S-O coupling constant and V_{trig} is the interaction energy of the ion with the trigonal field. The position of the $^2T_2$ level was not measured as the crystals were too small to observe this weak absorption; however, one would expect the $^2T_2 - {}^2E$ separation to be relatively independent of Dq according to Sugano and Tanabe [3]. While the free ion value for λ is greater than for Cr^{3+}, one would expect the greater covalency of Mn^{4+} to reduce its value in the crystal to where it is comparable to that of Cr^{3+} in the crystal. From Eq. (2) it would seem then that V_{trig} is greater by a factor of 2.7 than for Cr^{3+}. On the other hand, the ground state splitting goes as

$$D \sim \frac{\lambda^2 V_{\text{trig}}}{({}^4T_2 - {}^4A_2)^2} \tag{3}$$

so that even through the $^4T_2 - {}^4A_2$ separation is larger for Mn^{4+}, one would expect a larger D on the basis of the increased V_{trig}. Independent of whether or not Eq. (2) adequately describes the ^2E splitting, many authors have pointed out the inadequacies of Eq. (3). D is very sensitive to anisotropic S-O coupling [16], to configurationally mixed excited states [17], and perhaps to the odd components of the axial field [18]. It is apparent that the quantitative details of the axial field splitting are not well enough understood.

V. Thermoluminescence in R lines

Up till now, in discussing the properties of Mn^{4+} in Al_2O_3 we have emphasized the similarities to ruby. However, the need for charge compensation results in a striking thermoluminescent phenomenon. When the crystals are irradiated with uv light (< 3300 Å) at $79°K$ they change in color from amber to gray-violet. Upon warming to room temperature, intense sharp-line thermoluminescence in the R lines is observed starting at about $-70°C$, and the crystals return to their original amber color at the end of the thermoluminescence.

The electron paramagnetic resonance of the Mn^{4+} has been monitored when the crystals are irradiated with uv at low temperature as described above. In preliminary experiments with uv irradiation in situ, a decrease of more than 50% in the Mn^{4+} state has been achieved as is shown in Figure 4. The crystal contained a small amount of Fe^{3+} which can be seen in Figure 4a.

Mn^{4+} IN Al_2O_3
FREQ = 23 945 Mc; H II TO C−AXIS; TEMP = 1.6°K

(a)

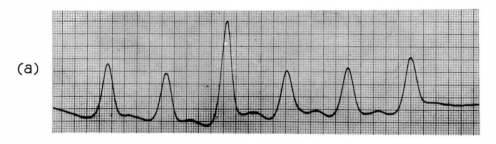

(b)

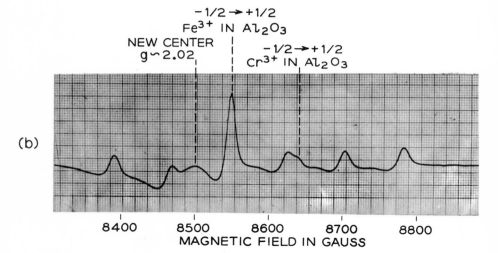

$-1/2 \rightarrow +1/2$
Fe^{3+} IN Al_2O_3

NEW CENTER
$g \sim 2.02$

$-1/2 \rightarrow +1/2$
Cr^{3+} IN Al_2O_3

MAGNETIC FIELD IN GAUSS

Figure 4a

ESR spectrum of Mn^4 in Al_2O_3 at 24 KMc and 1.6°K. This particular crystal contains a small amount of Fe^{3+} and lesser amounts of Cr^{3+} and Mn^{2+}. The Mn^{4+} is also easily seen at room temperature.

Figure 4b

Spectrum after irradiation in situ with uv Decrease of Mn^{4+} signal is greater than 50%. Similar effects are seen at 79°K.

as well as Cr^{3+} which is on the side of a Mn^{4+} h f s component and shows up in Figure 4b as the Mn^{4+} signal decreases. To further verify that the decrease of Mn^{4+} observed was real and did not perhaps correspond to an increase of Fe^{3+} or Cr^{3+} and decrease in Q of the cavity it was also checked relative to Cr^{3+} in MgO powder shielded in another part of the microwave cavity from the irradiating light. If the crystals are warmed, they thermoluminesce in the R_1 and R_2 lines and show the original ESR spectrum seen before irradiation.

A proposed model for the thermoluminescence is shown in Figure 5.

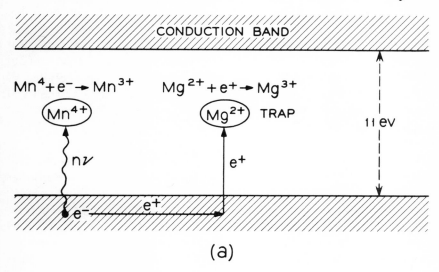

(a)

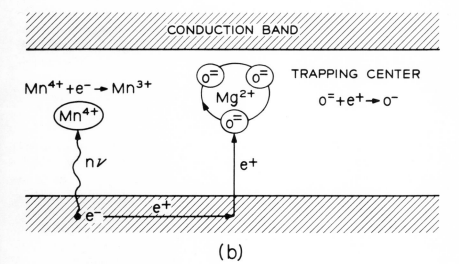

(b)

Figure 5

Proposed models for decrease of Mn^{4+} signal with uv irradiation and of trapping process.

The uv light removes an electron from the valence band which is captured by the Mn^{4+}, which in turn is converted to Mn^{3+}. This electron is easily captured by the Mn^{4+} as the Mn^{4+} looks like a positive center since it is in the trivalent Al site. The resultant hole moves in the valence band until it is trapped in the vicinity of the Mg^{2+} which looks like a negative center in the Al^{3+} site. In Figure 5a we show it trapped on a Mg^{2+} ion producing Mg^{3+}. A more likely model is Figure 5b wherein it is trapped on an O^{-2} next to an Mg^{2+} ion and resonance resonates between three equivalent oxygens surrounding the Mg^{2+} [19]. Either of these centers (Figure 5a or 5b) should give rise to an ESR spectrum and a new center at a g-value of 2.02 is observed simultaneously with the decrease of Mn^{4+} as shown in Figure 4b. This new center is being further studied by ESR to see if any further details of this center can be correlated with the proposed models.

Actually there is reason to believe that one is dealing with several different types of traps. The evidence for this is in the glow curve where two peaks are observed, one at about $-70°C$ and a smaller one at about $+80°C$. Moreover if one plots the thermoluminescent decay time, τ, at given temperature as a function of temperature one finds that it can not be described by a single exponential and that a minimum of two exponentials are needed as shown in Figure 6 and even this is not adequate. Moreover the decay could not be fitted by a single power law of T. Of course a simple exponential decay is only to be expected in a monomolecular process whereas we undoubtedly have at least a bimolecular process [20]. One notes an extrapolated lifetime of months or longer at $79°K$ for these traps. From the slopes of the plots of Figure 6, one can roughly estimate trap depths from the monomolecular expression for τ.

$$\tau \sim \text{const. } e^{\Delta/kT} \tag{4}$$

and one finds $\Delta \sim 0.25$ ev. Initial efforts to empty these traps by radiation of this wavelength have so far been unsuccessful, and the only way we have been able to empty them is by warming of the crystal. However, if one could find a way of rapidly emptying the traps, then the pump power needed to observe possible laser action in the R lines could be reduced. Namely, one could depopulate the Mn^{4+} ground state by uv irradiation, this requiring little power because of the long lifetime of the traps. Then just enough energy has to be supplied to bridge the gap between the trap depth and the ^2E level. The reduction in pumping power for maser action should be of the order of $[^2E - {}^4A_2]/\Delta$ where Δ is the trap depth beolw the ^2E level.

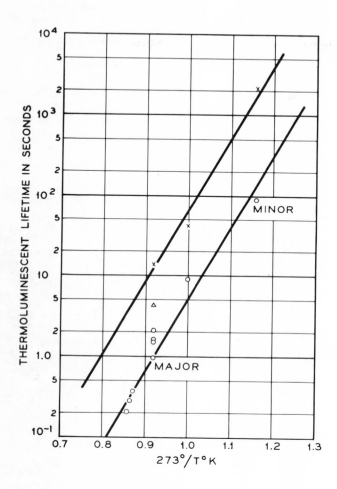

Figure 6

Thermoluminescent decay time of traps vs. temperature. At a given temperature, where two or more traps are indicated, "Major" refers to fact that most of decay can be described by that particular time constant. This same trap if followed to lower temperature, may no longer describe the major portion of the total decay and is labeled "Minor".

Acknowledgment

We wish to thank D. Linn, G. Devlin, E. Kelly and Miss B. Prescott for their experimental assistance and A. M. Clogston, V. Jaccarino, M. Peter and M. Sturge for helpful discussions.

124 S. GESCHWIND, P. KISLIUK, M. P. KLEIN, J. P. REMEIKA AND D. L. WOOD

[1] P. PRINGSHEIM, *Fluorescence and Phosphorescence* (Interscience Publishers, Inc., New York, 1949) who quotes E. TIEDE AND R. PIWONKA, *Chem. Ber.* **64,** 2252 (1931).
[2] P. A. KROGER, *Some Aspects of the Luminescence of Solids*, Elsevier Publishing Company, Inc., Amsterdam, Netherlands, 1948.
[3] S. SUGANO AND Y. TANABE, *J. Phys. Soc. Japan* **13,** 880 (1958).
[4] S. SUGANO AND TSUJIKAWA, *J. Phys. Soc. Japan* **13,** 899 (1958).
[5] D. S. MCCLURE, *Solid-State Physics* Academic Press Inc., New York, Vol. 9, 1959.
[6] J. OWEN, *Proc. Roy. Soc.* (*London*) **A227,** 183 (1955).
[7] P. KISLIUK AND W. S. BOYLE, *Proc. I.R.E.*, November, 1961, p. 2; quote SCHAWLOW AND DEVLIN.
[8] A. KIEL, *Phys. Rev.* **126,** 1292 (1962).
[9] R. H. SILSBEE, *Phys. Rev.* **128,** 1726 (1962).
[10] D. MCCUMBER, Private communication.
[11] K. A. MUELLER, *Phys. Rev. Letters* **2,** 341 (1959).
[12] H. G. ANDRESEN, *Phys. Rev.* **120,** 1606 (1960); *J. Chem. Phys.* **35,** 1090 (1961).
[13] W. LOW AND J. T. SUSS, *Phys. Rev.* **119,** 132 (1960).
[14] V. HEINE, *Phys. Rev.* **107,** 1002 (1957); J. H. WOOD AND G. W. PRATT, JR., *Phys. Rev.* **107,** 995 (1957); R. E. WATSON AND A. J. FREEMAN, *Phys. Rev.* **123,** 2027 (1961).
[15] A. A. MANENKOV AND A. M. PROKHOROV, *J. Exp. Theor. Phys.* (*U.S.S.R.*) **28,** 762 (1955); J. E. GEUSIC, *Phys. Rev.* **102,** 1252 (1956); M. ZARIPOV AND I. SHAMONIN *J. Exp. Theor. Phys.* (*U.S.S.R.*) **30,** 291 (1960).
[16] H. KAMIMURA, *Phys. Rev.* **128,** 1077 (1962).
[17] S. SUGANO AND M. PETER, *Phys. Rev.* **122,** 381 (1961).
[18] J. ARTMAN, Proc. Ist. Int. Conf. Paramagnetic Resonance, Academic Press, New York, 1963, p. 634
[19] This latter model was suggested to the author by Dr. Piet Cossee.
[20] M. E. Wise, *Physica* **17,** 1011 (1951).

Paramagnetic and Endor Spectrum of Cu^{3+} in Al_2O_3

W. E. Blumberg, J. Eisinger, S. Geschwind and J. P. Remeika

Bell Telephone Laboratories, New Jersey

ABSTRACT

We have studied the paramagnetic resonance of the ion Cu^{3+} (configuration $3d^8$ which is isoelectronic with Ni^{2+}) and obtained precise information about the electron-nuclear interactions of this ion by means of the ENDOR technique.

The Cu^{3+} entered the Al_2O_3 lattice as a substitutional impurity for Al. The ion exhibit is a spectrum typical of a center with $S = 1$ in an axially symmetrical site. Each electronic transition has four hyperfine components arising from nuclear spin 3/2. The lines corresponding to the two isotopes Cu^{63} and Cu^{65} were unresolved in the paramagnetic spectrum. The observed transitions yielded the following parameters. $D = -0.18838 \pm 0.00004$ cm^{-1}, $g_{\parallel} = 2.0784 \pm 0.005$ and $g_{\perp} = 2.0772 \pm 0.0005$.

By performing ENDOR experiments at 1.3°K we were able to observe $\Delta M_s = 0$, $\Delta M_I = \pm 1$ transitions with line widths of about 50 kc/s. These could be fitted satisfactorily only by postulating an effective field at the nucleus equal to $(1 + \delta) H_0$ where H_0 is the external field and $\delta = 0.0087$. Other interaction parameters are $A_{63} = -192.947 \pm 0.001$ mc/s; $A_{65} = -206.679 \pm 0.001$ mc/s; $B_{63} = -180.10 \pm 0.05$; $B_{65} = -192.916 \pm 0.05$; $e^2qQ^{63} = -0.17 \pm 0.001$ mc/s. The origin of δ and surprisingly small value for e^2qQ will be discussed.

The hyperfine structure anomaly $(A_{63}/A_{65})(g_{63}/g_{65}) - 1 = (0.0145 \pm 0.0008)$ per cent. Since this agrees with the value obtained for $s_{1/2}$ electrons in Cu as measured by atomic beam magnetic resonance we may conclude that the hyperfine interaction in Cu^{3+} has its origin in $s_{1/2}$ electrons polarized by s-d interactions.

Electron Spin Resonance and Spin-Lattice Relaxation of Ti³⁺ Ion in Corundum

L. S. KORNIENKO AND A. M. PROKHOROV

Institute of Nuclear Physics, Moscow State University

ABSTRACT

The electron paramagnetic spectra (EPR) and the spin-lattice relaxation of the Ti^{3+} ion in, corundum was investigated.

A single EPR line was observed at temperatures below 9°K and can be described by the spin-Hamiltonian

$$\hat{\mathscr{H}} = g_{\parallel}\beta H_z \hat{S}'_z + g_{\perp} \beta(H_x\hat{S}'_x + H_y\hat{S}'_y)$$

$$S' = \tfrac{1}{2},\ g = 1.067 \pm 0.001,\ g_{\perp} \approx 0.$$

The temperature dependence of the spin-lattice relaxation time τ_1 was investigated by the methods of continuous — and impulse — saturation in the region of 4.2°K–2°K. At 2°K τ_1 is $5 \cdot 10^{-2}$ sec and decreases sharply as the temperature increases to 4.2°K (by a factor of approximately 10^3). At 9°K line broadening occurs which permits the evaluation of $\tau_1 \sim 5 \cdot 10^{-8}$ sec at this temperature.

Electron spin resonance (ESR) absorption of the Ti^{3+} ions, isomorphously substituted for Al in a corundum crystal lattice was detected at liquid helium temperatures. Three crystals, containing about several hundredth mole percent of Ti were investigated using a wavelength of ~ 3 cm.

ESR spectrum comprises one resonance line of unusual asymmetrical shape with fast decrease at the high magnetic field slope (Figure 1).

Figure 1

Investigation of the line position at various angles between the magnetic field direction and the trigonal crystal axis shows that the spectrum can be described by the spin-Hamiltonian:

$$\hat{\mathscr{H}} = g_{\parallel}\beta H_z \hat{S}_z' + g_{\perp} \beta(H_x\hat{S}'_x + H_y\hat{S}'_y)$$

126

where $g_{\parallel}$ and $g_{\perp}$ are g-factors along the direction parallel and perpen-dicular to the trigonal crystal axis respectively, β—Bohr magneton, $\hat{S}'$—effective spin operator with $S' = 1/2$.

The g-factors, determined at the points, where the line intensity has its maximum value are

$$g_{\parallel} = 1.067 \pm 0.001, \; g_{\perp} \lesssim 0.1$$

The evaluation of $g_{\perp}$ was made by extrapolation from g-value dependence for $\theta = 0 - 60°$. The ESR lines were observed with a magnetic field of $6000 - 16,000$ gauss. A value was taken to obtain the best agreement with the calculated dependance $H = h\nu/g\beta$, where $g = (g_{\parallel}^2 \cos^2\theta + g_{\perp}^2 \sin^2\theta)^{1/2}$. This evaluation of $g_{\perp}$ is confirmed by the decreasing of the line intensity for Ti^{3+}, which for $\theta = 0°$ is approximately the same as the line intensities of small impurities Fe^{3+}, Cr^{3+}. The concentration of these impurities is approximately $10^3 - 10^4$ times smaller than that for Ti^{3+}. The maximum slope width ΔH for Ti^{3+} when $\theta = 0°$ at temperature $4.2°K$ was 50 gauss. The line shape and line width do not change when the temperature decreases to $1.55°K$. The angular variation of the line width shows that it cannot be described by the low $\Delta H = h\Delta\nu/g\beta$ width $\Delta\nu = $ const. In fact, the line broadening was more rapid, particulary for small angles. This can be accounted for by the small variations in the trigonal axis direction about the average position at the angle $0.5 - 1°$. The line conserves its asymmetrical shape for all magnetic field orientation.

At the temperature $\sim 9°K$ the line width increases and spin-lattice relaxa-tion time τ_1 was estimated as $5 \cdot 10^{-8}$ sec. τ_1 was also evaluated by the continuous wave saturation method. Supposing $g_{\perp} = 0.1$ we obtain that $\tau_1 \approx 10^{-4}$ sec for $4.2°K$ and $\approx 10^{-1}$ sec for $1.55°K$. This evaluation gave approximately the temperature dependance of τ_1 but its absolute values were practically unknown. In fact we did not know the exact values of $g_{\perp}$ and τ_2 as the former was very small and the latter could not be calculated be-cause the line shape indicated the presence of inhomogeneous broadening.

In order to measure the values of τ_1 more exactly a pulsed saturation method was used. At temperature $T = 2°K$ 20μsec microwave saturating pulses "burned out the hole" in the absorption line. The "hole" could be observed when the magnetic field directed along trigonal crystal axis was modulated with a frequency of 50 cps. Figure 2 represents the oscillogram of the relaxation process when the sweep is synchronized with the pulse frequency and the magnetic field passes through the resonance value eight times. The saturating pulse is seen at the first line. In the succeeding passages the

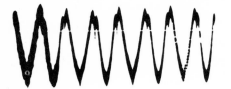

Figure 2

absorption line with a narrow "hole" is observed. The hole decays with characteristic time $\tau = (5 \pm 1) \cdot 10^{-2}$ sec.

If we accept that the "hole" width does not change than τ coincides with spin-lattice relaxation time τ_1. But the cross-relaxation through the absorption line also can decrease the "hole" and the hole width then ought to increase. In this case τ_1 must be longer then τ.

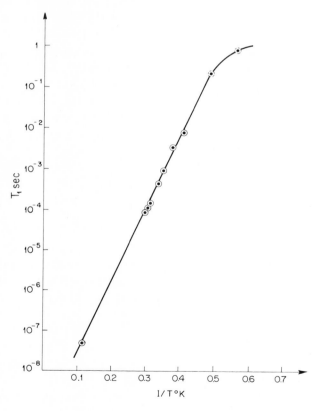

Figure 3

At a temperature of $4.2°K$ the pulse power was insufficient and the hole was not observed at all, in agreement with temperature depandence of τ_1 found from the continuous wave saturation method for $2 - 4.2°K$.

It was very difficult to observe the usual exponential decay pictures after the pulsed saturation. This is connected with the fact that hole width is very small if short well shaped monochromatic pulses are used. But using the nonmonochromatic saturating pulses such a decay picture could be obtained. With this technique the variation of τ_1 in the temperature range $2.5 - 3.5°K$ has been measured and temperature dependance of τ_1 is shown in Figure 3. It is clear from the figure that at temperatures $9 - 2.5°K$ τ_1 obeys the exponential law, and the splitting of the first excited level from the ground state can be evaluated as $30 - 35 \text{ cm}^{-1}$.

REFERENCES

[1]   L. S. KORNIENKO AND A. M. PROKHOROV, *JETP* **38,** 1651 (1960).
[2]   L. S. KORNIENKO, P. P. PASHININ AND A. M. PROKHOROV, *JETP* **42,** 65 (1962).

Paramagnetic Properties of Iron Group Ions in Tetrahedral Coordination

F. S. HAM AND G. W. LUDWIG

General Electric Research Laboratory, Schenectady, New York

ABSTRACT

The electronic structure and paramagnetic resonance spectra of iron group ions in tetrahedral coordination are reviewed. Energy levels are inverted compared with octahedral coordination, and crystal field splittings are smaller. Hybridization of $3d$ states with odd-parity states occurs, and covalent bonding with ligands may be large; both effects cause characteristic changes in resonance parameters. Tables are given of parameters for iron group ions in tetrahedral and near-tetrahedral symmetry.

I. Introduction

In this paper we review the energy level structure and paramagnetic resonance spectra of iron group ions in tetrahedral coordination [1–5]. Compared with the more familiar octahedral case, the crystalline field splitting of $3d$ states in tetrahedral symmetry usually is smaller and has the opposite sign. The tetrahedron's lack of inversion symmetry leads to hybridization of the $3d$ functions with functions of opposite parity, such as $4p$ and $4f$ functions of the central ion [6; 7]. Both d-p hybridization [8] and covalent bonding with neighboring ligands [9–11] affect resonance parameters by changing matrix elements of the orbital angular momentum, the spin-orbit interaction, and the hyperfine interaction, and both contribute to linear shifts in resonance parameters in an applied electric field [12–14]. The available experimental data support the view that covalent bonding frequently is important, but they permit estimates of the extent of d-p hybridization in only a very few cases. Areas are pointed out in which further study would be rewarding.

II. Energy levels in tetrahedral symmetry

We consider a transition metal ion at the center of an arrangement of four ligands at the corners of a tetrahedron. In the point ion approximation, ligands of charge $-Ze$ contribute the terms

$$V = + \frac{20}{\sqrt{3}} \frac{Ze^2}{a^4} xyz - \frac{35}{9} \frac{Ze^2}{a^5}(x^4 + y^4 + z^4 - \frac{3}{5}r^4)$$

to the potential energy of an electron on the central ion, if a is the ion-ligand separation. The first term, V_3, is odd under inversion and reflects the lack of inversion symmetry. The second term, V_4, is identical with the cubic term contributed by the six neighbors in octahedral coordination except that the coefficient is 4/9 as large and of opposite sign.

There is a close correspondence between the electronic structure of transition metal ions in tetrahedral and in cubic symmetry, a result of the fact that the symmetry group T_d of the tetrahedron is a subgroup of the full cubic group O_h and is isomorphic with the rotation group of the cube [15]. The simplest case is that of a single $3d$ electron: in either symmetry the five orbital states split into groups of three and two belonging to the representations t_2 and e:

$$t_2: \quad xy, \; yz, \; zx$$

$$e: \quad z^2 - \tfrac{1}{2}(x^2 + y^2), \quad (\sqrt{3}/2)(x^2 - y^2). \tag{2}$$

Assuming the potential (1) and neglecting admixture of other states, we obtain for the splitting (defined as $+10Dq$) between the states

$$E(e) - E(t_2) = -\frac{20}{27} \frac{Ze^2}{a^5} \langle r^4 \rangle, \tag{3}$$

where $\langle r^4 \rangle$ is the expectation value of r^4 for the $3d$ electron. In this approximation the splitting is proportional to the coefficient of V_4 and is independent of V_3. Hence whereas in octahedral symmetry e lies above t_2 ($Dq > 0$), in tetrahedral symmetry the e states are lower and the splitting is 4/9 as large. Qualitatively similar conclusions may be reached with models [9; 11; 16] more sophisticated than the point ion approximation.

In paramagnetic resonance of iron group ions our primary concern is with the lowest energy levels of ions having ground state free ion configurations $3d^n$. The lowest Russell-Saunders term of each of these configurations has maximum multiplicity; the terms of interest are then ^2D, ^3F, ^4F, ^5D, and ^6S. A tetrahedral potential lifts the orbital degeneracy of these terms as follows [5; 15]:

$$\begin{aligned} D &\to T_2(3) + E(2), \\ F &\to T_1(3) + T_2(3) + A_2(1), \\ S &\to A_1(1), \end{aligned} \tag{4}$$

where the degeneracy of the representation is given in parantheses. We assume that the crystalline potential is sufficiently weak compared to the Coulomb interaction of the electrons so that mixing with higher free ion terms may be neglected. The relative energies of the resulting crystal-field terms may then be expressed as follows using the one-electron parameter Dq:

D terms: $E(E) - E(T_2) = \pm\, 10\, Dq.$

F terms: $E(T_2) - E(A_2) = (5/4)\, [E(T_1) - E(T_2)] = \pm\, 10\, Dq.$

The lowest crystal-field term (for $Dq < 0$ and the weak-field case) for each of the configurations $3d^n$ is given in Figure 1. This figure provides a convenient mnemonic in identifying the lowest crystal-field term, although it is not a rigorous description of the occupation of one-electron states in the ground terms of $3d^3$ and $3d^8$.

The degeneracy of terms of orbital symmetry T_1 and T_2 is lifted further when spin-orbit interaction (assumed weaker than the crystalline potential)

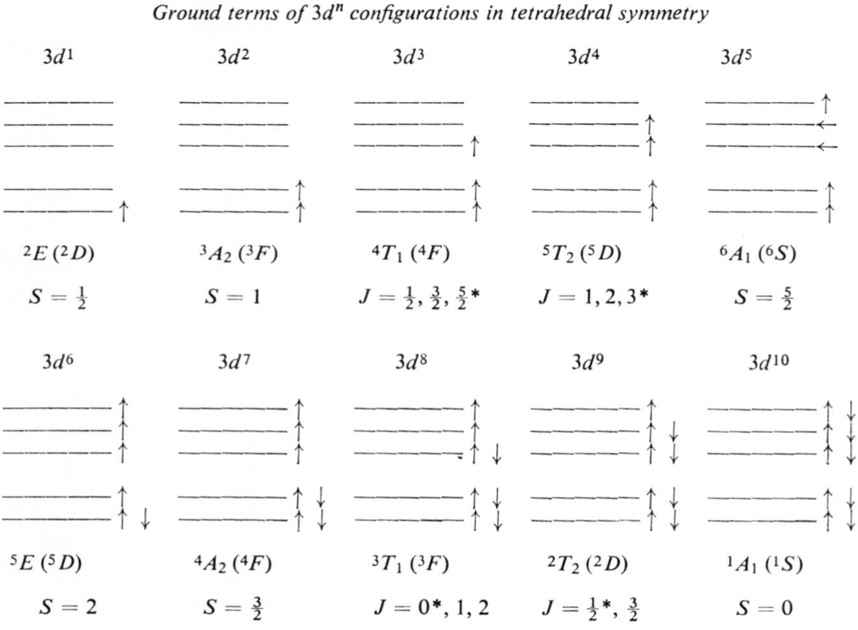

Ground terms of $3d^n$ configurations in tetrahedral symmetry

Figure 1

Ground crystal-field terms of iron grop ions with $3d^n$ configurations in tetrahedral symmetry ($Dq < 0$; weak crystal field). The upper group of three lines denotes the 3-fold degenerate one-electron t_2 states, the lower group of two lower energy e states. The distribution of electrons among the t_2 and e states and their relative spin orientation are indicated schematically by the arrows. The ground crystal-field term of the ion is noted beneath each diagram, and in parentheses the lowest free ion term, from which it is derived. Also noted are the spin S of this term and the effective total angular momentum J of the levels into which the term is split in first order by the spin-orbit interaction. The value of J marked with an asterisk should have the lowest energy. Levels with $J > 3/2$ and the ^5E term are split further in order λ^2/Dq by the spin-orbit interaction.

is taken into account. As in cubic symmetry, the matrix elements of the orbital angular momentum L among the T_1 or T_2 states are proportional to those of an effective orbital angular momentum operator $\mathfrak{L}$, with $\mathfrak{L} = 1$ [17]. The different groups of states are characterized by their value of the effective total angular momentum J where $J = \mathfrak{L} + S$ is an operator analogous to the total angular momentum $L + S$ of the free ion. The possible values of J are indicated in Figure 1.

The ground states of some ions in tetrahedral symmetry have no counterpart in octahedral coordination. For example, $3d^4$ in tetrahedral symmetry differs from octahedral $3d^1$ in having $S = 2$, and from octahedral $3d^6$ in that the ordering of the J levels is inverted because of the opposite sign of the spin-orbit interaction.

Since the crystalline field splitting in tetrahedral symmetry is relatively small, we expect relatively large perturbations of the ground state by states in which an electron has been excited across the $t_2 - e$ gap.

III. Hybridization with odd parity states of the central ion

The term V_3 in the potential leads to hybridization of the $3d$ states with states of the central ion having odd parity [6; 7]. Hybridization of $t_2 d$ states occurs with p and f states and with other states of higher L. (Odd functions belonging to the representation t_{1u} of O_h belong to t_2 of T_d.) Neglecting all but the p- and f-admixtures, we have for the hybridized one-electron t_2 orbitals

$$\psi_{xy} = \alpha d_{xy} + \beta p_z + \gamma f_z$$
$$\psi_{yz} = \alpha d_{yz} + \beta p_x + \gamma f_x$$
$$\psi_{zx} = \alpha d_{zx} + \beta p_y + \gamma f_y.$$

The lowest states having a symmetry similar to that of the e $3d$ states are those belonging to e_u of O_h from $L = 5$. Consequently the hybridization of e $3d$ states is assumed small.

We shall take the point of view that the hybridization of many-electron states can be taken into account by replacing all one-electron t_2 orbitals by the hybridized orbitals (6) [6; 8]. The effect of such hybridization on the paramagnetic properties of an ion may then be deduced from one-electron matrix elements of the orbital angular momentum L and the spin-orbit interaction $\mathscr{H}_o$ [18].

For the d part of the t_2 functions, $L = -\mathfrak{L}$; for the p part, $L = \mathfrak{L}$; and for the f part, $L = -(3/2)\mathfrak{L}$. Hence the matrix elements of L and $\mathscr{H}_{so}$ among the functions (6) are

$$\langle\, t_{2i}\,|\,\mathbf{L}\,|\,t_{2j}\,\rangle = -(\alpha^2 - \beta^2 + \frac{3}{2}\gamma^2)\,\langle\, t_{2i}\,|\,\mathfrak{L}\,|\,t_{2j}\,\rangle$$

$$\langle\, t_{2i}\,|\,\mathscr{H}_{so}\,|\,t_{2j}\,\rangle = -(\alpha^2\zeta_d - \beta^2\zeta_p + \frac{3}{2}\gamma^2\zeta_f)\langle\, t_{2i}\,|\,\mathfrak{L}\cdot\mathbf{S}\,|\,t_{2j}\,\rangle,$$

where ζ_d, ζ_p, and ζ_f are the one-electron spin-orbit parameters for d, p and f states. The effect of d–p hybridization (which is presumably more important than d–f hybridization) on the matrix elements is thus two-fold: (1) the contribution of the d functions is reduced by the factor α^2; (2) the p part of the orbitals (6) introduces a contribution of opposite sign proportional to β^2.

Matrix elements of $\mathfrak{L}$ and $\mathscr{H}_{so}$ among e states vanish, while those between t_2 and e are simply reduced from the pure d case by the factor α.

As an example of how a particular resonance property is affected by d–p hybridization we consider the hyperfine interaction [8]. The relevant operator is [17]

$$\mathscr{H}_{hf} = 2\gamma\beta_0\beta_N\left\{\frac{(\mathbf{L}-\mathbf{S})\cdot\mathbf{I}}{r^3} + \frac{3(\mathbf{r}\cdot\mathbf{S})(\mathbf{r}\cdot\mathbf{I})}{r^5} + \frac{8\pi}{3}\delta(\mathbf{r})(\mathbf{S}\cdot\mathbf{I})\right\} \qquad (9)$$

Omitting the contact term, we can represent $\mathscr{H}_{hf}$ for d and for p states by [17]

$$(\mathscr{H}_{hf})_d = P_d\left\{(\mathbf{L}\cdot\mathbf{I}) - \frac{2}{21}\left[\frac{3}{2}(\mathbf{L}\cdot\mathbf{S})(\mathbf{L}\cdot\mathbf{I}) + \frac{3}{2}(\mathbf{L}\cdot\mathbf{I})(\mathbf{L}\cdot\mathbf{S}) - 6(\mathbf{S}\cdot\mathbf{I})\right]\right\} \quad (10)$$

$$(\mathscr{H}_{hf})_p = P_p\left\{(\mathbf{L}\cdot\mathbf{I}) - \frac{2}{5}\left[\frac{3}{2}(\mathbf{L}\cdot\mathbf{S})(\mathbf{L}\cdot\mathbf{I}) + \frac{3}{2}(\mathbf{L}\cdot\mathbf{I})(\mathbf{L}\cdot\mathbf{S}) - 2(\mathbf{S}\cdot\mathbf{I})\right]\right\} (11)$$

where

$$P_{d,p} = 2\gamma\beta_0\beta_N\langle r^{-3}\rangle_{p,d}$$

For the hybridized t_2 states (6) the hyperfine operator takes the form

$$(\mathscr{H}_{hf})_{t_2} = A\,(\mathfrak{L}\cdot\mathbf{I}) + B(\mathbf{S}\cdot\mathbf{I}) + C[(\mathfrak{L}\cdot\mathbf{S})(\mathfrak{L}\cdot\mathbf{I}) + (\mathfrak{L}\cdot\mathbf{I})(\mathfrak{L}\cdot\mathbf{S})]$$
$$+ D(\mathfrak{L}_x^2 S_x I_x + \mathfrak{L}_y^2 S_y I_y + \mathfrak{L}_z^2 S_z I_z) \qquad (12)$$

with

$$A = -\alpha^2 P_d + \beta^2 P_p \qquad\qquad C = -\frac{3}{7}\alpha^2 P_d - \frac{3}{5}\beta^2 P_p$$

$$B = -\frac{4}{7}\alpha^2 P_d + \frac{4}{5}\beta^2 P_p \qquad D = +\frac{12}{7}\alpha^2 P_d \qquad (13)$$

A typical matrix element of (12) is

$$\langle\,\mathfrak{L}_z = \pm 1, S_z = \tfrac{1}{2}\,|\,\mathscr{H}_{hf}\,|\,\pm 1, \tfrac{1}{2}\,\rangle = [\pm A + \tfrac{1}{2}B + (C + \tfrac{1}{2}D)]I_z. \quad (14)$$

The p and d functions make contributions of opposite sign to the coefficients A, B, and $(C + \frac{1}{2}D)$.

For many-electron states obtained from $3d^n$ configurations using the hybridized t_2 orbitals, we may now evaluate the g-factor and the spin-orbit and hyperfine interactions of the whole ion from the one-electron matrix elements of e and t_2 states. Although the results are complicated by perturbations from excited states (and are further complicated when distortions from tetrahedral symmetry occur), they may be stated qualitatively as follows: Interactions depending on matrix elements of the orbital angular momentum, spin-orbit interaction, and hyperfine interaction (aside from the contact term) among the t_2 states have contributions of opposite sign from d and p components (and would even reverse sign if the admixture of p were sufficiently large). Interactions arising from matrix elements between t_2 and e states (such as most of the perturbation terms of the ground state arising from excited states of the many-electron configuration) are unaffected by $d-p$ hybridization except for the factor α, the amplitude of the d contribution to the t_2 state. Interactions depending on $e-e$ matrix elements are unchanged.

Several estimates are available of the extent of $d-p$ hybridization for tetrahedral complexes. Ballhausen and Liehr [6] have estimated from crystal field calculations for $CuCl_4^=$ and $CoCl_4^=$ that the $4p$ admixture is much less than 1%. Calculations by Weakliem yield similar results for other systems [19]. If $d-p$ hybridization is in general as small as this one has little hope of identifying its effect on the usual resonance parameters. However, Bates et al. [8] have estimated for Cu^{2+} in the organic complex copper ($\alpha\alpha'Br$) dipyrromethene that the p-admixture is 20–30% and is responsible for cancelling an anisotropic hyperfine interaction which would be expected for a $3d$ model of the Cu^{2+} ion but which was not observed. Other crystals may exist in which $d-p$ hybridization is equally large. In particular, departures from the point ion approximation may enhance the p admixture.

The ions for which effects of $d-p$ hybridization on the paramagnetic resonance spectrum should be most pronounced are those for which in the scheme of Figure 1 there is orbital degeneracy in the ground state arising from the t_2 level, namely $3d^3$, $3d^4$, $3d^8$, and $3d^9$. However, $3d^3$ (^4F) and $3d^8$ (^3F) are complicated because the ground term $^4T_1$ ($^3T_1$) may be mixed substantially by the crystal field with terms of the same symmetry and multiplicity arising from the ^4P (^3P) terms of the same configuration [20]. This mixing also makes a contribution of opposite sign to that of the ground term in the orbital part of the g-factor and in the spin-orbit interaction.

The most promising configurations for unequivocal observation of effects of $d-p$ hybridization are thus $3d^4$ and $3d^9$.

IV. Covalent bonding

In tetrahedral coordination the t_2 states on the central ion have the proper symmetry to form σ-bonds with the four ligands, while the e states do not [6]. This is the reverse of the situation pertaining in octahedral coordination [9; 10]. Both t_2 and e states may form π bonds with the ligands.

Covalent bonding may be expected to change matrix elements in a manner similar to that found in octahedral coordination. However, many of the crystals in which tetrahedral coordination occurs have a strongly covalent character, so that covalent effects may be expected to be pronounced. That this is so is shown in Section VI by the empirical correlations between the covalency of the crystal and such resonance parameters as the hyperfine interaction, g-factor, and cubic field splitting parameter a of S-state ions. A satisfactory theory of these effects is not now available.

V. Electric dipole matrix elements

A further consequence of the absence of inversion symmetry is that electric dipole matrix elements may be finite between states derived from the original $3d^n$ configuration, because of both $d-p$ hybridization on the central ion and covalent bonding with the ligands. Ballhausen and Liehr have estimated the resulting enhancement of intensities of optical transitions[6].

Finite electric dipole matrix elements can influence the resonance spectrum by making the resonance parameters depend linearly on an applied dc electric field[12–14]. Such effects are discussed in other papers in this volume [21]. We note here that an electric field $\mathscr{E}_z$ along the z cubic axis has two independent orbital matrix elements of importance which are linear in the strength of $d-p$ mixing in the t_2 states and also linear in the strength of covalent bonding with the ligands. One is between the t_2 states and may be represented by the operator

$$\mathscr{H}_{e\mathscr{L}} = -p\mathscr{E}_z(\mathfrak{L}_x\mathfrak{L}_y + \mathfrak{L}_y\mathfrak{L}_x).$$

The other is between the t_2 state with $\mathfrak{L}_z = 0$ and one of the e states. The former has the predominant effect when the ground term of the ion has orbital degeneracy due to t_2.

Effects of an applied electric field on resonance thus offer a direct measurement of the extent of the breakdown of parity and thereby represent an important tool for the further study of tetrahedral ions. However, they may not provide a clear distinction between $d-p$ hybridization on the central ion and covalent bonding with neighboring ligands.

VI. Discussion of observed paramagnetic resonance spectra

Relatively few ions have been studied in tetrahedral coordination by paramagnetic resonance. The most extensive series of such observations for iron group ions has been made in various semi-conductors, notably silicon and the II-VI compounds[22]. Spectra have also been observed in spinel, garnet, and a few other inorganic and organic crystals.

In Table I we have listed resonance parameters for ions in tetrahedral symmetry, while those for lower symmetries for which the environment of the ion is a distorted tetrahedron are listed in Table II[8; 23–40]. Dq is

TABLE I

Paramagnetic resonance parameters of iron group ions in tetrahedral symmetry*

Ion	Con-figuration	Host	S	g	Units of 10^{-4} cm^{-1}		Reference
					a	A	
V^{51}	$3d^2(?)$	ZnTe	1(?)	1.917		57.8	36
Cr^{53}	$3d^2$	Si	1	1.9962		12.54	22
Mn^{55}	$3d^2$	Si	1	2.0259		−63.09	22
	$3d^5$	ZnAl$_2$O$_4$	5/2	2.0002	< 3	−74.9	33
	$3d^5$	ZnS	5/2	2.0021	+ 8.0	−63.7	38 [24, 26]
	$3d^5$	ZnSe	5/2	2.0051		−61.7	36 [25]
	$3d^5$	ZnTe	5/2	2.0105	+ 30	−56.1	36
	$3d^5$	CdTe	5/2	2.0069	+ 28	−57.3	36[25,34,39]
	$3d^5$	Ge	5/2	2.0061	+ 8.9	−42.7	27
	$3d^5$	Si	5/2	2.0058	+ 26.1	−40.5	22
Fe	$3d^5$	GaP	5/2	2.025	+ 390		36
Co^{59}	$3d^7$	ZnS	3/2	2.248		1.8	35
	$3d^7$	ZnSe	3/2	2.270			35
	$3d^7$	ZnTe	3/2	2.2972		17.5	35
	$3d^7$	CdTe	3/2	2.3093		23.4	35

* Interstititial ions in silicon have been omitted.

negative, as expected, for all cases in the Tables for which the sign of Dq may be determined from the resonance spectrum. We have however omitted from Table I the various interstitial ions in silicon [22; 41] (see below), for which Dq is positive.

The available evidence for the most part agrees [42] with the prediction of the point ion approximation that Dq should be about half as large for ions in tetrahedral coordination as in the corresponding octahedral cases. The most comprehensive data supporting this conclusion come from studies of optical spectra; a full discussion is given in the review by McClure[43]. Recent experiments by Weakliem [19], for example, give for $Co(3d^7)$ values of Dq of -330, -375, and -390 cm^{-1} in CdS, ZnS, and ZnO respectively, in contrast to Low's value of $+960$ cm^{-1} in MgO[44].

TABLE II

Paramagnetic resonance parameters of iron group ions in near-tetrahedral symmetry

Ion	Con-figu-ration	Host	S	g	Units of 10^{-4} cm^{-1}			Reference
					a	D	A	
V[51]	$3d^2$	CdS	1	1.934($\parallel$), 1.932($\perp$)		± 1130	$\mp 63(\parallel)$, $\mp 66(\perp)$	36
Mn[55]	$3d^5$	ZnO	5/2	2.0016	+6*	−216.9	−76.0	29
	$3d^5$	CdS	5/2	2.0029	+4*	+8.2	−65.3	29 [25, 34]
	$3d^5$	ZnS	5/2	2.0016	+8*	−105	−65	28 [23, 24]
	$3d^5$	CdSe	5/2	2.003			−61.5	30
	$3d^5$	MgTe	5/2	2.013			−58.1	30
Fe[57]	$3d^5$	ZnO	5/2	2.0060	39	−594	9.0	40
Fe**	$3d^5$	$Y_3Ga_5O_{12}$	5/2	2.0047	+62	−880		37
	$3d^5$	CdS	5/2	2.01	+60*	−30		31
Co[59]	$3d^7$	Cs_3CoCl_5	3/2	2.32($\parallel$), 2.27($\perp$)		-3.1×10^4		3
	$3d^7$	CdS	3/2	2.269($\parallel$), 2.27($\perp$)		$> 2 \times 10^4$	4.6($\parallel$), < 12($\perp$)	36
Ni[6]	?	Ge	1/2	$g_1 = 2.0294$ $g_2 = 2.0176$ $g_3 = 2.1128$			$A_1 \leqq 1.6$ $A_2 = 12.2$ $A_3 = 10.3$	32
Cu	$3d^9$	Copper (aa'Br) dipyrro-methene	1/2	$g_1 = 2.084$ $g_2 = 2.069$ $g_3 = 2.283$			$A_1 \cong A_2 \cong A_3 \cong 0$	8

* These values represent $(a–F)$ rather than a.

** Spectra which may be due to Fe^{3+} at tetrahedral sites in beryl reported by M. Dvir and W. Low, *Phys. Rev.* **119**, 1587 (1960).

Estimates of Dq from the resonance spectra may be obtained for the ions $V(3d^2)$ and $Co(3d^7)$ from the shift in the g-factor of the orbital singlet ground state[4]

$$g - 2 \cong \frac{4\lambda}{5Dq}$$

Using for the spin-orbit parameter λ a value that is 70% of the free ion value [11], we obtain from the g-shifts of Tables I and II the following rough values for Dq:

V $(3d^2)$	in CdS	-860 cm^{-1}
	in ZnTe	-690 cm^{-1}
Co$(3d^7)$	in ZnS	-400 cm^{-1}
	in CdTe	-325 cm^{-1}

This value for $Co(3d^7)$ in ZnS is a bit larger than Weakliem's -375 cm^{-1}[19]. Typical values for these ions in octahedral coordination are given by McClure[41]: $V(3d^2)$, 1800 cm^{-1}; $Co(3d^7)$, 1000 cm^{-1}. Thus our expectation is confirmed that in tetrahedral coordination Dq is roughly $-4/9$ of its value in the corresponding octahedral case, resulting in relatively large perturbations of resonance parameters from excited states.

Since most observations of resonance for ions in tetrahedral coordination have been for ions having ground states that are orbital singlets, there are only a few cases from which we might hope to obtain estimates of d–p hybridization from the available spectra. Of the two ions in the Tables which appear to have orbital degeneracy (or near-degeneracy) in their ground states, a detailed analysis of the spectrum of Ni$^-$ in germanium has not been given, the configuration of the ion not being known with certainty. Accordingly the only case remaining is that of Cu^{2+} in the organic complex copper ($\alpha\alpha'$Br) dipyrromethene, for which Bates et al. [8] estimated from the absence of an observable hyperfine interaction that the ground state has 20–30% admixture of $4p$. No parameters describing shifts of resonance parameters in an applied electric field have so far been reported for any of the ions of Tables I and II.

Although in tetrahedral coordination, the interstitial ions in silicon studied by Ludwig, Woodbury, and Ham [22; 41] have been omitted from Table I because they are anomalous in that they show positive values for Dq (e is above t_2). Large shifts of the resonance parameters of these centers in an applied electric field have been observed [13; 21]; these shifts and the unperturbed values of the resonance parameters are not accounted for simply by d–p hybridization on the central ion or by covalent bonding with the nearest neighbor ligands. The model that is evolving for these centers involves more extended orbitals and is sufficiently different from the ionic model used as a basis for the discussion of this paper to make discussion of these centers inappropriate here.

A number of empirical correlations are evident between the resonance parameters in Tables I and II and the covalent character of the host crystal. As Van Wieringen [25] and Matumura [30] have pointed out, the hyperfine parameter A of Mn $(3d^5)$ decreases in magnitude with increasing covalent bonding, while the g-factor increases in this sequence. A has the value -97.8×10^{-4} cm^{-1} for the strongly ionic case of Mn^{2+} in CaF$_2$ [45]; in Tables I and II it decreases through the sequence of ligands O, S, Se, and Te to values of about -40×10^{-4} cm^{-1} for Ge and Si. This large hyperfine interaction of Mn$(3d^5)$ arises from a contact interaction which is now believed to result from exchange polarization of the spins of the $1s$, $2s$ and $3s$ electrons [46]. The contribution to A of each these inner shells should depend on the ion's environment and in particular on the extent of covalent bonding, but in view of the cancellations among these contributions it is not clear why the variation of A from ligand to ligand in different host crystals is as regular as it seems to be.

Another correlation is between covalency and large values found for the cubic splitting parameter a of the $3d^5$ $^6S_{5/2}$ ground state of Mn$(3d^5)$ and Fe$(3d^5)$. Gabriel, Johnston, and Powell [47] have calculated from the crystal field model that a should increase roughly as the third to sixth power of $|Dq|$, being positive for most interesting values of Dq and λ. Values of a for Mn^{2+} in octahedral coordination range from $+3 \times 10^{-4}$ cm^{-1} to $+11 \times 10^{-4}$ cm^{-1} for the Tutton salts, double nitrates, and fluosilicates [3], while for Mn^{2+} in MgO Low obtained $a = +18.6 \times 10^{-4}$ cm^{-1} [48]. For Fe^{3+}, a is $\sim +130 \times 10^{-4}$ cm^{-1} in the alums [3], $+203.8 \times 10^{-4}$ cm^{-1} in MgO [38], and $+185 \times 10^{-4}$ cm^{-1} for *octahedral* sites in yttrium gallium garnet [37]. The expectation that a should in general be substantially smaller in tetrahedral coordination is not borne out. Indeed in a number of the semiconductors a is larger for Mn$(3d^5)$ [and for Fe$(3d^5)$ in GaP] than in any octahedral case. Hall, Hayes, and Williams [39] have noted that the values for Mn$(3d^5)$ in ZnO and CdTe are larger than those predicted by the theory of Gabriel et al. [47] by factors of 10 and 100 respectively. It thus appears that bonding with the ligands may greatly increase a above the value expected for a given Dq for the simple crystal field model [34; 39], although there does not appear to be a quantitative correlation between values of a and the degree of covalent bonding indicated by the size of the hyperfine parameter A.

If covalent bonding is important, substantial hyperfine interaction with the ligands is to be expected. While relevant data are not available for most of the ions in the Tables, such superhyperfine structure has been found for a number of the ions in silicon [22] and in a few other cases. Indeed Dorain [29] and Lambe and Kikuchi [34] have found for $Mn(3d^5)$ in CdS and CdTe that easily resolvable structure appears as a result of hyperfine interaction with cadmium ions occupying the twelve second nearest neighbor sites.

VII. Conclusion

The few existing paramagnetic resonance data for iron group ions in tetrahedral coordination reveal trends which distinguish their spectra from those of corresponding ions in octahedral coordination, but further studies are needed before the electronic structure of the ions can be understood in detail. In particular, it is not yet clear how important d–p hybridization on the metal ion may be: while crystal-field calculations indicate it may be small, the paramagnetic resonance data on one appropriate ion suggest a large mixing. Further study of ions with orbital degeneracy (or near-degeneracy) in the ground state should resolve this question. Another important problem is that of clarifying the effects of covalent bonding on the resonance spectra; the tetrahedrally coordinated ions offer an excellent opportunity for examination of these effects, for in many cases both the degree of bonding and the resulting changes in the resonance parameters are large. The study of the effects of an applied electric field on spectra should prove particularly interesting, especially if such effects supplement data on hyperfine interaction with the ligands as a means of determining quantitatively the degree of covalent bonding or of distinguishing between such bonding and d–p mixing on the central ion.

REFERENCES

[1] For general reviews of the methods and results of paramagnetic resonance see references [2–4]; for a recent review of crystal field theory see reference 5.

[2] W. Low, *Paramagnetic Resonance in Solids*, Academic Press, New York, 1960.

[3] K. D. BOWERS AND J. OWEN, *Repts. Progr. Phys.* **18**, 304 (1955).

[4] B. BLEANEY AND K. W. H. STEVENS, *Repts. Progr. Phys.* **16**, 108 (1953).

[5] J. S. GRIFFITH, *The Theory of Transition-Metal Ions*, Cambridge University Press, Cambridge, 1961.

[6] C. J. BALLHAUSEN AND A. D. LIEHR, *J. Mol. Spectroscopy* **2**, 342 (1958).

[7] W. LOW AND M. WEGER, *Phys. Rev.* **118**, 1119 (1960).

[8] C. A. BATES, W. S. MOORE, K. J. STANDLEY AND K. W. H. STEVENS, *Proc. Phys. Soc.* (London) **79**, 73 (1962).

[9]   K. W. H. STEVENS, *Proc. Roy. Soc. London* **A219**, 542 (1953).

[10] M. TINKHAM, *Proc. Roy. Soc. London*, **A236**, 535, 549 (1956).

[11] W. MARSHALL AND R. STUART, *Phys. Rev.* **123**, 2048 (1961).

[12] N. BLOEMBERGEN, *Science*, **133**, 1363 (1961); *Phys. Rev. Letters* **7**, 90 (1961).

[13] G. W. LUDWIG AND H. H. WOODBURY, *Phys. Rev. Letters* **7**, 240 (1961).

[14] F. S. HAM, *Phys. Rev. Letters* **7**, 242 (1961).

[15] We employ the notation of Reference 5 in referring to irreducible representations of symmetry groups.

[16] J. H. VAN VLECK, *J. Chem. Phys.* **3**, 803 (1935).

[17] A. ABRAGAM AND M. H. L. PRYCE, *Proc. Roy. Soc. London* **A205**, 135 (1961).

[18] The same conclusions can also be reached by the method of configuration mixing (Reference 7) whereby V_3 is viewed as perturbing the terms of the $3d^n$ configuration by admixing terms of the same T_d symmetry from higher odd configurations such as $3d^{n-1} 4p$ and $3d^{n-1} 4f$.

[19] H. A. WEAKLIEM, *J. Chem. Phys.* **36**, 2117 (1962).

[20] A. ABRAGAM AND M. H. L. PRYCE, *Proc. Roy. Soc. London* **A206**, 173 (1951).

[21] See for example G. W. LUDWIG AND F. S. HAM, this volume.

[22] A review of electron spin resonance studies in semiconductors has been given by G. W. LUDWIG and H. H. WOODBURY in *Solid State Physics*, Academic Press, New York, 1962, Vol. 13, p. 223.

[23] E. E. SCHNEIDER AND T. S. ENGLAND, *Physica* **17**, 221 (1951).

[24] W. D. HERSHBERGER AND H. N. LEIFER, *Phys. Rev.* **88**, 714 (1952).

[25] J. S. VAN WIERINGEN, *Disc. Faraday Soc.* **19**, 118 (1955).

[26] L. M. MATARRESE AND C. KIKUCHI, *J. Phys. Chem. Solids* **1**, 117 (1956).

[27] G. D. WATKINS, *Bull. Am. Phys. Soc.* **2**, 345 (1957).

[28] S.P. KELLER, I. L. GELLES AND W. V. SMITH, *Phys. Rev.* **110**, 850 (1958).

[29] P.B. DORAIN, *Phys. Rev.* **112**, 1058 (1958).

[30] O. MATUMURA, *J. Phys. Soc. Japan*, **14**, 108 (1959).

[31] J. LAMBE, J. BAKER AND C. KIKUCHI, *Phys. Rev. Letters* **3**, 270 (1959).

[32] G. W. LUDWIG AND H. H. WOODBURY, *Phys. Rev.* **113**, 1014 (1959).

[33] R. STAHL-BRADA AND W. LOW, *Phys. Rev.* **116**, 561 (1959).

[34] J. LAMBE AND C. KIKUCHI, *Phys. Rev.* **119**, 1256 (1960).

[35] F. S. HAM, G. W. LUDWIG, G.D. WATKINS AND H.H. WOODBURY, *Phys. Rev. Letters* **5**, 468 (1960).

[36] H. H. WOODBURY AND G. W. LUDWIG, *Bull. Am. Phys. Soc.* **6**, 118 (1961).

[37] S. GESCHWIND, *Phys. Rev.* **121**, 363 (1961).

[38] W. M. WALSH, *Jr. Phys. Rev.* **122**, 762 (1961).

[39] T. P. P. HALL, W. HAYES AND F. I. B. WILLIAMS, *Proc. Phys. Soc. London*, **78**, 883 (1961).

[40] W. M. WALSH, JR. AND L. W. RUPP, *Jr. Phys. Rev.* **126**, 952 (1962).

[41] G. W. LUDWIG, H. H. WOODBURY AND F. S. HAM (to be published).

[42] Such agreement may be fortuitous: a correct description of the effect of the crystalline potential and of covalent bonding may be very much more complicated. See, for example, R.G. SHULMAN AND S. SUGANO, *Phys. Rev. Letters* **7**, 157 (1961).

[43] D. S. McCLURE, in *Solid State Physics*, Academic Press, New York, 1959, Vol. 9, p. 399.

[44] W. LOW, *Phys. Rev.* **109**, 256 (1957).

[45] J. M. BAKER, B. BLEANEY AND W. HAYES, *Proc. Roy. Soc. London* **A247**, 141 (1958).

[46] R. E. WATSON AND A. J. FREEMAN, *Phys. Rev.* **123,** 2027 (1961).
[47] J. R. GABRIEL, D. F. JOHNSTON AND M. J. D. POWELL, *Proc. Roy. Soc. London* **A264,** 503 (1961).
[48] W. LOW, *Phys. Rev.* **105,** 793 (1957).

DISCUSSION

A. YARIV, USA: Some recent work at the Bell Telephone Laboratories (Dietz, Kamimura and Yariv) revealed an unusually large hyperfine interaction for Cu^{2+} in the tetrahedral coordination of ZnO, $|A| = 224 \times 10^{-4}$ cm^{-1} corresponding to a nuclear field per spin of $\sim$ 660,000 Φ. The increased covalent bonding in tetrahedral coordination was generally assumed to decrease the hyperfine interaction, so that our observation may require modification of the existing theories.

Paramagnetic Resonance of Cr in CdS

T. L. ESTLE, G. K. WALTERS AND M. DEWIT

Texas Instruments Incorporated, Dallas 22, Texas, U.S.A.

ABSTRACT

The paramagnetic resonance of Cr in CdS has been studied at low temperatures. Six Cr centers, differing only in their orientation, are present in equal numbers. Each resonance has a $g_\perp \leq 0.02$; consequently no $\Delta M = \pm 1$ transitions are observed. The results can be interpreted using the spin-Hamiltonian, $\mathscr{H} = g_\parallel' \beta H_z S_z' + \Delta S_x'$, with $S' = 1/2$, $g_\parallel = 7.747$ and $\Delta/h = 4506$ Mc/s, and where the z-axis of the Cr center makes an angle of $57.8°$ with the crystal c-axis. The lines broaden at about $6°$K and are unobservable above about $20°$K. The hyperfine splitting constants parallel to the z axis of the center are 5.6 gauss for the nearest Cd nuclei and 13.8 gauss for Cr^{53} in an enriched sample. We attribute the resonance to substitutional Cr^{++} with a Jahn-Teller distortion approximately along the directions bisecting the lines to the nearest sulfur neighbors. There are six such directions, three from each of the two non-equivalent substitutional sites. The resultant crystalline field quenches the orbital angular momentum leaving a spin 2 state lowest. The observed resonance occurs between the lowest two levels, which are an admixture of $M_s = \pm 2$ produced by a zero field splitting, Δ, comparable to $h\nu$.

I. Introduction

Ions of the first transition group, which have partially filled $3d$ shells have been extensively studied in octahedral coordination. In contrast, the data on these ions in tetrahedral coordination are much less extensive, although the somewhat similar eight-coordinated fluorite lattice has received considerable attention.

The most important difference between $3d$ ions in octahadral and tetrahedral complexes is that the order of the energy levels derived from the ground term is inverted. The three t_2 or $d\varepsilon$ orbitals have the lowest energy in an octahedral complex, whereas the two e or $d\gamma$ orbitals are lowest in tetrahedral coordination. This difference in ordering, plus other characteristics of tetrahedral coordination, such as lack of inversion symmetry, a smaller Dq and different tendencies of the complex to distort, implies in general that the $3d$ ions will behave quite differently in the two types of coordination. In addition, crystals having tetrahedral coordination, such as those with the zinc blende or wurtzite structure, possess large interstices in which impurities may reside.

For the reasons outlined above, we have studied a number of $3d$ impurities in crystals with the zinc blende or wurtzite structure. An interesting example is chromium in cadmium sulfide, which has the wurtzite structure shown diagramatically in Figure 1.

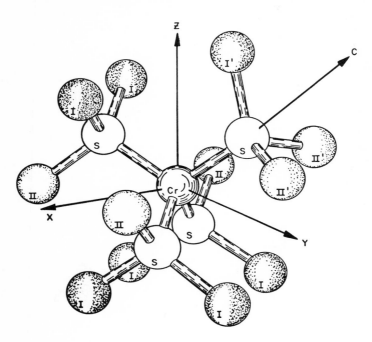

Figure 1
Substitutional site in the wurtzite structure.

Paramagnetic resonance studies have been made on Mn^{++} [1;2] Fe^{3+} [3], Co^{++} and V^{3+} [4] in CdS. In each case, the measurements are consistent with the impurity occupying a Cd site with no decrease in the symmetry of the site. Dorain and Locker [5] have recently reported an independent study of Cr in CdS [6].

Section II will be devoted to a presentation of the experimental results and a somewhat phenomenological description of the center. It starts with a description of the samples followed by a qualitative description of the methods of measurements. Finally, the hyperfine structure is described and some additional observations are listed. Section III discusses the results in terms of several specific models. Best agreement with experiment is obtained for a substitutional Cr^{++} model.

II. Experimental results

Single crystals of cadmium sulfide were obtained from the Eagle-Picher Company. The crystals were covered with a saturated solution of a chromium salt, usually chromic nitrate, and heated in order to drive off the water. The samples were then sealed in evacuated quartz ampoules with small amounts of sulfur and heated to temperatures ranging from 900°C to 1100°C for varying lengths of time. The crystals were either cooled slowly or quenched by dropping the quartz ampoule into cold water. After removing the crystal from the ampoule, the surface layer was removed by scraping, lapping and etching. The resultant crystals were uniformly colored and therefore presumably uniform in chromium concentration.

At 1.3°K six groups of hyperfine lines are observed in all samples. Each group of lines is identified with a different Cr center, with the centers differing only in the orientation of their principal axes. The effective g-values are about 8 and 0 along and perpendicular to the z axes of the centers. The z axes make an angle of 57.8° with the crystalline c axis and have a 60° periodicity perpendicular to the c axis. The component in the (00.1) plane bisects the angle between two of the crystalline a axes. The intensity of each group is greatest with H_1 parallel to the z axis of the center and zero if H_1 is perpendicular to this axis. The intensities of the six groups are approximately equal for equivalent orientations.

The experimental results, except for the hyperfine structure, can be described with the spin-Hamiltonian:

$$\mathcal{H} = g'_{\parallel}\beta H_z S'_z + \Delta S'_x, \tag{1}$$

where $S' = 1/2$. The measured values for the parameters are $g'_{\parallel} = 7.747 \pm 0.003$ and $\nu_0 \equiv \Delta/h = 4506 \pm 6$Mc/s or $\Delta = 0.1503 \pm 0.0002$ cm^{-1}. Since $g_{\perp}$ is zero no allowed $\Delta M = \pm 1$ transitions occur. However, the zero-field splitting, Δ, mixes the two states and a $\Delta M = 0$ transition occurs when a component of H_1 is along the z axis of the center. The dependence of the magnetic field for this transition upon frequency and upon θ, the angle of the field with the z axis, is given by

$$H = \frac{h\nu\sqrt{1 - \nu_0^2/\nu^2}}{g_{\parallel}\beta\cos\theta}. \tag{2}$$

The form of this dependence was verified experimentally.

The zero-field splitting, ν_0, was measured by comparing the magnetic field for resonance at two different frequencies but at a fixed angle. This was accomplished by employing cavities which resonated at both frequencies and making the measurements in succession with no changes in the geometry other than the direction of H_1. Measurements were made using 8.37 Gc/s and 9.59 Gc/s, and 9.29 Gc/s and 24.45 Gc/s. The results were the same to within less than the experimental error.

Having determined ν_0, the value of $g'_{\parallel}$ was obtained from the lowest magnetic field at which resonance occurred as the orientation of the sample was varied. This was accomplished by rotating the sample in a vertical plane inside a cylindrical cavity resonant in the TM_{110} mode and rotating the magnetic field in a horizontal plane. In this way the sample could be oriented to within $0.2°$ of the desired direction. The angle of the z axis of the center with the c axis was obtained by measuring the magnetic field for resonance of the three other centers observable when H is parallel to the z axis of one center. With $g'_{\parallel}$ and Δ known, one can calculate θ from Eq. 2. This value of θ, along with the $60°$ periodicity of the spectrum perpendicular to the c axis, enables one to obtain two independent determinations of the angle between the z and c axes. The average value is $57.8 \pm 0.1°$.

A Hamiltonian of the form given in Eq. 1 would result if the $\pm M$ levels of a system with integral spin were far removed from the remaining levels. The most likely interpretation is that they are the $M = \pm 2$ levels for $S = 2$. The zero-field splitting can then result from the cubic field, which couples $M = \pm 2$ in first order, or from a rhombic field, which must be present for reasons of symmetry and which gives a second order coupling. An axial field larger than any other term in the $S = 2$ Hamiltonian will be directed along the z axis. The value of $g_{\parallel}$ for the spin 2 system is then 1.937 ± 0.001 if only a cubic field is present, or about 1.5% higher if the rhombic field produces the splitting Δ [7]. This is fairly close to the free spin value and indicates an appreciable quenching of the orbital angular momentum.

Each of the six groups of lines has a structure produced by a hyperfine interaction with nearby Cd nuclei [8]. There are two isotopes of Cd with non-zero nuclear spins, Cd^{111} and Cd^{113}. Both have $I = 1/2$, natural abundances of 12.75% and 12.26% respectively, and nuclear moments differing by less than 5%. Figure 2 shows an example of the structure for a sample in which the resolution is good. In addition to the Cd hyperfine structure the hyperfine interaction with Cr^{53} ($I = 3/2$) has been observed in samples with natural abundance (9.55% Cr^{53}) and in samples which have been enriched to 99% in Cr^{53}. Figure 2 shows some lines due to Cr^{53} in natural abundance. The effect of the hyperfine interactions is to add terms to Eq. 2 giving

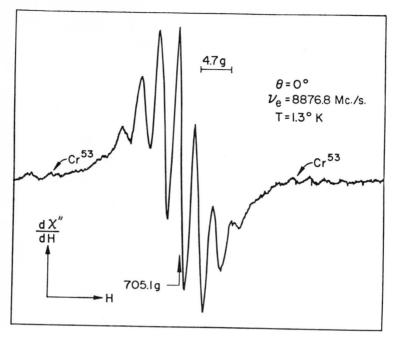

Figure 2

Observed cadmium hyperfine structure of a slowly cooled sample.

$$H = \frac{h\nu \sqrt{1 - \nu_0^2/\nu^2}}{4g_{\parallel}\cos\alpha \; \cos\theta} + \frac{M_I A}{g_{\parallel}\beta\cos\theta} + \sum_i \frac{M_{Ii} K_i}{g_{\parallel}\beta\cos\theta}, \qquad (3)$$

where A, K_i, and $g_{\parallel}$ refer to spin 2, $\cos\alpha$ is a parameter introduced by the rhombic field, and i is summed over the equivalent Cd nuclei. The angular dependence has been verified for both the Cd and the Cr^{53} hyperfine structure. The value of $A/g_{\parallel}\beta$, the hyperfine splitting for Cr^{53}, is 13.82 ± 0.04 gauss. The Cd hyperfine splitting, $K_i/g_{\parallel}\beta$, is 5.55 ± 0.15 gauss.

The Cd hyperfine structure is characterized by a roughly symmetrical group of lines with relative intensities, taken proportional to the peak to peak amplitude of the derivatives, of about 1.00, 0.71, 0.25, 0.03 with H along the z axis and for samples showing good resolution. An irregular shape of some of the hyperfine lines in slowly cooled samples may indicate additional unresolved structure. The cadmium hyperfine structure becomes unresolvable for values of θ greater than about 30°. The loss of resolution seems to depend on the direction in which H is rotated away from the axis. The structure is usually slightly asymmetric. The asymmetry and loss of resolution are worst for samples which are quenched and best for those which are cooled very slowly. The relative intensities also vary from sample to sample, being somewhat smaller for the quenched samples. A study of the intensities as a function of temperature between 1.3°K and 4.2°K indicates that we are observing the ground state and that excited states exist about 4 cm^{-1} above the ground state. These would presumably be the states with $M = \pm 1, 0$. As the temperature is raised above 4°K, the lines broaden rapidly. The Cd hyperfine structure becomes unresolved at about 6°K and the line is too broad to be observable by 20°K. No signs of saturation could be detected at 1.3°K.

Preliminary results by Lin [9] on the static susceptibility of Cr doped CdS seem to indicate the presence of levels lying roughly 200 cm^{-1} above the ground state.

The optical absorption spectrum of one of our samples was examined at room temperature [10]. No bands similar to those reported by Pappalardo and Dietz [11] were seen. This may be a result of the rather low concentration of Cr in the sample (~ 30 ppm). Therefore, it is not known whether the centers seen by resonance are related to the bands observed by Pappalardo and Dietz.

Single crystals of ZnO and hexagonal ZnS doped with Cr have also been examined and show no resonances similar to the ones described above. Lines corresponding to $\Delta M = \pm 1$ transitions, probably due to another charge state of Cr, were seen in ZnS as well as in many of the CdS crystals.

III. Discussion

A number of models which might produce a spin 2 ground state can be postulated. The configurations d^4 and d^6 both have $S = 2$ in crystalline fields which are not too strong. If an axial field in the appropriate direction quenches the orbital angular momentum, then the observed results can be obtained. The d^4 configuration would result from Cr^{++}, taking an ionic picture, whereas d^6 could result from neutral Cr if the $4s$ levels are higher than the $3d$ levels, as might be expected in a solid [12]. There are two likely sites for the impurity, substitution for a Cd or in an interstice. The substitutional site is tetrahedrally coordinated (see Figure 1), while the interstitial site is surrounded by six sulfurs and six cadmiums on two interpenetrating octahedra (see Figure 3). The latter site probably behaves very much like the usual case of octahedral coordination. The

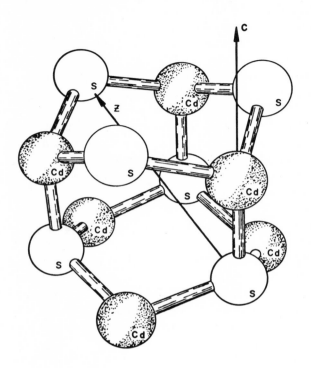

Figure 3
Interstice in the wurtzite structure.

symmetry of both these sites is C_{3v}. However, a tetragonal distortion of the predominantly cubic environment of both sites is approximately along the direction measured for the z axis of the center.

The configurations d^4 and d^6 both produce a ^5D term which splits into an orbital doublet, ^5E, and an orbital triplet, $^5T_2$, in a cubic field. For substitutional d^4 and interstitial d^6, $^5T_2$ is lowest, whereas ^5E is lowest for the other two cases. A tetragonal crystalline field will remove the orbital degeneracy of ^5E but a trigonal field will not. The $^5T_2$ level splits into a doublet and a singlet in both tetragonal and trigonal fields. All the orbital singlets derived from the ^5D term in a tetragonal field combine with the spin functions $\chi(M)$ to form the linear combinations $[\chi(2) + \chi(-2)]$ and $[\chi(2) - \chi(-2)]$. The functions then always belong to different, one dimensional representations. However, these two representations remain degenerate up to second order in the spin orbit interaction and are therefore expected to be very close together. One of the orbital singlets derived from ^5E will have these $M = \pm 2$ levels lowest with $g_\parallel < 2$ and of about the observed magnitude, both of which are in agreement with the observations. The other orbital singlet has $g_\parallel \simeq 2$ and $M = \pm 2$ highest. The orbital singlet derived from $^5T_2$ will have $g_\parallel < 2$ for d^4, but for d^6 $g_\parallel$ may be less than or greater than 2. In an axial field the $M = \pm 2$ levels will be highest. The work of Tinkham [7] indicates that in a rhombic field this order may be changed and $M = \pm 2$ may be lowest.

Isolated substitutional Cr^{++} and interstitial Cr^0 are neutral in this lattice, whereas isolated interstitial Cr^{++} has a charge of $+ 2$ and isolated substitutional Cr^0 has a charge of $- 2$. Local charge compensation is likely in the case of the latter two models. Defect association for the former two cases is not necessary to obtain charge neutrality; although association with neutral defects may occur. Substitutional Cr^0 requires a positively charged defect and a nearest interstice is the only close geometrically acceptable site. The combination of a $+ 2$ ion in an interstice and a neutral atom in a positive ion site seems rather unlikely. Interstitial Cr^{++} requires a negatively charged defect for charge compensation. This could be provided by a vacancy in one of the Cd sites surrounding the interstice [13].

In the event that defect association does not occur, the axial crystalline field must be explained by a Jahn-Teller type of distortion. Such a distortion is likely for the doublet since the trigonal field produced no splitting and spin-orbit interaction provides only a small splitting ($\lambda \simeq 50\,\mathrm{cm}^{-1}$). In the case of the orbital triplet, the work of Dunitz and Orgel [14] indicates tetrahedral d^4 to be prone to undergo a Jahn-Teller distortion while octahedral d^6 is not. In order for the former to occur, the combined effect of the trigonal field and spin-orbit interaction must be too small to stabilize the undistorted complex.

The cadmium hyperfine structure probably provides the most definitive evidence available to help differentiate between the various models. Figure 4 shows the result of a calculation of the relative intensities of the hyperfine lines for an interaction with a given number of equivalent Cd nuclei. Complete resolution is assumed and both isotopes with $I = 1/2$ are considered to have the same magnetic moment (they differ by less than 5%) and a total abundance of 25.2%. A number of factors will tend to make the observed intensities smaller than the calculated ones. The incomplete resolution, which is frequently accentuated by strains from rapid cooling, and the interference of the $M_I = \pm 1/2$ Cr^{53} hyperfine lines are examples of such factors. With this in mind the observations appear to be consistent with an appreciable interaction with about seven Cd nuclei, probably not less than six or more than eight. There seems to be an indication of additional

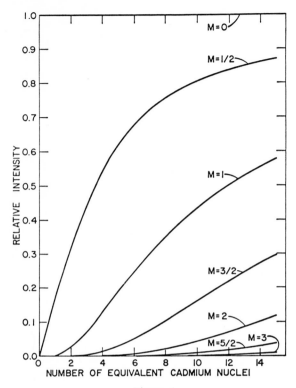

Figure 4

Calculated relative intensities of the lines in the cadmium hyperfine structure as a function of the number of equivalent cadmium nuclei. The two Cd isotopes with non-zero spin have a spin of 1/2, were treated as identical, and assumed to have a total abundance of 25.2%.

weak interactions possibly from a few more Cd's and with a splitting comparable to the line width.

An interstitial model is difficult to make consistent with these observations. One starts with six Cd nuclei, or five in the case of a Cd vacancy in the Cd octahedron. Of these six, three probably lie closer to the impurity than the other three in an undistorted arrangement (see Figure 3). A tetragonal distortion may reduce this equivalence further. In addition, the d-orbitals have varying amounts of overlap with the Cd's because of their angular dependence. Thus the equivalence of the Cd nuclei will again be reduced. It would be rather surprising if this were to result in a hyperfine structure resembling six or more equivalent cadmiums.

In contrast the substitutional models have twelve Cd nuclei with which interaction may occur. No large differences in spacing exist in the absence of a distortion. However a t_2 orbital, such as would be unoccupied for d^4, will be directed so as to overlap and therefore interact strongly with type II nuclei and probably II' but not type I or I' (see Figure 1). Hence if this interaction is subtracted from an isotropic interaction with twelve cadmiums, we obtain an interaction with the six type I nuclei and the type I' nucleus which is probably appreciable, plus a smaller interaction with II'.

Thus the substitutional model is consistent with the amplitudes of the observed structure, although the magnitude of the splitting does seem somewhat large for a substitutional impurity.

A number of additional experiments are planned in order to more clearly indicate the nature of the defect. These include a more careful study of the temperature dependence, in particular the dependence of line width upon temperature. Observation and a careful study of transitions between higher lying states would be of value. The possibility of observing other charge states should be explored, and crystals doped with donors and acceptors are being investigated for this purpose. Finally, the study of Cr in similar crystals, especially those with the zinc blende structure may be quite informative.

IV. Conclusion

Although the explanation of the properties of Cr in CdS in terms of a spin 2 system seems well founded, the explanation in terms of a specific model for the impurity center is much less definite. On the basis of our present experimental information it would appear that substitutional Cr^{++} with a tetragonal Jahn-Teller distortion fits better than the other models considered.

REFERENCES

[1] P. B. DORAIN, *Phys. Rev.* **112**, 1058 (1958).

[2] J. LAMBE AND C. KIKUCHI, *Phys. Rev.* **119**, 1256 (1960).

[3] J. LAMBE, J. BAKER AND C. KIKUCHI, *Phys. Rev. Letters*, 3 270 (1959).

[4] H. H. WOODBURY AND G. W. LUDWIG, *Bull. Am. Phys. Soc.* **6**, 118 (1961) and private communication from G. W. Ludwig.

[5] P. B. DORAIN AND D. LOCKER, *Bull. Am. Phys. Soc.* **7**, 306 (1962) and private communication.

[6] We learned of the work of Dorain and Locker after the majority of this work was completed. These authors ascribe the resonance to interstitial Cr^{++} in a crystalline field with predominantly cubic and axial components. The most important difference in experimental findings is their failure to observe the Cd hyperfine structure which leads us to a different interpretation.

[7] M. TINKHAM, *Proc. Roy. Soc.* A236, 535, 549 (1956). See also J. S. GRIFFITHS, *The Theory of Transition-Metal Ions*, Cambridge, 1961, p. 355.

[8]   Similar "super"-hyperfine structure has been observed in Mn^{++} and V^{3+} in CdS. See references 1, 2 and 4.

[9]   Private communication from Chun C. Lin.

[10]   This measurement was kindly performed by R. Hilton.

[11]   R. PAPPALARDO AND R. E. DIETZ, *Phys. Rev.* **123,** 1188 (1961).

[12]   G. W. LUDWIG AND H. H. WOODBURY, *Phys. Rev. Letters* 5, **98** (1960).

[13]   This model was suggested by S. Geller who pointed out that the preference shown by Cr for octahedral coordination might prevent it from moving into the vacancy.

[14]   J. D. DUNITZ AND L. E. ORGEL, *J. Phys. Chem. Solids* **3,** 20 (1957).

Optical and Magnetic Behaviors of $Ni^{2+} \cdot 6H_2O$ Complex in Crystalline Salts

A. Bose, R. Chatterjee and A. S. Chakraborty

Indian Association for the Cultivation of Science, Cal-32, India

ABSTRACT

Optical absorption spectra, paramagnetic resonance and magnetic anisotropy of several hydrated salts of octahedrally six coordinated Ni^{2+} ion have been correlated by assuming a small orthorhombic field superimposed on the predominant cubic field, arising from the charged atoms surrounding the Ni^{2+} ion and acting upon its original free ion energy state, d^8, ^3F.

The orthorhombic field is assumed to consist of a quartic and also the usual quadratic component. In calculating the energy separations of the spectroscopic levels under the above fields, we have considered the interactions between the $^3F, ^3P, ^1D, ^1G$ and ^1S states but omitted the small shifts due to spin-orbit coupling while for the magnetic anisotropy we have included the admixtures due to spin-orbit coupling, though the small high frequency contributions from the ^3P and other states coud be neglected.

Theory

Tanabe and Sugano [1] have calculated the coulomb and octahedral field matrices for $d^8(Ni^{2+})$ configuration and have shown that a d-electron in an octahedral field can either occupy a triply degenerate level t_2, of energy $-4\,Dq$ or a doubly degenerate level e, of energy $6\,Dq$, where the energy difference $10\,Dq$ is a measure of the cubic field strength.

Taking the crystalline field Hamiltonian of the usual from

$$\mathscr{H} = \sum D(x_i^4 + y_i^4 + z_i^4) + [A_2 x_i^2 + B_2 y_i^2 - (A_2 + B_2)z_i^2] +$$
$$+ \frac{3}{4} B_4 [x_i^4 - y_i^4 + 6y_i^2 z_i^2 - 6z_i^2 x_i^2] \tag{1}$$

and operating with it on the cubic field wavefunctions [2] for the ^3F and ^3P triplet states of Ni^{2+} ions, we set up the respective secular determinants which on solving by suitable unitary transformations, give the following eigenvalues for ^3F states:

$$E_1 = -4Dq + 3(\sigma - \delta) - 5\gamma - [16Dq^2 + 144\sigma^2 + 72\sigma\delta + 24Dq(\sigma - \delta) +$$
$$+ \gamma(100\,Dq + 120\sigma - 60\delta + 160\gamma)]^{\frac{1}{2}}$$

$$E_2 = -4Dq + 3(\sigma + \delta) + 5\gamma - [16Dq^2 + 144\sigma^2 - 72\sigma\delta + 24Dq(\sigma + \delta) + \\ + \gamma(160\gamma - 100\,Dq - 120\sigma - 60\,\delta)]^{\frac{1}{2}}$$

$$E_3 = -4Dq - 6\sigma - [16Dq^2 - 48Dq\cdot\sigma + 36\sigma^2 + 60\delta^2 + 15\gamma^2]^{\frac{1}{2}}$$

$$E_{,1} = -4Dq + 3(\sigma - \delta) - 5\gamma + [16Dq^2 + 144\sigma^2 + 72\sigma\gamma + 24Dq(\sigma - \delta) + \\ + \gamma(100\,Dq + 120\sigma - 60\delta + 160\gamma)]^{\frac{1}{2}}$$

$$E_{,2} = -4Dq - 6\sigma + [16\,Dq^2 - 48\,Dq\cdot\sigma + 36\sigma^2 + 60\delta^2 + 15\gamma^2]^{\frac{1}{2}}$$

$$E_{,3} = -4\,Dq + 3(\sigma + \delta) + 5\gamma + [16Dq^2 + 144\sigma^2 - 72\,\sigma\delta + 24\,Dq(\sigma + \delta) + \\ + \gamma(160\,\gamma - 100\,Dq - 120\,\sigma - 60\,\delta)]^{\frac{1}{2}}$$

$$E_4 = -18\,Dq$$

and for ^3P: (2)

$$E_{,,1} = -2\sigma$$

$$E_{,,2} = -\tfrac{1}{2}\sigma + \tfrac{1}{2}[9\sigma^2 + 4\delta^2]^{\frac{1}{2}}$$

$$E_{,,3} = -\tfrac{1}{2}\sigma - \tfrac{1}{2}[9\sigma^2 + 4\delta^2]^{\frac{1}{2}}$$ (3)

where

$$\left. \sigma = \frac{a(A_2 + B_2)}{2}, \quad \delta = \frac{a(A_2 - B_2)}{2}, \quad \gamma = \frac{3}{4}b\,B_4 \\ 12\,q'D = Dq \right\}$$ (4)

where q, a, b are ratios of matrix elements of the different orders of the field calculated for a system of 8-electrons to those for one electron.

The spectroscopic energy levels are now calculated using Eqs. (2) and (3) together with the field matrices of Tanabe and Sugano and are compared with the experimental results of Hartmann and Müller [3] for $NiSO_4\cdot 6H_2O$ and $NiSO_4\cdot 7H_2O$ crystals at 291° and 68°K as shown in Tables I and II.

To calculate the expression for magnetic susceptibility we include the spin-orbit interaction which removes the three fold spin-degeneracy of the orthorhombic field ground state of Ni^{2+} ion in the second-order. Proceeding in the usual manner, we get the susceptibility expression, which differs from Schlapp and Penney [4] including the fourth-order rhombic field and a second-order term in ζ, as follows:

$$K_i = -8N\beta^2\alpha_i + \frac{8N\beta^2}{3kT}(1 + 8\zeta_i\alpha_i + 16\,\zeta_i^2\alpha_i^2)\left(1 + \frac{\theta_i}{kT}\right)$$ (5)

where $i = 1, 2, 3$ refer to the orthorhombic axes of the crystalline field and $\theta_1 = -\tfrac{2}{3}\,\zeta_i^2(2\alpha_1 - \alpha_2 - \alpha_3)$ and a similar expression for θ_2 and θ_3. ζ_i is the

TABLE I

Absorption maxima

	$B = 980$ cm^{-1}		$C = 4608$ cm^{-1} (Racah coefficients)	
Maximum	NiSO$_4$·7 H$_2$O		NiSO$_4$·6 H$_2$O	
	Temperature $= 291°$K	Temperature $= 68°$K	Temperature $= 291°$K	Temperature $= 68°$K
	$Dq = 845$cm^{-1}	$Dq = 870$cm^{-1}	$Dq = 860$cm^{-1}	$Dq = 870$cm^{-1}
	$\sigma = -80$cm^{-1}	$\sigma = -80$cm^{-1}	$\sigma = -82$cm^{-1}	$\sigma = =80$cm^{-1}
	$\delta = -9$cm^{-1}	$\delta = -10$cm^{-1}	$\delta = -14$cm^{-1}	$\delta = -9$cm^{-1}
	$\gamma = -24$cm^{-1}	$\gamma = -30$cm^{-1}	$\gamma = -30$cm^{-1}	$\gamma = -30$cm^{-1}
A_1	7929	8081	7907	8086
A_2	8447	8698	8593	8697
	(8270)		(8430)	
B	8698	9049	8939	9059
	(8770)		(8900)	
C	13719	14051	13900	14046
	(13736)	(14100)	(13974)	(14100)
D	13900	14299	14195	14312
	(13930)	(14246)	(14110)	(14266)
E	15116	15504	15369	15504
	(15152)	(15565)	(15450)	(15565)
a	15730	16454	16446	16454
	(15526)	(15909)	(16130)	(15933)
b	23670	24671	24747	24671
	(21980)	(22830)	(22470)	(22730)
F	25827	26200	26048	26200
	(25410)	(25770)	(25720)	(25920)
G'	26067	26440	26292	26440
G	26068	26442	26294	26442
	(25760)	(25920)	(26060)	(26175)
c	25936	26043	26006	26043
	(26236)	(26300)	(26565)	(26643)
d	29426	29676	29576	27676
	(28740)	(28900)	(29240)	(28490)
e'	34680	36033	35845	36033
	(35000)	(34000)	(35000)	(34500)
f'	35160	36520	36324	36520
	(35900)	(35700)	(35600)	(35300)
h	63756	66149	65986	66149

The values in parentheses are the experimental values of Müller [3].

TABLE II

Susceptibility and anisotropy

Salts	Temp. °K	Field parameters. cm^{-1}	$\chi_1 - \chi_2$ × 10^6	$\chi_1 - \chi_3$ × 10^6	$\bar{\chi}$ × 10^6
NiSO$_4$·7H$_2$O	291°	$Dq = 845$, $\sigma = -80$ $\delta = -9$, $\gamma = -24$ $\bar{\zeta} = -300$	39 (40)	159 (162)	4728
	68°	$Dq = 850$, $\sigma = -80$ $\delta = -10$, $\gamma = -30$ $\bar{\zeta} = -300$	568 (555)	1278 (1275)	19289
Ni(NH$_4$SO$_4$)$_2$· 6H$_2$O	300°	$Dq = 850$, $\sigma = -60$ $\delta = -10$, $\gamma = -16$ $\bar{\zeta} = -270$ $\alpha_1 = -12.25 \times 10^5$ $\alpha_2 = -11.77 \times 10^5$ $\alpha_3 = -11.28 \times 10^5$ $\varphi_1 = 3.5$ $D = -2.12$ (-2.24) $E = -0.71$ (-0.38) $g = 2.244$ $(2.25 \pm .05)$	93.64 (93.80)	93.29 (91.50)	4438 (4307)

			$\chi_\perp - \chi_\parallel$ × 10^6		$\bar{\chi}$ × 10^6
NiSO$_4$·6H$_2$O	291°	$Dq = 860$, $\sigma = -82$ $\sigma = -14$, $\gamma = -30$ $\bar{\zeta} = -310$	83.2 (80.8)		4693 (4770)
	68°	$Dq = 870$, $\sigma = -80$ $\delta = -8$, $\gamma = -30$ $\bar{\zeta} = -310$	450 (467)		19694

spin-orbit coupling coefficient for the crystal and includes a covalency factor due to the overlap of the 3d charge cloud with the s- and p-charge clouds of the surrounding O-atoms. α_1, α_2, α_3 are complicated functions of the cubic, quadratic and quartic field coefficients Dq, σ, δ and γ and are written as

$$\alpha_1 = \frac{p^2}{E_4 - E_3'} + \frac{q^2}{E_4 - E_3}$$

$$\alpha_2 = \frac{r^2}{E_4 - E_1'} + \frac{s^2}{E_4 - E_1}$$

$$\alpha_3 = \frac{t^2}{E_4 - E_2'} \quad \frac{u^2}{E_4 - E_2}$$

where p, q, r, s, t, u are the unitary matrix transformation coefficients used to diagonalise the quadratics of the orthorhombic field.

Comparing the expression of susceptibility (Eq. 5) with that of Griffiths and Owen's [5] expression obtained from spin-Hamiltonian, we get expressions for D, E, and g as

$$D = 2\zeta^2 (2\alpha_1 - \alpha_2 - \alpha_3)$$
$$E = 2\zeta^2 (\alpha_2 - \alpha_3)$$
$$g = 2(1 + 4\zeta\alpha_1 + 8\zeta^2 \alpha_1{}^2)$$

Using the available structural data for the crystals, and the values of the spectroscopic energy levels as already found, it is possible to calculate by trial and error the magnetic anisotropies of the crystals and check these against the paramagnetic resonance data (Table II) where available. The calculated anisotropy are found to be in good agreement (see Table II) with the accurate anisotropy data between 300°K and 90°K [6] assuming an appreciable thermal change in the crystal field coefficients due to thermal expansion of the lattice and to the spin-lattice relaxation effects, and about 20 to 30% covalency overlap.

REFERENCES

[1]   Y. TANABE AND S. SUGANO, *J. Phys. Soc. Jap.* **9**, 753, (1954).

[2]   B. BLEANEY AND K. W. H. STEVENS, *Rep. Progr. Phys.* **16**, 108, 1953.

[3]   H. HARTMANN AND H. MÜLLER, *Farad. Soc. Disc.* **26**, 49 (1958); H. MÜLLER, (1957), Thesis.

[4]   R. SCHLAPP AND W. G. PENNEY, *Phys. Rev.* **42**, 666, 1932.

[5]   J. H. E. GRIFFITHS AND J. OWEN, *Proc. Roy. Soc.* A.**213**, 459 (1952).

[6]   A. BOSE, S. K. MITRA AND S. K. DUTTA, *Proc. Roy. Soc.* A. **248**, 153 (1958).

PART II

ESR SPECTRA OF RARE EARTH AND URANIUM ELEMENTS

A. Experimental results of ESR spectra of $4f^n$ and $5f^n$ ions

Paramagnetic Resonance of Irradiated CaF$_2$ Containing Rare Earth Salts

W. Hayes and J. W. Twidell

The Clarendon Laboratory, Oxford

ABSTRACT

Effects of 50 kv X-rays on synthetic undoped CaF$_2$ and on CaF$_2$ containing rare earth impurities have been investigated using ESR techniques. Irradiations have been carried out in a microwave cavity at temperatures between 20°K and room temperatures and the induced electron excess and electron deficient centers have been investigated. The structure of the self-trapped hole in CaF$_2$ has been determined and it has been shown that rare earth impurity ions which dissolve initially in CaF$_2$ in the trivalent state on cubic lattice sites provide trapping centers for electrons. Effects of electron irradiations on CaF$_2$ at room temperature have also been investigated.

Calcium fluoride belongs to the O_h^5 space group, the structure being a simple cubic array of fluorine ions with calcium ions at alternate body centers. Many rare earth ions dissolve readily in the trivalent state on substitutional lattice sites in CaF$_2$. Charge compensation may be achieved by a F$^-$ ion in a nearest interstitial site [1; 2] or by the presence of O^{2-} ions on anion sites [3]; the reduction of lattice symmetry by associated charge compensating defects is readily detected by ESR methods. In some cases charge compensation is remote and the ESR spectrum shows the cubic symmetry of the fluorine lattice [4].

We are at present investigating the effects of X-rays on CaF$_2$ containing rare earth ions using ESR and optical methods; the irradiations are carried out over a wide temperature range. We shall report here some results of investigations on CaF$_2$: Tm and on CaF$_2$: Ho.

A crystal of CaF$_2$ containing about 0.05% Tm which had been grown by the Stockbarger method did not show a resonance at X-band down to 20°K. The crystal was then X-irradiated at 77°K and the ESR spectrum was investigated without allowing the crystal to warm up. Two different spectra were observed. One of these spectra is isotropic and may be fitted to the spin-Hamiltonian

$$\mathcal{H} = g\beta\mathbf{H}\cdot\mathbf{S} + A\mathbf{I}\cdot\mathbf{S} \tag{1}$$

with $S = \frac{1}{2}$, $I = \frac{1}{2}$, $g = 3.453 \pm 0.003$ and $|A| = 368 \pm 2 \times 10^{-4}\,\text{cm}^{-1}$. There are two strong hyperfine lines, which arise from transitions with

$\Delta m_I = 0$; these bracket a weak line arising from the transitions m_S, $m_I = +\frac{1}{2}$, $\pm\frac{1}{2} \leftrightarrow -\frac{1}{2}$, $\mp\frac{1}{2}$. The two strong lines show a partly resolved structure arising from interaction with the fluorine ligands. The spectrum is assigned to Tm^{2+} which is isoelectronic with Yb^{3+} ($4f^{13}\ ^2F_{7/2}$); we find that the g-value of Yb^{3+} in the cubic crystal field of CaF_2 is 3.441 ± 0.003. This result shows that electrons released by the irradiation were captured by Tm^{3+} ions which must have been initially on cubic lattice sites since it is unlikely that associated charge compensating defects would be mobile at 77°K. A detailed discussion of the g-and $|A|$-values of Tm^{2+} has been given by Hayes and Twidell [5]. The nuclear moment of ^{169}Tm has been measured by Ritter [6] who finds $\mu = .229 \pm 0.003$ n.m. and we calculate an effective value of $\langle r^{-3}\rangle = 10.9$ a.u. for Tm^{2+} from the formula

$$|A|/g = \frac{2\beta\beta_n\mu_n}{I}\ \langle r^{-3}\rangle\ \frac{\langle J\|N\|J\rangle}{\langle J\|\wedge\|J\rangle}.$$

This value is close to the value of 10.80 a.u. estimated by interpolation between the values of $\langle r^{-3}\rangle$ calculated by Judd and Lindgren [8] for Tm atoms (10.51 a.u.) and Tm^{3+} (10.98 a.u.).

The other ESR spectrum observed upon irradiation of CaF_2 : Tm crystals at 77°K arises from the self trapped hole. The hole is located for about 98% of the time on fluorines 1 and 2 (see Figure 1) and about 2% of the time on

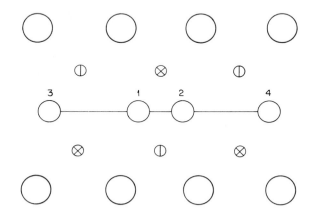

Schematic representation of the self-trapped hole in CaF_2. $\otimes$ calcium ions at the centers of fluorine cubes above the plane of the paper. $\oplus$ calcium ions at the centers of fluorine cubes below the plane of the paper. $\bigcirc$ fluorine ions in the plane of the paper; the self-trapped hole is located on fluorines 1, 2, 3 and 4.

fluorines 3 and 4. The centers have axial symmetry about a cube edge and there are three distinguishable centers in the magnetic unit cell. The ESR spectrum has been fitted to the spin-Hamiltonian

$$\mathscr{H} = g_{\parallel}\beta H_z S_z + g_{\perp}\beta(H_x S_x + H_y S_y) + A I_z S_z + B(I_x S_x + I_y S_y) + A' I'_z S_z$$
$$+ B'(I'_x S_x + I'_y S_y)$$

with $S = \frac{1}{2}$ and $I = I_1 + I_2$ where $I_1 = I_2 = \frac{1}{2}$ are the spins of the fluorine nuclei 1 and 2; $I' = I_3 + I_4$ where $I_3 = I_4 = \frac{1}{2}$ are the spins of the fluorine nuclei 3 and 4. We find $g_{\parallel} = 2.001 \pm 0.001$, $g_{\perp} = 2.020 \pm 0.001$, $|A| = 840.7 \pm 1.0 \times 10^{-4} \text{cm}^{-1}$, $|B| = 45.7 \pm 2.0 \times 10^{-4} \text{cm}^{-1}$, $|A'| = 14.1 \pm 0.3 \times 10^{-4} \text{cm}^{-1}$ and $|B'| \leq 4 \times 10^{-4} \text{cm}^{-1}$. The lines observed with the external magnetic field perpendicular to the axis of the center have a fluorine satellite structure [2] with line intensity ratios $1:10:35:10:1$ and spacing 4.5 ± 0.7 G; the calculated spacing is 4.2 G.

An optical absorption band arising from the self-trapped hole has been observed at 350 mμ by G. D. Jones (unpublished). This would appear to be the analogue of the $^2\Sigma_u^+ \leftrightarrow {}^2\Sigma_g^+$ transition of the self-trapped hole in LiF(F_2^-) which has been observed at 348 mμ by Delbecq, Hayes and Yuster [9]. The centers in CaF_2 decay at 138°K with emission of luminescence but there is no noticeable reduction in the concentration of Tm^{2+} ions at this temperature; the Tm^{2+} ions are annealed out by heating the crystal to about 550°C. The presence of thulium in the irradiated crystals enhances the initial rate of formation of self-trapped holes because of the electron trapping properties of the Tm^{3+} ion.

In experiments carried out so far with CaF_2:Ho crystals, the behavior of holmium appears to be similar to that of thulium. No resonance is observed at X or K band in unirradiated crystals; this seems to indicate that the ground state of Ho^{3+} ($4f^{10} \, ^5I_8$) in the cubic field of CaF_2 is the singlet, Γ_1, a result which is not inconsistent with the calculations of Lea, Leask and Wolf [10]. After X-irradiation at room temperature an isotropic spectrum with an eight line hyperfine structure is observed at 4°K. The K-band spectrum has been fitted to the spin-Hamiltonian (1) with $S = \frac{1}{2}$, $I = 7/2$, $g = 5.910 \pm 0.005$ and $|A| = 1308 \pm 3 \times 10^{-4} \text{cm}^{-1}$. This spectrum arises from $^{165}Ho^{2+}$ which is isoelectronic with Er^{3+} ($4f^{11} \, ^4I_{15/2}$). If we assume that the ground state of Ho^{2+} in CaF_2 is (see Lea, Leask and Wolf)

$$\Gamma_6 = 0.5818 \left| J_z = \pm\frac{15}{2} \right\rangle + 0.3307 \left| J_z = \pm\frac{7}{2} \right\rangle$$
$$+ 0.7182 \left| J_z = \mp\frac{1}{2} \right\rangle + 0.1910 \left| J_z = \mp\frac{9}{2} \right\rangle$$

we find that $g = 5g_j$. The value of g_j has been measured for the holmium atom $(4f^{11}5S^2\ ^4I_{15/2})$, using an atomic beam method, by Goodman, Kopferman and Schlüpman [11] and found to be 1.19516 ± 0.00010. Since the g_j for the holmium atom is not expected to be significantly different from that of Ho^{2+} we may calculate $g = 5.975$ for Ho^{2+}. However a detailed discussion of the measured g-value must await experiments at other frequencies.

Baker, Hayes and Jones [12] find that $g = 6.78 \pm 0.01$ for Er^{3+} in the cubic field of CaF_2 and this is consistent with the ground state

$$\Gamma_7 = 0.6332 \left| J_z = \pm \frac{13}{2} \right\rangle + 0.5819 \left| J_z = \pm \frac{5}{2} \right\rangle$$

$$- 0.4507 \left| J_z = \mp \frac{3}{2} \right\rangle - 0.2393 \left| J_z = \mp \frac{11}{2} \right\rangle$$

which, allowing for the breakdown of Russell-Saunders coupling, gives a calculated $g = 6.77$. The fact that different ground states exist for the isoelectronic ions Ho^{2+} and Er^{3+} on cubic sites in CaF_2 is due, presumably, to different ratios of the fourth to sixth order crystal field parameters for these ions.

The hyperfine interaction $a\mathbf{I}\cdot\mathbf{J}$ of the holmium atom has been measured [11] and found to be $|a| = 800.583 \pm 0.003$ Mcs. This value may be compared with our value of $|a| = |A|/5 = 783 \pm 2$ Mcs; the difference between the observed $|a|$ values for the holmium atom and Ho^{2+} may be due largely to the effects of core polarization.

REFERENCES

[1]   B. BLEANEY, P. M. LLEWELLYN AND D. A. JONES, *Proc. Phys. Soc.* **B69**, 858 (1956).

[2]   J. M. BAKER, W. HAYES AND M. C. M. O'BRIEN, *Proc. Roy. Soc.* **A254**, 273 (1960).

[3]   J. SIERRO, *J. Chem. Phys.* **34**, 2183 (1961).

[4]   W. LOW, *Phys. Rev.* **118**, 1608 (1960).

[5]   W. HAYES AND J. W. TWIDELL, *J. Chem. Phys.* **35**, 1521 (1961).

[6]   G. J. RITTER, *Phys. Rev.* in the press.

[7]   R. J. ELLIOTT AND K. W. H. STEVENS, *Proc. Roy. Soc.* **A218**, 553 (1953).

[8]   B. R. JUDD AND I. P. K. LINDGREN, *Phys. Rev.* **122**, 1802 (1961).

[9]   C. J. DELBECQ, W. HAYES AND P. H. YUSTER, *Phys. Rev.* **121**, 1043 (1961).

[10] K. R. LEA, M. J. M. LEASK AND W. P. WOLF, *J. Phys. Chem. Solids*, in the press.

[11] L. S. GOODMAN, H. KOPFERMAN AND K. SCHLUPMAN, *Naturwiss.* **5**, 1 (1962).

[12] J. M. BAKER, W. HAYES AND D. A. JONES, *Proc. Phys. Soc.* **73**, 942 (1959).

ESR of Rare Earth Ions in Irradiated and Thermally Treated CaF$_2$*

W. LOW

Department of Physics, The Hebrew University of Jerusalem, Israel

AND

U. RANON

Department of Physics, Israel Atomic Energy Commission Laboratories, Rehovoth, Israel

ABSTRACT

Single crystals of CaF$_2$ containing various rare earth ions were irradiated by γ-rays at the Israel Research Reactor and treated thermally.

Conversions of trivalent ions to other valencies as well as changes in the point symmetry were observed.

I. Introduction

It is by now well established that trivalent rare earth ions at low concentration occupy substitutional sites in the crystal lattice of calcium fluoride. The crystal field potential acting on the rare earth ion is usually either of cubic, tetragonal or trigonal point symmetry. In the cubic case the original crystal field symmetry is preserved and charge compensation is effected far away from the paramagnetic ion. Tetragonal symmetry is obtained by an interstitial F$^-$ ion in an adjacent nearest neighbor cube. Trigonal symmetry is thought to arise from a substitutional O^{2-} ion taking the place of one F$^-$ at the corner of the cube. Paramagnetic resonance spectra of rare earth ions have sometimes been observed in which a fraction of the ions are exposed to one kind of symmetry and another fraction to a different one. In a previous communication we have reported a summary of results of such different point symmetry spectra for a number of rare earth ions [1]. We have also shown that it is possible to change the point symmetry by means of heat treatment [2].

We report here some effects of γ-irradiation on the electron spin resonance spectra of rare earth ions in CaF$_2$. Two main effects can be distinguished:

(1) The conversion of a trivalent ion into a different valence state.

* The research reported in this document has been sponsored in part by Air Force Office of Scientific Research, OAR, through the European Office, Aerospace Research, United States Air Force.

167

(2) The conversion of one point symmetry into another.

We shall illustrate this in three cases, namely, for the elements ytterbium (Yb), thulium (Tm) and terbium (Tb), and shall comment briefly on holmium (Ho) and cerium (Ce).

II. Experimental results and discussions

The experiments were carried out at X-band and at temperatures of 14°K, 20°K and 77°K. The doped CaF_2 crystals were obtained from "Semi-Elements" Inc. and Dr. R. W. H. Stevenson of Aberdeen. The concentration of the rare earth ions was given as 0.01%–0.5% but was probably less by a factor of 5.

The crystals were γ-irradiated at room temperature in the Israel Research Reactor at Nachal Soreq, with total dosage exceeding 10^6 roentgens. The neutron dosage was very low. The crystals change color after irradiation.

1. *Ytterbium (Yb)*

The spectrum of trivalent ytterbium has been observed in two kinds of point symmetries:

(a) A cubic field spectrum having $g = 3.441 \pm 0.002$ [3],

(b) A trigonal field spectrum with the trigonal axis along a body diagonal [1;4]. This spectrum has been discussed in detail and may be represented by the following spin-Hamiltonian:

$$\mathcal{H} = g_\parallel \beta H_z S_z + g_\perp \beta (H_x S_x + H_y S_y) + A S_z I_z + B(S_x I_x + S_y I_y)$$
$$+ Q \left[I_z^2 - \tfrac{1}{3} I(I+1) \right]$$

with

$$S = 1/2, \quad {}^{171}I = 1/2, \quad {}^{173}I = 5/2.$$

The measured and calculated parameters are given in Table I. In calculating the nuclear magnetic moments we used the value of $\langle r^{-3} \rangle$ given by Lindgren [5].

The trigonal spectrum

Before describing the effects of γ-irradiation we would like to make a few comments on the interpretation of the trigonal spectrum. Sierro [6] has observed two different trigonal spectra of Gd^{3+} in CaF_2 upon hydrolysis of the crystal. When hydrolyzing a crystal containing Gd^{3+} in cubic sites, he first obtained a tetragonal spectrum caused by interstitial F^- ions. Further hydrolysis caused the appearance of a trigonal spectrum attributed to OH^- replacing an F^- ion. Still further hydrolysis gave another trigonal spectrum which he explained to arise from O^{2-} taking the place of an F^- ion. The charge compensation by an oxygen ion can explain the observed spectra of Yb^{3+} in the trigonal symmetry. Heating the crystals in an atmosphere of hydrogen to 500°C causes a new trigonal spectrum to appear with a slightly different $g_{\parallel}$ factor. Presumably this second trigonal spectrum can be attributed to an OH^- taking the place of the F^- at one of the corners of the cube.

Both trigonal spectra, however, show a complication not found so far in other rare earth spectra in CaF_2. If the spectrum is observed along the trigonal axis all lines are doubled and of equal intensity as seen in Figure 1.

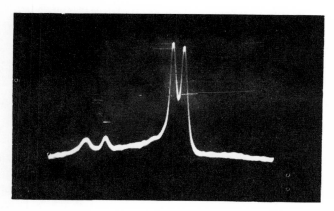

Figure 1

Doubling of Yb^{3+} lines in a trigonal site. (The weaker doublet is a hfs line of 171Yb).

The separation of the two lines is 18 ± 1 gauss and is anisotropic, decreasing as the external field is rotated away from the trigonal axis. At right angles to the trigonal axis, i.e. along $g_{\perp}$, the two lines cannot be resolved. The g factors of the two lines are listed in Table I as $g_{\parallel}^{(1)}$ and $g_{\parallel}^{(2)}$.

The doublet separation is larger than that expected from a pure dipolar interaction with an adjacent fluorine ion. Such an interaction is of the order of 11 gauss. Similarly it cannot be explained by a spin flip of the F^- ion which would give rise to a satellite spectrum separated by the NMR frequency.

A possible explanation of the doubling is to assume that the electronic configuration of the Yb ion is $4f^{13}(ns)$ rather than $4f^{13}$, with the outer s electron weakly bound. The spectrum can be described by $^2F(ns)$ in which the two possible spin orientations of the s electrons in the external field would give the doublet splitting in the cubic crystal field. It is important to note

TABLE I

Measured and calculated parameters of Yb^{3+} : CaF_2 in a trigonal field

$g_\parallel^{(1)} = 1.323 \pm 0.002$	$g_\perp^{(1)} = 4.389 \pm 0.004$
$g_\parallel^{(2)} = 1.328 \pm 0.002$	$g_\perp^{(2)} = 4.389 \pm 0.004$
$|^{171}A| = (359 \pm 2)\,10^{-4}\,\mathrm{cm}^{-1}$	$|^{173}A| = (96 \pm 1)\,10^{-4}\,\mathrm{cm}^{-1}$
$|^{171}B| = (1174 \pm 5)\,10^{-4}\,\mathrm{cm}^{-1}$	$|^{173}B| = (320 \pm 3)\,10^{-4}\,\mathrm{cm}^{-1}$
	$|^{173}Q'| = (85 \pm 3)\,10^{-4}\,\mathrm{cm}^{-1}$
$|^{171}\mu_N| = (0.52 \pm 0.05)\,n.m.$	$|^{173}\mu_N| = (0.70 \pm 0.05)\,n.m.$
	$|^{173}Q| = (2.6 \pm 0.2)$ barns

The second trigonal spectrum is given by the same Hamiltonian but

$g_\parallel^{(2)} = 1.421 \pm 0.002$

$g_\parallel^{(1)} = 1.425 \pm 0.002$

$g_\perp = 4.389 \pm 0.004$

that this doubling was not observed for Er^{3+} which was an accidental impurity in some of these crystals.

Radiation effects

Crystals showing the trigonal spectrum (b) were irradiated and examined. It was found that the intensity of the spectrum (b) diminished to less than 5%. An isotropic spectrum appeared (called spectrum (c)) which was similar to the cubic spectrum (a) and had the same g-value. However, when observed along a cube axis a distinct superstructure was resolved which consisted of at least 13 components. A recording of such a pattern is shown in Figure 2. The line width is 1.5 gauss and the separation of the components is (3.0 ± 0.2) gauss.

When the irradiated crystals were heated in vacuum to 500°C for an hour, the new spectrum (c) (cubic) disappeared completely while the intensity of the original (b) spectrum remained about 5%. Subsequent irradiation by γ-rays caused the reappearance of the cubic spectrum (c) with the superstructure and no change in the intensity of spectrum (b).

We have also irradiated a crystal showing originally a cubic (a) spectrum. No changes in the spectrum nor any superstructure were observed. Optical examination of crystals showing trigonal spectrum (b) indicates that the crystal contains a considerable fraction of the ytterbium in the divalent state. Yb^{2+} has f^{14}-electrons and is, therefore, diamagnetic.

These experimental facts can be possibly fitted by means of the following model:

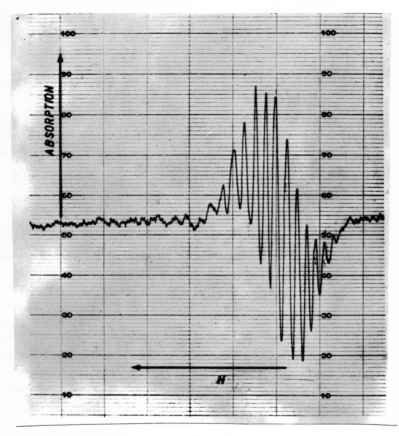

Figure 2

Superstructure lines in the spectrum of γ-irradiated $CaF_2:Yb^{+3}$.

The γ-irradiation causes partial conversion of Yb^{3+} into Yb^{2+} and the converse:

$$Yb^{3+} \text{ (trigonal)} \xrightarrow{\gamma} Yb^{2+}$$

$$Yb^{2+} \text{ (cubic)} \xrightarrow{\gamma} Yb^{3+} \text{ (cubic)}$$

The second reaction will preserve the cubic symmetry. Yb^{2+} replaces Ca^{2+} i.e. an ion having the same valence, and, therefore, should not cause a change in the cubic point symmetry. The γ-ray probably causes only a change of the valence but no change in the point symmetries.

Heat treatment causes the reverse reaction:

$$Yb^{3+} \text{ (cubic)} \xrightarrow{\text{heat}} Yb^{2+}$$

This was verified by heating crystals showing a cubic spectrum (a) to 1000°C in vacuum. The spectrum disappeared completely, indicating the probable conversion into Yb^{2+}. Subsequent irradiation caused the reappearance of the Yb^{3+} (c) spectrum. We have here, therefore, an example of a conversion from one valence state to another and the indirect conversion from one point symmetry to another. In the case of cubic symmetry the two following reactions may take place:

$$Yb^{3+} \text{ (cubic (a))} \xrightarrow{\text{heat}} Yb^{2+}$$

$$Yb^{2+} \text{ (cubic)} \longrightarrow Yb^{3+} \text{ (cubic (c))}$$

Because of the superposition of these two spectra the super hyperfine structure is not resolved.

Superstructure

The superstructure of 13 or more lines is observed both for the even isotopes as well as for each of the hyperfine lines of the spectrum. The relative intensities of the superstructure lines are given in the first row of Table II. Only the first 7 lines are tabulated since the spectrum is symmetric about the central line.

The superstructure is not resolved as the external magnetic field is rotated from the [100] direction. A similar structure to the one observed along the [100] direction is seen along the [110] direction.

We have so far no satisfactory explanation for the superstructure lines. The isotropic nature of the Yb^{3+} spectrum suggests a cubic point symmetry and therefore one is naturally led to examine an interaction with eight nearest neighbor F^- nuclei. However, this would give rise to only 9 lines along [100], with the relative intensities indicated in the second row of Table II.

TABLE II

Experimental and theoretical relative intensities of satellite lines in the spectrum of irradiated CaF_2; Yb^{3+} along the [100] direction

1) Experimental	1 ± 0.5	4 ± 1	9 ± 1	18 ± 3	30 ± 2	41 ± 2	44
2) Perfect cube			0.6	5	17.5	35	44
3) Three cubic fields with 6 gauss separation	0.3	3	10	22	35	42	44
4) Two tetrahedra $a = 2b = 6$ gauss	1	4	10	20	31	40	44

See text for explanation of (2), (3) and (4).

Multiple spin flips, as observed by Baker et al. [7] give rise to a spectrum with separation between adjacent lines equal to the NMR frequency of fluorine. In our case this would be about 1.6 gauss which is only 50% of the observed separation. This appears to rule out the possibility of multiple spin flips as the only mechanism of the superstructure.

We have considered three other possible models:

(i) Configuration $f^{13}(ns)$ which has a weakly bound s electron. The electron is supposed to be spread over the next nearest neighbor (*n.n.n*) fluorines which are about 5 Å distant. Along the [100] direction the 24 *n.n.n* would give rise to 25 lines in addition to 9 *n. n* lines. It is difficult to understand, however, why such a superstructure is only observed in the case of the cubic field spectrum but not in the case of the trigonal spectrum (b).

(ii) Assuming that there exist three nearly cubic sites differing only slightly in their g factor, one could get 13 lines by superposition of three nine-line patterns, shifted by 6 gauss relative to each other. The relative intensities of such a superposition are given in the third row of Table II. The relative intensities in this case correspond closely to those found experimentally.

(iii) Suppose that the cube of F^- ions, surrounding the paramagnetic ion, is distorted into two adjacent unequal tetrahedra. These could be formed by slightly moving four F^- ion towards the paramagnetic ion along the cube body diagonals and moving the remaining four away from it along the same axes. This is indicated in Figure 3. The spin-Hamiltonian describing the spectrum when observed along [100] can be written:

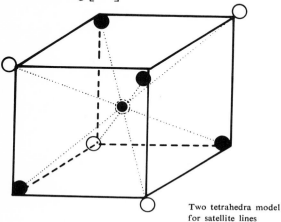

Two tetrahedra model
for satellite lines

Figure 3

Distortion of regular cube into two tetrahedra (white and black circles respectively).

$$\mathscr{H} = g\beta H_z S_z + A\mathbf{S}\cdot\mathbf{I} + aI_z^{(a)}S_z + bI_z^{(b)}S_z, \quad I_z^{(a)} = I_z^{(b)} \leqq 2 \quad S_z = \pm 1/2.$$

Here the first two terms describe the ordinary cubic spectrum of Yb^{3+}, the fluorine of two tetrahedera respectively and $S_z = \pm 1/2$. These two host terms give rise to 25 lines since $(2 I^{(a)} + 1)(2 I^{(b)} + 1) = 25$. If one chooses a suitable ratio a/b, i.e.: $a = 2b = 6$ gauss one obtains 13 lines with separation of 3 gauss and relative intensities as given in the fourth row of Table II. It is seen that these intensities are in fair agreement with the experimental results.

Kiro [8] has observed 13 or more superstructure lines in the spectrum of cerium in CaF_2. However, his spectrum could be explained in the main by assuming a multiple spin flip plus dipole-dipole interaction with the charge compensating, interstitial, F^- nucleus.

2. Thulium (Tm)

Crystals of CaF_2 containing Tm^{2+} gave rise to a spectrum of two lines of equal intensity at 20°K. The lines were broad, highly anisotropic and had an extremum at a very low field. Maximum intensity was obtained with the external field parallel to the rf field. The two lines indicate a nuclear spin $I = 1/2$ corresponding to ^{169}Tm. The high anisotropy and very low field extremum indicate an axial site, a very large $g_{\parallel}$ and $g_{\perp} \cong 0$. This is consistent with a transition between two close lying singlets of Tm^{3+}.

Upon irradiation with γ-rays an isotropic spectrum was observed, identical with the one reported by Hayes and Twidell [9] who obtained this spectrum by X-ray irradiation. This spectrum is attributed to Tm^{2+}, which is isoelectronic with Yb^{3+}. A detailed discussion of the measured g factor and hyperfine splitting was given by Hayes and Twidell. Our results agree here with those reported by these authors. The spin-Hamiltonian is given

$$\mathscr{H} = g\beta\mathbf{H}\cdot\mathbf{S} + A\,\mathbf{S}\cdot\mathbf{I}$$

with

$$g = 3.455 \pm 0.003$$

$$|A| = (369 \pm 2) \times 10^{-4} \text{ cm}^{-1}.$$

Using a value of $\langle r^{-3} \rangle = 75.10^{24} \text{ cm}^{-1}$ interpolated from the values for Tm I and Tm IV given by Lindgren [5] we obtain for the nuclear magnetic moment:

$$|\mu_N| = (0.23 \pm 0.02) \, n.m.$$

This value is in good agreement with 0.229 ± 0.003 obtained by Ritter [10] using atomic beam techniques. A typical spectrum is shown in Figure 4.

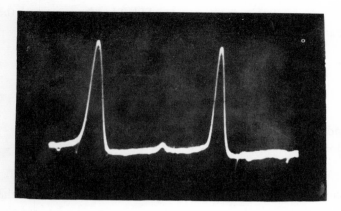

Figure 4
Spectrum of Tm^{2+} in CaF_2.

The two intense lines are the hyperfine structure lines while the weak central line is a so-called "forbidden" transition of the type

$$\triangle M = \pm 1, \quad \triangle m = \mp 1.$$

We have here a clear case of valence conversion by γ-rays. We are, however, not certain that the Tm^{3+} ions which were converted into Tm^{2+} have all been in a cubic site prior to irradiation. There are two reasons which speak against this possibility:

(a) Some of our crystals contained in addition to Tm, Er^{3+} ions for which an axial spectrum was observed. If Er^{3+} in a cubic site were present it could have been easily detected. It is unlikely that a fraction of Tm would go preferentially into a cubic site whereas a different rare earth ion, in the same crystal and under the same crystal-growing conditions, would go into a different site.

(b) It seems to us unlikely that γ-irradiation would preferentially convert Tm^{3+} ions in cubic sites into Tm^{2+}, and not do the same to Tm^{3+} ions in an axial site.

We are, therefore, inclined not to reject the possibility that the compensating ion is only weakly bound and is relatively mobile.

3. Terbium (Tb)

We have observed a spectrum of Tb^{3+} in an axial field at 20°K which could be described by the following spin-Hamiltonian:

$$\mathscr{H} = g_{\parallel}\beta H_z S_z + g_{\perp}\beta(H_x S_x + H_y S_y) + A S_z I_z + \triangle_x S_x + \triangle_y S_y.$$

This spectrum has already been reported [1]. The parameters of the spin-Hamiltonian are:

$$g_\parallel = 17.9 \pm 0.2 \qquad\qquad g_\perp \cong 0$$

$$|A| = (2130 \pm 40)\cdot10^{-4}\ cm^{-1}$$

$$|\triangle| = (1750 \pm 50)\cdot10^{-4}\ cm^{-1}$$

Using Lindgren's [5] value $\langle r^{-3} \rangle = 54 \times 10^{24}\ cm^{-3}$ we obtain for the nuclear moment

$$|\mu_N| = (1.6 \pm 0.2)\ n.\,m.$$

Recently Forrester and Hempstead [11] made a detailed study of the Tb^{3+} spectrum using a very wide range of frequencies and determined the parameters to a much higher degree of accuracy. They obtained:

$$g_\parallel = 17.768 \pm 0.020$$

$$g_\perp < 0.25$$

$$|\triangle| = 5.134 \pm 0.006\ kMc/s = (1713 \pm 2)\cdot10^{-4}\ cm^{-1}$$

$$|A| = 6.26 \pm 0.01\ kMc/s = (2088 \pm 3)\cdot10^{-4}\ cm^{-1}$$

Upon irradiation the crystals showed a many line spectrum clearly observable at 77°K. The spectrum is highly anisotropic and consists of many four-line groups. These four lines are the hyperfine structure caused by the nuclear spin $I = 3/2$ of the 100% abundant ^{159}Tb. At X band many lines were observed at low fields and some quartets at fields slightly higher than $g = 2$. In addition, quartets were observed with extrema at about 6000 and 8700 gauss. No other lines were observed up to a field of 14000 gauss. The large number of lines, the small hyperfine splitting and the fact that the spectrum is observed at 77°K without broadening of the lines point to the possibility of an S configuration and to Tb^{4+}.

The spectrum is unstable and at room temperature reduces rapidly to the Tb^{3+} spectrum. However, by keeping the crystals in liquid nitrogen, it is possible to observe the Tb^{4+} spectrum a few weeks after irradiation.

The point symmetry of the new spectrum is as yet not determined. However, it is certain that the symmetry is neither cubic nor tetragonal.

The hyperfine splitting gives $A = 38 \pm 2$ gauss. Assuming that $g = 2$ and the same amount of unpaired S electron as for Eu^{2+} or Gd^{3+} in CaF_2 we obtain a magnetic moment of the order of 2.2 $n.m.$, which seems large compared with that found from the Tb^{3+} spectrum.

4. *Holmium (Ho)*

A crystal containing Ho^{3+} showed the eight line spectrum. These were very broad and anisotropic and indicated an axial site.

Upon irradiation many new lines appeared but we have not as yet interpreted the spectrum.

5. *Cerium (Ce)*

Irradiation of crystals containing Ce on tetragonal sites did not give rise to any new lines or to a superstructure.

Acknowledgments

We are grateful to Professor L. E. Orgel for illuminating discussions regarding the superstructure spectrum of Yb^{3+} and to Dr. R. W. H. Stevenson of the University of Aberdeen for supplying some of the crystals.

REFERENCES

[1]   W. Low, Proc. Int. Conf. on Magnetism and Crystallography, Kyoto (1961). This paper gives references of the work of other authors.
[2]   E. FRIEDMAN AND W. LOW, *J. Chem. Phys.* **33**, 1275 (1960).
[3]   W. Low, *Phys. Rev.* **118**, 1608 (1960).
[4]   W. LOW AND U. ROSENBERGER, *Comptes Rendus* **254**, 1771 (1962).
[5]   I. LINDGREN, *Nuclear Phys.* (in press).
[6]   J. SIERRO, *J. of Chem. Phys.* **34**, 2183 (1961).
[7]   J. M. BAKER, W. HAYES AND M. C. M. O'BRIEN, *Proc. Roy. Soc.* (London) **A254**, 273 (1960).
[8]   D. KIRO, M. Sc. Thesis, Jerusalem (1962).
[9]   W. HAYES AND J. W. TWIDELL, *J. Chem. Phys.* **35**, 1521 (1961)
[10] G. J. RITTER, *Phys. Rev.* (in press).
[11] P. A. FORRESTER AND C. E. HEMPSTEAD, *Phys. Rev.* **126**, 923 (1962).

Paramagnetic Resonance of U^{3+} and U^{4+} in Calcium and Strontium Fluoride

R. S. TITLE

IBM Thomas J. Watson Research Center, Yorktown Heights, N. Y.

ABSTRACT

The substitution of U^{3+} and U^{4+} ions for the divalent cation in CaF_2 or SrF_2 creates a charge unbalance at the cation site. In order for charge neutrality in the crystal to be preserved the presence of compensating negative charges is required. Different orientations of the uranium ions and the compensating charges may lead to different symmetries at the uranium sites. Paramagnetic resonance techniques were used to determine the symmetry at the uranium ions. In addition to the previously observed U^{3+} ions in sites of tetragonal symmetry, U^{3+} ions in sites of cubic symmetry have been identified in CaF_2. Observations of U^{4+} ions in trigonal sites have been made both in CaF_2 and SrF_2. These centers in CaF_2 had been previously attributed by Porto and Yariv to be due to U^{3+}. Both paramagnetic and optical data are presented to show that these centers are in fact U^{4+} ions. A model is given for the U^{4+} site, suggested both from the paramagnetic data and from the details of the chemical preparation of the crystal.

The spectrum of Fe^{+3} in cubic symmetry was also observed in CaF_2.

I. Introduction

The spectra of several rare earth ions have been found useful for optical maser action. The crystal lattices in which these ions are incorporated must have certain physical properties consistent with optical maser operation. Among these the effect of the crystalline field on the absorption and emission spectra of the rare earth ion is of special interest. This effect may be complicated in the case of a trivalent ion such as Nd^{3+} or U^{3+}, incorporated substitutionally for the divalent cation in such lattice as CaF_2 or $CaWO_4$. This creates a charge unbalance of plus one at the cation site. To preserve charge neutrality in the crystal, a negative charge must be incorporated somewhere in the lattice. Due to the relatively high temperature of preparation of these crystals ($> 1450\,°C$) the negatively charged defect may diffuse to the vicinity of the trivalent rare earth ion. The symmetry at the rare earth ion in such charge associated pairs will differ from that normally present at the cation site. As will be shown below for CaF_2, there are several ways in which charge aasociation between the rare earth ion and a negatively charged defect may take place. This results in the possibility of the rare earth ion being present in any one of several crystalline symmetries, each affecting the optical spectrum

178

in a different way. In this paper, the determination by paramagnetic resonance techniques of the symmetry at the uranium sites in CaF_2 and SrF_2 will be presented. This case of uranium is of added interest in that not only is there the possibility of different symmetries, but as will be shown the uranium may be also incorporated as U^{4+} in these crystals.

Both CaF_2 and SrF_2 have the cubic fluorite structure. This consists of simple cubes of fluorine ions with the divalent cation, Ca^{++} or Sr^{++}, at the center of alternate cubes (Figure 1). The substitution of U^{3+} for the

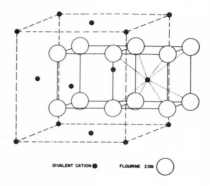

DIVALENT CATION ●   FLOURINE ION ◯

Figure 1
The fluorite lattice.

divalent cation creates a charge unbalance which may be compensated in several ways[1]. a) An F^- ion may be incorporated interstitially in the center of one of the adjacent F^- cubes. This will lead to tetragonal symmetry at the U^{3+} site about each of the three cubic axes. b) A Group VI B ion such as O^{-2} may substitute for a F^- ion. If this takes place at one of the F^- ions next to the U^{3+} ion the symmetry at the U^{3+} site will be trigonal. c) A Group I ion such as Na^+ may substitute for a divalent cation. Any one of several symmetries is possible depending on the relative orientation of the Na^+ and U^{3+} ions. d) Two U^{3+} ions may be incorporated in place of three divalent cations. The symmetry will depend on the relative orientation of the three centers involved but may in general be expected to be of low symmetry. e) Compensation may be by any of the above mechanisms but the compensating negative charge may be several lattice distances from the U^{3+} site. The symmetry at the U^{3+} site would then be that of the cubic fluorite lattice. f) The symmetry would also be cubic if the compensation were by conduction electons. Such compensation has been observed for trivalent rare earth ions in CdF_2[2].

Incorporation of U^{4+} substitutionally for the divalent cation requires compensation by two negative charges. Since UO_2 crystallizes in the fluorite structure (Lattice constant $a = 5.47A$ cf. CaF_2 $a = 5.45A$ and SrF_2 $a = 5.86A$), it is not likely that the compensation may be by the replacement of two F^- ions by O^{2-} ions. If these are at opposite corners of the cube of negative ions surrounding the U^{4+} ion, the symmetry will be trigonal. Other orientations of the O^{2-} ions lead to lower symmetry at the U^{4+} site.

Measurements on trivalent uranium in these crystals have been previously made. Resonances in CaF_2 and SrF_2 of U^{3+} ions in tetragonal symmetry have been reported by Bleaney el al.[1]. Vincow and Low[3] report the observation in CaF_2 of very weak resonances in the [110] direction which they attribute to U^{3+} ions in cubic symmetry. Their assignment is however open to question since the g-values and the orientational dependence of the observed resonances did not agree with the theory advanced for these ions by Bleaney[4]. They argue that the departure is due to the fact that the theory of Bleaney is no longer valid when the cubic field splittings of the energy levels are comparable to those caused by spin-orbit couplings and that this is the case for the $5f$ electrons of U^{3+}. Spectroscopic evidence[5], however, indicates that the field splittings for U^{3+} are still small compared to those of spin-orbit coupling. Measurements on U^{3+} ions in cubic symmetry whose g-values and orientational dependence are in agreement with the theory of Bleaney[4] will be given in this paper indicating that the conclusions reached by Vincow and Low[3] on the basis of their erroneous assignment are not valid.

The observation in CaF_2 of U^{3+} ions with trigonal symmetry has been reported by Porto and Yariv[6]. It will be shown in this paper, however, that these centers in sites of trigonal symmetry are tetravalent uranium rather than trivalent uranium.

II. The paramagnetic resonance spectra

The resonance spectra of several uranium doped CaF_2 and SrF_2 crystals were examined at liquid helium temperatures. In general these crystals showed the uranium to be present in several different symmetries in the same crystal. Two crystals were unique, however, one CaF_2 and one SrF_2. These showed the uranium to be present in trigonal symmetry only. The details of the observed spectra will now be given:

A. *Tetragonal symmetry*

Resonances of U^{3+} in tetragonal symmetry were observed in both CaF_2 and SrF_2. The g-values of these resonances are the same as those first reported by Bleaney et al.[4].

B. *Cubic symmetry*

The typical crystal of CaF_2 showed about ten per cent of the resonances to be due to U^{3+} ions in cubic symmetry. The ground state of the $5f^3$ configuration of U^{3+} is $^4I_{9/2}$. In a field of cubic symmetry this splits into a Γ_6 doublet and two Γ_8 quartets with one of the Γ_8 quartets lying lowest[3]. The resonances within the lowest lying quartet will be anisotropic even in cubic field[4]. This arises due to the addition of a term of the form $(H_z J_x^3 + H_y J_y^3 + H_z J_z^3)$ to the usual $g\beta$ **J·H** term in the Hamiltonian. The observed orientational dependence of the cubic resonance in a (110) plane is given in Figure 2. The solid lines in Figure 2 are the theoretically predicted orientational dependence of the two strongest transitions within the Γ_8 quartet. It will be observed that the observed points are in good agreement with the theory. The small departures that do exist may be due to the neglect of sixth order terms in the crystalline field potential. The

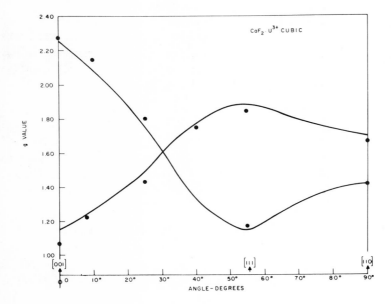

Figure 2

Variation in a (110) plane of CaF_2 of the two strongest transitions within the lowest Γ_8 quartet of U^{3+} in cubic symmetry.

agreement obtained is comparable to that obtained for Nd^{3+} $(4f^3)$ in a cubic field [3]. It may be concluded that although the crystalline field splittings are somewhat larger for the $5f^3$ configuration than for $4f^3$ they are still small enough compared to spin-orbit splittings to allow the Hamiltonian proposed by Bleaney[4] to be used for the $5f^3$ configuration. The opposite conclusion reached by Vincow and Low[3] is due to their erroneous identi-fication of the weak resonances they observed as due to U^{3+} ions in cubic symmetry.

C. *Trigonal symmetry*

Some of the CaF_2 and SrF_2 crystals showed uranium in sites of trigonal symmetry. In the two previously mentioned crystals this was the only observed symmetry. In the case of CaF_2 the g-values are $g = 3.27 \pm 0.03$, $g = 0 \pm 0.2$. For SrF_2 they are $g = 2.87 \pm 0.03$, $g = 0 \pm 0.2$. The trigonal sites in CaF_2 are identical to those previously reported by Porto and Yariv[4] and attributed by them to U^{3+}. Evidence will be presented to show that these are in fact U^{4+} centers.

In Figure 3 the resonance spectrum for a crystal of CaF_2 containing only these centers is shown. The plot is of the derivatives of the resonance absorption curve. The sharp line is due to DPPH. Those marked A, B, and C are to due uranium. It will be noticed that the resonance due to DPPH is symmetrical showing equal positive and negative values for the derivative of the absorption curve. The resonances of uranium are asymmetrical being much sharper on the high field side of the curve and hence emphasizing the

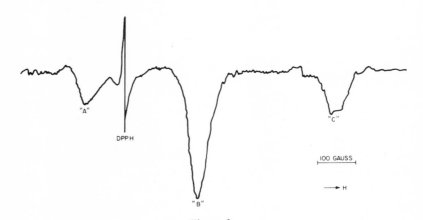

Figure 3

Paramagnetic resonance spectrum of CaF_2 containing uranium in sites with trigonal symmetry. The spectrum was taken with the magnetic field oriented in the (110) plane 3–1/2° from the [001] direction.

negative value of the derivative. The resonances were taken with the magnetic field oriented in the (110) plane of the crystal in a direction 3–1/2 degrees from the [001] direction. The resonances marked A and C are due to centers with their axes of symmetry along the [111] axes lying in the (110) plane. The resonance marked B is due to those centers whose axes of symmetry are along the [111] axes not in this plane. There are two such axes both making equal angles with any particular direction in the (110) plane. This accounts for the approximate two to one size of the resonance marked B compared to those marked A and C.

A plot of the variation in a (111) plane of the resonances of uranium in trigonal symmetry for a crystal of SrF_2 is shown in Figure 4. In this plane in

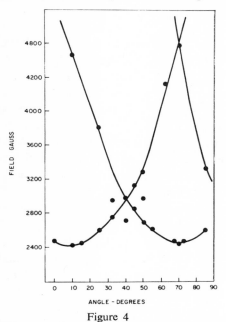

Figure 4

Variation in a (111) plane of the uranium sites in trigonal symmetry in SrF_2.

trigonal symmetry there is a minimum in the magnetic field at which the resonance occurs which repeats at sixty degree intervals. The g-value at this minimum is equal to $1/3\,(8\,g_\parallel^2 + g_\perp^2)^{1/2}$. At the same angle as the minimum, a second resonance should be observed with a g-value equal to $1/3\,(2g_\parallel^2 + 7g_\perp^2)^{1/2}$. Reference to Figure 4 shows that these resonances were observed at magnetic fields in the ratio of approximately two to one indicating that the g-values are in the ratio of one to two. This can occur only if $g_\perp = 0$. The value for $g_\parallel = 2.87 \pm 0.03$. The lines were found to be asymmetrical with the steep side again on the high field side of the line. The g-values were measured at the point on the high field side of the line where the derivative is equal to zero.

The characteristics of the observed uranium resonances from sites in trigonal symmetry in CaF_2 and SrF_2 are (1) a $g_\perp$-value equal to zero and (2) an asymmetrical resonance absorption curve. Such resonances can be shown to arise from tetravalent uranium rather than trivalent uranium. U^{4+} has an $5f^2$ configuration with a $^3H_4$ ground state. The nine fold degeneracy of the ground state will be split in a field of trigonal symmetry into three singlets and three doublets. The doublets are non-Kramers doublets and may be split by fields of lower symmetry. Such fields may arise from small local imperfections in the crystal. The magnetic characteristics of a split non-Kramers doublet have been given by Baker and Bleaney[7]. The $g_\perp$-value is predicted to be zero and also the shape of the absorption line is expected to be asymmetrical as was observed for the above uranium resonances. The asymmetrical shape arises from the nature of the interactions with the small local fields. These can be represented by a Hamiltonian of the form $H = g_\parallel \beta H_z S_z + \Delta_x S_x + \Delta_y S_y$ where Δ_x and Δ_y are the splittings of the doublet caused by the small departure of the field from trigonal symmetry. The values of Δ_x, Δ_y are not unique but form a distribution of values since they represent the effect of random local departures at the uranium sites from trigonal symmetry. The solution of the above Hamiltonian leads whose separation is given by: $h\nu = [(g_\parallel \beta H_z)^2 + \Delta^2]^{1/2}$ where $\Delta^2 = \Delta_x^2 + \Delta_y^2$. Since Δ enters as the square, the sign of Δ is not important. As a result the resonance absorption line will be asymmetrical. It will rise slowly on the low field side showing the effect of the random distribution of the values of Δ. When Δ has the value 0 the line will fall comparatively sharply, corresponding to the natural width of the line.

It was also pointed out by Baker and Bleaney[7] that the transition probability between levels of a non-Kramers doublet is a maximum when the microwave magnetic field, H_{rf}, is parallel to the D C magnetic field, H_{DC}. This was checked by placing a crystal of CaF_2 in the form of a 5 mm cube into a rectangular X-band cavity operating in a TE_{102} mode. The angle between H_{rf} and H_{DC} could thus be varied by rotation of the magnet. The results obtained are shown in Figure 5. Because of the large size of the crystal these results should be regarded as qualitative only. The solid line represents the variation in intensity observed for the resonance of uranium in sites of trigonal symmetry. It is noticed that the uranium resonance has a maximum transition probability when H_{rf} is parallel to H_{DC}. For comparison, measurements were made on a different paramagnetic impurity in the crystal and the results are given by the dotted line. The transition in this case was between levels of a Kramers doublet for which the maximum transition probability occurs when H_{rf} is perpendicular to H_{DC}.

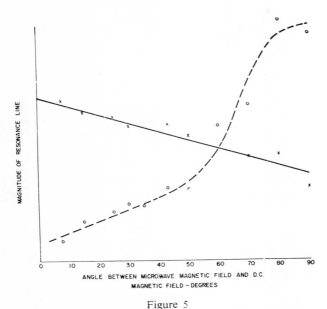

Figure 5

Variation of the intensity of the resonance lines as a function of the angle between the microwave magnetic field and the DC magnetic field.

The measured characteristics of the uranium resonances in sites of trigonal symmetry namely $g_{\perp} = 0$, an asymmetrical line shape and a maximum transition probability when H_{rf} and H_{DC} are aligned leads to the conclusion that these sites are due to tetravalent uranium rather than trivalent uranium as assumed by Porto and Yariv[6]. Trivalent uranium ($5f^3$, $^4I_{9/2}$) splits into five Kramers doublets in a field of trigonal symmetry. A Kramers doublet cannot be further split in fields of lower symmetry. It can be split by an applied magnetic field. The transition between the split levels would give an absorption line of symmetric shape and maximum transition probability with H_{rf} perpendicular to H_{DC}.

The identification of the trigonal centers as due to U^{4+} has been confirmed by the observation of the optical absorption spectrum of these crystals[8]. Although there is some overlap in the absorption bands of U^{3+} and U^{4+} there is a distinct band characteristic of U^{4+} which occurs around 1.6μ.

This was first observed in several U^{4+} salts by Dreisch and Kollscheuer[9]. The absorption spectra of the crystals of CaF_2 and SrF_2 that paramagnetic resonance measurements showed to have only U^{4+} ions are given in Figures 6 and 7. It will be noticed that the absorption bands characteristic of U^{4+}

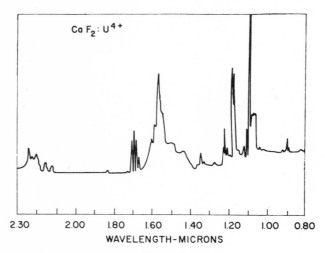

Figure 6
Optical absorption spectrum of $CaF_2 : U^{4+}$.

are prominent. By contrast a crystal of CaF_2 which the paramagnetic resonant results showed to contain trivalent but no tetravalent uranium is shown in Figure 8. This absorption spectrum is characteristic of U^{3+}[10]. In crystals containing mixtures of U^{3+} and U^{4+} a correlation could always be made between the magnitude of U^{4+} optical absorption and the U^{4+} paramagnetic resonance spectrum.

A correlation could also be made between the amount of tetravalent uranium in a crystal and the method by which it was prepared. The crystals were grown by the Stockbarger technique[11]. Lead difluoride was added to the original mixture in order to remove any oxygen present in the samples. The samples in which the greatest amount of tetravalent uranium was found were the ones held at elevated temperatures for the shortest time (about 24 hours). These crystals would therefore have the greatest amount of oxygen. This would tend to confirm the model suggested earlier for the incorporation of U^{4+} in CaF_2 and SrF_2. The U^{4+} is incorporated substitutionally for the divalent cation. The two excess positive charges at the U^{4+} site are compensated by the substitution of two O^{2-} ions for the two F^- ions located at

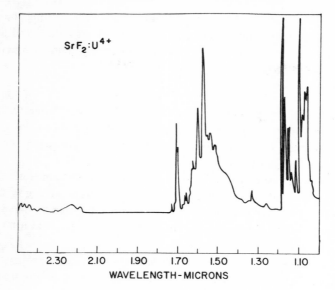

Figure 7
Optical absorption spectrum of $SrF_2 : U^{4+}$.

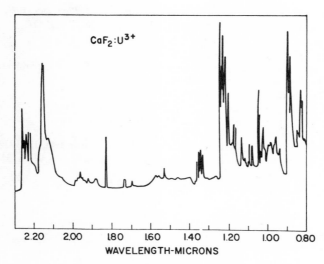

Figure 8
Optical absorption spectrum of $CaF_2 : U^{3+}$.

the opposite corners of the cube of negative ions surrounding the U^{4+} ion. As previously mentioned UO_2 has the fluorite structure and its lattice constant is very similar to that of CaF_2 and SrF_2. The symmetry at the U^{4+} site would be trigonal.

D. *Other resonances*

In addition to the uranium resonances reported above other weaker resonances were observed at liquid helium temperature both in CaF_2 and SrF_2. These may be due to uranium ions in lower symmetry or possibly due to impurity ions as yet unidentified.

Some of the crystals of CaF_2 were observed to contain Fe^{3+} in cubic symmetry. Measurements made at room temperature give $g = 2.003$ and $|a| = 242 \pm 1$ gauss. Some of the lines were observed to have fluorine hyperfine structure. These results will be reported in detail at a later date.

Acknowledgments

The author acknowledges discussions with Drs. P. P. Sorokin, R. W. Keyes and W. V. Smith. In addition he would like to thank John Scardefield who grew some of the crystals, Norman Stemple for X-ray orientations of the crystals and Eugene Tynan for aid in the paramagnetic measurements. The optical data were taken by G. D. Pettit.

REFERENCES

[1]   B. BLEANEY, P. M. LLEWELLYN, AND D. A. JONES, *Proc. Phys. Soc.* **B69**, 858 (1956).

[2]   J. D. KINGSLEY AND J. S. PRENER, *Phys. Rev. Letters* **8**, 315 (1962).

[3]   G. VINCOW AND W. LOW, *Phys. Rev.* **122**, 1390 (1961).

[4]   B. BLEANEY, *Proc. Phys. Soc.* **A73**, 939 (1959).

[5]   P. P. SOROKIN AND M. J. STEVENSON, *Advances in Quantum Electronics*, Edited by J. R. SINGER, Columbia University Press, 1961, p. 66.

[6]   S. P. S. PORTO AND A. YARIV, *J. Appl. Phys.* **33**, 1620 (1962).

[7]   J. M. BAKER AND B. BLEANEY, *Proc. Roy. Soc.* **A245**, 156 (1958).

[8]   R. S. TITLE, P. P. SOROKIN, M. J. STEVENSON, G. D. PETTIT, J. SCARDEFIELD AND J. R. LANKARD, *Phys. Rev.* **128**, 62 (1962).

[9]   W. DREISCH AND O. KALLSCHEUER, *Zeit. f. Physik. Chem.* **B45**, 19 (1939).

[10] G. D. BOYD, R. J. COLLINS, S. P. S. PORTO, A. YARIV, AND W. A. HARGREAVES, *Phys. Rev. Letters* **8**, 269 (1962).

[11] D. C. STOCKBARGER, *J. Opt. Soc. Amer.* **39**, 731 (1949).

Paramagnetic Resonance and Charge Compensation of Tetravalent Uranium (U^{4+}) in Calcium, Strontium, and Barium Fluorides

A. YARIV

Bell Telephone Laboratories, Incorporated,
Murray Hill, New Jersey

ABSTRACT

A new electron spin paramagnetic resonance spectrum in CaF_2 doped with uranium is attributed to U^{4+}. The spectrum possesses axial symmetry about the [111] directions and is describable by a spin-Hamiltonian with $g_\perp = 0 \pm 0.15$ and $g_\parallel = 3.238 \pm 0.005$ at 4.2°K. The trigonal symmetry is due to the presence of charge compensating O^{2-} ions along the [111] directions. Similar results are observed in $SrF_2:U^{4+}$ and $BaF_2:U^{4+}$. The U^{4+} spectra are absent in crystals grown under reducing conditions.

Introduction

Paramagnetic resonance studies of uranium have been limited mostly to the trivalent ion [1;2;3]. Ghosh, Gordy and Hill [4] have reported a resonance in UF_4, unfortunately the powder form of the sample and the high concentration made the interpretation difficult. Paramagnetic resonance on solid solutions of $ThO_2:U^{4+}$ has been observed by Llewellyn [5] with $g \approx 2.7$. In this paper we report on a paramagnetic resonance spectrum observed in single crystals of CaF_2 doped with $\sim 0.1\%$ of uranium. The spectrum consists in general of four lines possessing a threefold symmetry about the [111] cube diagonals. This spectrum is assigned to U^{4+} ions substituting for Ca^{2+} ions. The extra positive charge $(+2e)$ is believed to be compensated by two O^{2-} ions replacing two F^- ions along any of the [111] directions, thus giving rise to the observed trigonal spectrum. The assignment of this spectrum to the U^{4+} ion $(5f^2)$ rather than to the U^{3+} ions $(5f^3)$ is based on certain features of the paramagnetic resonance which can be explained if we assume a low lying non-Kramer's doublet arising from an even number of electrons. This assignment is strengthened further by the dependence of the U^{4+} spectrum on the crystal growing conditions. The bulk of the investigation was devoted to CaF_2 host crystals. The presence of U^{4+} was detected also in SrF_2 and BaF_2.

189

Experimental results and their interpretation

The observed spectrum consists of four lines possessing threefold symmetry about the [111] axes. This symmetry is believed to be due to the presence of an interstitial O^{2-} along one of the [111] directions as is discussed in the next section. The site symmetry is C_{3v} and it causes the free ion ninefold degeneracy to be split into three doublets and three singlets.

$$2A_1 + A_2 + 3E_1$$

The observed ESPR spectrum is due to transitions between the Zeeman split levels of the lowest lying doublet.

The four lines observed with an arbitrary orientation of the magnetic field are each due to U^{4+} sites compensated by two O_2^- ions along one of the four [111] directions. The data discussed in this paper were taken with the magnetic field in the (110) plane so that two of the four sites become equivalent and only three lines are observed.

Each of the three lines is describable by a spin-Hamiltonian

$$\mathscr{H} = \beta[g_\parallel S_z H_z + g_\perp(S_x H_x + S_y H_y)] + \Delta_x S_x + \Delta_y S_y \tag{1}$$

where $S = \frac{1}{2}$, the "z" direction is the direction of the trigonal axis for the site in question, β, $g_\parallel$, and $g_\perp$ have their conventional meaning. Δ_x and Δ_y account for the random departure from perfect axial symmetry [6].

Diagonalization of the spin-Hamiltonian leads to

$$H = \frac{[(h\nu)^2 - \Delta^2]^{\frac{1}{2}}}{\beta[g_\parallel^2 \cos^2\theta + g_\perp \sin^2\theta]^{\frac{1}{2}}} \tag{2}$$

where $\Delta^2 = \Delta_x^2 + \Delta_y^2$, h and ν are Planck's constant and the rf frequency, respectively, and θ is the angle between the applied magnetic field of magnitude H and the "z" axis. For the best fit between the experimental data and Eq. (2) we have at 4.2 °K

$$|g_\parallel| = 3.238 \pm 0.005$$

$$g_\perp = 0 \pm 0.15.$$

If we assume that Δ^2 is distributed about its nean value with Gaussian distribution we obtain

$$\langle \Delta^2 \rangle^{\frac{1}{2}} \simeq 2 \times 10^{-17} c \cdot g \cdot s \sim 0.1 \text{ cm}^{-1}.$$

Figure 1 shows the variation of the observed magnetic field H as a function of ϕ, the angle between the applied magnetic field and the [001]

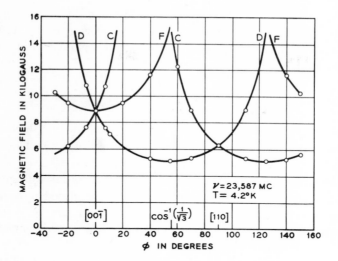

Figure 1

Variation of the resonance magnetic field for the trigonal sites as a function of the angle between the magnetic field and the trigonal axis. The magnetic field is in the (110) plane. The solid curve is based on Eq. (2) with $\Delta = 0$ and $g_{\parallel} = 3.238$, and $g_{\perp} = 0$. The circles are experimental points.

axis. With the magnetic field applied in the (110) plane, two of the four trigonal lines are due to sites whose axes lie in the (110) plane at $54.76°$ and $-54.76° \left(\pm \cos^{-1} 1/\sqrt{3} \right)$ with respect to the $[00\bar{1}]$ direction. The spectra of these sites are labeled C and D respectively. The remaining two trigonal sites are equivalent and give rise to a single line which is labeled, in Figure 1, as F.

The angle θ, between the applied magnetic field and each of the four trigonal axes, is given by

$$\theta_C = \phi + \cos^{-1} \frac{1}{\sqrt{3}} = \phi + 54.76°$$

$$\theta_D = \phi - \cos^{-1} \frac{1}{\sqrt{3}} = \phi - 54.76° \qquad (3)$$

$$\theta_F = \cos^{-1} \left(\frac{\cos\phi}{\sqrt{3}} \right)$$

where ϕ is the angle between the magnetic field vector and the [001] direction.

The solid curves of Figure 1 were obtained by using Eq. (2) with $g_\perp = 0$, $|g_{\parallel}| = 3.238$, $\Delta = 0$ and the respective values of θ as given by Eqs. (3). When $\phi = 0°$, i.e., when the applied magnetic field is parallel to one of the cube edges, we have

$$|\theta_C| = |\theta_D| = \theta_F| = |\cos^{-1} \frac{1}{\sqrt{3}}|$$

and the three spectra coincide. The extrema of each of the three spectra occur at the maxima and minima of $|\cos\theta|$ as given by Eq. (3). This constitutes sufficient proof for the trigonal symmetry of the sites.

Small deviations from perfect alignment of the crystal will spoil the perfect equivalence of the two sites which give rise to spectrum F and the atter appears as a doublet. The doublet separation is zero at $\phi = 0$ and increases as ϕ is increased from zero toward 90°. The experimental points in Figure 1 are those of the center of gravity of the doublet.

Since the transition intensity between the two levels, $S = \pm \frac{1}{2}$, of the low lying doublet are proportional to Δ^2, it follows that the line shape is asymmetric. This is due to the fact that a spin packet characterized by a certain value of Δ^2 will absorb more energy than a similar number of spins at a lower Δ^2 whose resonance field, in consequence of Eq. (2), is lower. This causes the resonance line to drop sharply on the high field side and to possess a more gentle slope on the low field side. This is indeed what is observed. The estimate $\langle \Delta^2 \rangle^{1/2}$ is based on the distance between the peak and the base of the line on the high field side where $\Delta^2 = 0$. Another consequence of $g_\perp$ being zero, which is verified experimentally, is the ineffectiveness of the component of the rf magnetic field at right angles to the trigonal axis in inducing transitions.

An absorption run obtained at 4.2°K with $\phi = 40°$ is shown in Figure 2.

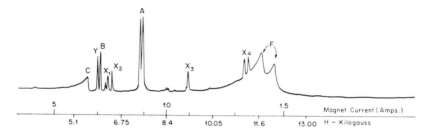

Figure 2

Actual absorption run at $\phi = 40°$. The ordinate is proportional to $\chi'' H_{1z}$. The abscissa is marked by the magnetic field values.

No field modulation is employed so that the ordinate is proportional to $\chi'' H_{1z}$. Only line C and the doublet F are present at this orientiation. Line D occurs at a value of H which is outside our reach. The crystal orientation is such that the rf magnetic field is nearly perpendicular to the trigonal axes of sites C and D, a fact which explains the relative weakness of their absorption as compared to that of the two F sites.

The lines labeled as A and B arise from the tetragonal U^{3+} sites discussed by Bleaney et al. [1]. The compensation axis for the site giving rise to line B is the [001] direction and is contained, along with the magnetic field, in the (110) plane. The sites with axes along the [010] and [100] directions are magnetically equivalent when $\bar{H}$ is in the (110) plane and give rise to line A. Small deviations from perfect alignment will split this line into a doublet. The remaining lines: X_1, X_2, X_3, X_4 and Y_1 belong to yet another site which, we believe, is due to U^{3+} ions compensated by F^- ions in the next nearest interstitial positions. These sites are found in all the crystals in which the U^{4+} spectrum is found. They lack an axis of symmetry and their detailed description is set aside for a future paper.

Since the value of $g_\parallel$ is given approximately by $g_\parallel \sim 2\Lambda M$, with $M = 2$ and Λ the Landé-g factor (equal to 0.8), we conclude that the wavefunctions of the doublet are dominated by $|2\rangle$ and $|-2\rangle$. Since admixture of $\Delta M = \pm 3, \pm 6$ is allowed by the perturbation Hamiltonian for C_{3v} symmetry. The total wavefunctions can be written as [7;8].

$$|\alpha\rangle = a|4\rangle + b|1\rangle + C|-2\rangle$$
$$|\beta\rangle = a|-4\rangle - b|-1\rangle + C|2\rangle \qquad (5)$$

where $a < c > b$. The minus sign preceding the $|-1\rangle$ ket is necessary in order to make

$$g_\perp = 2\langle\alpha|L_x + 2S_x|\beta\rangle = 0.$$

The paramagnetic resonance data is not sufficient to solve for a, b, c. We can only write two equations:

$$a^2 + b^2 + c^2 = 1$$

which is the normalization condition and

$$g_\parallel = 2\langle\beta|J_z|\beta\rangle = 4a^2 + b^2 - 2c^2 = 3.238$$

for the three unknowns a, b and c. To solve for a, b and c it is necessary to use optical absorption data. We have neglected the added admixture from the $^3H_5$ level.

As mentioned earlier the matrix element $\langle \alpha | J_z | \beta \rangle$ is zero when $|\alpha\rangle$ and $|\beta\rangle$ are given by Eq. (5). The effectiveness of the "z" component of the rf magnetic field in inducing transitions is attributed to further admixture, caused by local departures from C_{3v} symmetry, which makes possible $\Delta M = 0$ transitions.

Experimental notes

The experiments were conducted at 4.2 °K. Strong resonance signals were also observed at 20°K but not at 78°K. This is probably due to short thermal relaxation times at the latter temperature. The paramagnetic resonance spectrometer was of the superheterodyne type, with an intermediate frequency of 60 mc, capable of covering the the 21–24 kmc range. The signal and local oscillator power were provided by two stabilized 2K33 klystrons. The sample cavity operated in the TE_{011} mode with the sample placed at its center. The sample and cavity orientation were such that the rf magnetic field at the sample position was always perpendicular to the dc magnetic field.

The coupling of the cavity as well as the sensitivity of the receiver to χ'' or χ' were controlled by a variable coupling scheme which was previously described by J. P. Gordon [9]. Magnetic fields of up to 15 kilogauss were provided bv a 12 inch Varian magnet rotatable about a vertical axis.

The charge compensation

The extra positive charge, $+2e$, introduced into the lattice by replacing Ca^{2+} by U^{4+} must be compensated by some excess negative charge or by cation deficiency [1; 8; 10; 11].

Two compensation models are proposed:

a) Two F^- ions situated on opposite sides of the body diagonal, one on each side of the central U^{4+} ion, are replaced by two O_2^- ions.

b) An O_2^- ion occupies the first interstice along the [111] direction, i.e., the center of the cube sharing a corner with the cube containing the U^{4+} ion.

Either mechanism will give rise to a trigonal spectrum of the type observed. Mechanism (a) is believed to be more likely since it corresponds to a lower electrostatic energy and since the trigonal spectrum in $CaF_2:Gd^{3+}$ was shown by Sierro [12] to be due to an O_2^- ion replacing an F^- ion. Similar conclusions about $CaF_2:Tb^{3+}$ have been reached by Forrester and Hempstead.

A confirmation for the role played by O^{2-} ions in the charge compensation was provided by the dependence of the concentration of U^{4+} on the growing conditions. The crystals were grown by W. A. Hargreaves, using the Stockbarger-Bridgeman method in which a graphite crucible containing molten CaF_2 and uranium was gradually lowered through a heating induction coil. If the crucible and the melt were kept at $\sim 100°C$ above the melting temperature for ~ 2 hours before cooling, no trace of U^{++} was found in the crystal. This is probably due to the reduction action of the graphite crucible. The compensation mechanisms postulated above depend on the presence of oxygen in the melt. If the oxygen is removed by the carbon, compensation cannot take place and the uranium enters the crystal as U^{3+} in tetragonal sites and the compensation is achieved by interstitial F^- ion.

We have referred to the trigonal spectrum of U in CaF_2 on two previous occasions [14; 15] as being due to $CaF_2: U^{3+}$. This assignment was in error as is evident from this paper and should be corrected to $CaF_2:U^{4+}$.

Investigation of SrF_2 and BaF_2 trigonal spectra were also observed in single crystals of SrF_2 and BaF_2 and are also attributed to U^{4+}. The lines doped with uranium are considerably broader and weaker which is probably due to the larger amount of strain present in these crystals. The spin-Hamiltonian parameters as determined for these crystals are:

$$SrF_2:U^{4+}$$
$$g_\| = 2.85 \pm 0.05 \text{ at } 4.2°K$$
$$g_\perp \sim 0$$

$$BaF_2:U^{4+}$$
$$g_\| \sim 3 \text{ at } 4.2°K$$
$$g_\perp \sim 0$$

The accuracy of the measurements was limited by the width of the lines.

It may be of interest to note in this connection that the present investigation arose out of an effort to lower the threshold for optical maser action in $CaF_2:U^{3+}$ and that only after the complete elimination of the U^{4+} ions did the threshold become low enough so that continuous operation, rather than pulsed, was achieved [14].

Acknowledgments

It is a pleasure to acknowledge the extremely helpful communication with Professor B. Bleaney who first suggested the possibility of the U^{4+} spectrum. W. A. Hargreaves of "Optovac Inc.," provided the many crystals investigated and was instrumental in establishing the correlation between the growing conditions and the U^{4+} concentration. We have also benefited from many discussions with Dr. J. P. Gordron and from the able experimental assistance of J. M. Dziedzic.

REFERENCES

[1]   B. BLEANEY, P. M. LLEWELLYN AND D. A. JONES, *Proc. Phys. Soc.* (*London*) **A69,** 858 (1956).

[2]   G. VINCOW AND W. LOW, *Phys. Rev.* **122,** 1390 (1961).

[3]   C. A. HUTCHINSON, R., P. M. LLEWELLYN, E. WONG AND B. P. DORAIN, *Phys. Rev.* **102,** 292 (1956).

[4]   S. N. GHOSH, W. GORDY AND D. G. HILL, *Phys. Rev.* **96,** 36 (1954).

[5]   P. M. LLEWELLYN, Thesis, Oxford, 1956.

[6]   B. BLEANEY, P. M. LLEWELLYN, M. H. L. ROYCE AND G. R. HALL, *Phil. Mag.* **45,** 991 (1954).

[7]   B. R. JUDD, *Proc. Roy. Soc.* (*London*) **A232,** 458 (1955).

[8]   W. LOW, *Paramagnetic Resonance in Solids*, Academic Press, New York and London, 1960, p. 12.

[9]   J. P. GORDON, *Rev. of Scient. Instr.* **32,** 658 (1961).

[10a] P. P. FEOFILOV, *J. Phys. Radium* **17,** 656 (1956).

[10b] P. P. FEOFILOV, *Doklady Akad. Nauk.* SSSR **99,** 731 (1954).

[11] I. V. STEPANOV AND P. P. FEOFILOV, *Soviet Physics Doklady* (Engl. Transl.) **1** 350 (1956).

[12] JEROME SIERRO, *Journ. of Chem. Phys.* **34,** 2183 (1961).

[13] P. A. FORRESTER AND C. F. HEMPSTEAD, *Phys. Rev.*, to be published.

[14] G. D. BOYD, R. J. COLLINS, S. P. S. PORTO, A. YARIV AND W. A. HARGREAVES, *Phys. Rev. Letters* **8,** 269 (1962).

[15] S. P. S. PORTO AND A. YARIV, *Journ. of Appl. Phys.* **33,** 1620 (1962).

DISCUSSION

W. LOW, Israel: Have you observed the hyperfine structure from U^{235} and have you analyzed the hyperfine structure caused by the fluorine ions?

A. YARIV, U.S.A.: We have not observed the hyperfine structure of U^{235}. We have looked at the super hyperfine structure due to the fluorine ions. They have perfect binomial distribution corresponding to $n = 24$. There are only 8 nearest neighbors and 24 next nearest neighbors so the structure is very mystifying.

Electron Spin Resonance and Spin-Lattice Relaxation for the Yb^{3+} Ion in CdF$_2$

P. P. PASHININ AND A. M. PROKHOROV

P. N. Lebedev Physical Institute, USSR Academy of Sciences, Moscow

ABSTRACT

The results of the investigation of the EPR spectrum of Yb^{3+} ion in CdF$_2$ are cited in this work. The constants of the cubic spin-Hamiltonian were determined at the temperature of 4.2°K and at the frequency of 9100 Mc. The distance to the first excited level Γ_8 was evaluated through the changes of the g-factor of the ground state in high magnetic fields. The value obtained for this splitting has been confirmed by the investigation of the temperature dependence of the integral intensity of the EPR line in the region from 4.2°K to 60°K. The results of the experiments on the spin-lattice relaxation at temperatures from 2°K to 77°K are given in this paper. Samples with various Yb concentrations were investigated. In the helium temperature range the relaxation is due to first order processes, and $T_1 \sim T^{-1}$. At higher temperatures the Raman scattering predominates, and at temperatures over 15°K, $T_1 \sim T^{-7}$.

Electron Spin Resonance (ESR) spectrum for the Yb^{3+} ion in a cubic matrix of CdF$_2$ was investigated at frequencies 9100, 37150 and 73300 Mc/s. The decrease in g-value with increasing frequency of observation and temperature dependence of absorption line integral intensity at temperatures of $4 \div 60$°K has been measured. This yields the value of ground state splitting in crystalline electric fields. Spin-lattice relaxation time T_1 has been studied as a function of concentration and temperature at 4–60°K at wavelengths $\lambda = 3$ cm, and $\lambda = 10$ cm. It has been found that at liquid helium temperatures $T_1 \sim T^{-1}$ and it is proportional to the frequency and inversely proportional to the concentration of the paramagnetic ions. At liquid nitrogen temperatures $T_1 \sim T^{-7}$ and it does not change with frequency and concentration.

The ESR spectrum of Yb^{3+} ion in a single crystal of CaF$_2$, supposed to possess cubic symmetry, has been investigated earlier by W. Low [1]. The ground state of Yb^{3+} having the electron configuration $_4f^{13}$ is $^2F_{7/2}$. This state is split by a cubic electric field into two twofold levels Γ_6, Γ_7 and one fourfold level Γ_8. In Ca$_2$F and CdF$_2$ crystals, as ESR shows, [1; 2] the lowest level is Γ_7. The behavior of energy levels in the presence of a combined crystalline electric field and external static magnetic field H can be easily calculated [3; 4] and the positions of magnetic sublevels of the doublet

197

Γ_7 do not depend on the angles between the field direction and crystallo-graphic axes and are given by:

$$E_+ = 1/2(5c + 7d + a) - 1/2[(5c + 7d + 2a)^2 + 12a^2]^{\frac{1}{2}}$$

$$E_- = 1/2(5c + 7d - a) - 1/2[(5c + 7d - 2a)^2 + 12a^2]^{\frac{1}{2}}$$

(1)

where c and d are the fourth- and sixth-order cubic field constants, $a = g_\tau\beta H$, and g-factor Lande $g_\tau = 8/7$.

The separation between Γ_7 and the next level Γ_8 when the external mag-netic field is zero is $\delta = 5c + 7d$. For weak magnetic fields, when $a \ll \delta$ the roots in (1) can be approximated by a power series in a/δ. Then the first-order approximation shows that the ESR spectrum of the lower state of Yb^{3+} ion can be described by the cubic spin-Hamiltonian with effective spin $S = 1/2$ and a spectroscopic splitting factor $g = 3g_\tau$. Since there are odd isotopes of ytterbium Yb^{171} (natural abundance 14.3%, nuclear spin $I = 1/2$) and Yb^{173} (natural abundance 16.1%, $I = 5/2$), the spin-Hamilton-ian takes the form:

$$\hat{H} = g\beta HS + ASI$$

(2)

where A is the hyperfine coupling constant. The evaluation of δ from the infrared absorption of Yb^{3+} in CaF_2 [1], and CdF_2 [2] shows that its magni-tude has the order of dozens of cm^{-1}. Therefore for the description of paramagnetic resonance experiments at high frequencies the first approxima-tion appeared to be insufficient and the next terms in series (1) should be taken into consideration. In this case an ESR line is described by the same spin-Hamiltonian (2), where the g-factor changes with magnetic field as follows:

$$g = 3g_\tau\left[1 - 4\left(\frac{g_\tau\beta H}{\delta}\right)^2\right]$$

(3)

The crystals investigated have been grown from the melt in the evacuated furnace by the usual Stockbarger method. The initial chemical material, supplied as precipitated colorless powder of CdF_2, was previously thoro-ughly mixed with Yb_2O_3. The crystals with concentration of Yb by weight in powder 0.1; 0.05; 0.01% were grown at different annealing conditions.

The observation of ESR absorption has shown that in all samples Yb^{3+} ions replace isomorphously Cd^{2+} and the paramagnetic ion surroundings conserves the cubic symmetry. A signal can be easily observed at the temper-ature just below 77°K. At the frequency 9100 Mc/s the following row of spin-Hamiltonian constants was obtained:

$$g = 3.436 \pm 0.001$$

$$A^{171} = [883 \pm 1.5] \cdot 10^{-4} \text{ cm}^{-1} \qquad (4)$$

$$A^{173} = [242 \pm 0.4] \cdot 10^{-4} \text{ cm}^{-1}$$

The quantities A/g and the nuclei magnetic moments ratio for two odd isotopes are in a good agreement with those found by W. Low for CaF_2 [1]. The measurements at 37150 Mc/s show that the g-factor decreases very slowly when the frequency increases, but its change is beyond the estimated experimental error. For the frequency 73300 Mc/s its value is:

$$g = 3.431 \pm 0.001$$

A large relative error in Δg permits according to [3] only rough estimation of $\delta \simeq 50$ cm^{-1}. The possibility to observe the resonance line at liquid nitrogen temperatures, which is rather unusual for the rare earth ions, allows the evaluation of δ by measuring the temperature variation of absorption line integral intensity. For this purpose the method was used to measure as a check the intensity of $(3/2 \leftrightarrow 1/2)$ transition for Cr^{3+} in Al_2O_3 with magnetic field parallel to the c-axis of ruby. The results for the region $60 \div 4°K$ show that the intensity increases more rapidly than $1/T$. If we put that zero field splittings between Γ_6, Γ_8 and Γ_8, Γ_7 are in the ratio 3 : 5 then the temperature dependence of the line intensity can be accounted for with $\delta = 70$ cm^{-1}. This value is liable to be more accurate than that obtained from g-factor measurements. Then the overall ground state splitting is found to be 110 cm^{-1}. This is in good agreement with infrared absorption measurements [2], which give two lines with separation 116 cm^{-1}. It is to be noted that our attempts to detect an ESR signal of the excited states Γ_6, Γ_8 at liquid nitrogen temperatures were not successful. It may mean that at these temperatures spin-lattice relaxation of the excited states magnetic sublevels is faster than that for the ground state.

For the more accurate definition of δ, the infrared spectroscopic observations at different temperatures and with designs of high resolution should be carried out [5].

The spin-lattice relaxation time T_1 in the temperature range 2–77°K for the Yb^{3+} concentration 0.1; 0.05 and 0.01 % was measured at frequencies of 9100 and 3200 Mc/s. At low temperature the pulse saturation method was used [6], but at liquid nitrogen temperatures T_1 was derived from the absorption line broadening. The experimental results are presented in the Table.

TABLE

Concentration	0.1%		0.05%		0.01%	
$T°K$	$\lambda = 3$ cm	$\lambda = 10$ cm	$\lambda = 3$ cm	$\lambda = 10$cm	$\lambda = 3$cm	$\lambda = 10$ cm
2°	$3.2 \cdot 10^{-4}$	—	$5.5 \cdot 10^{-4}$	—	$2.3 \cdot 10^{-3}$	$7.5 \cdot 10^{-4}$
4.2°	$1.5 \cdot 10^{-4}$	—	$2.5 \cdot 10^{-4}$	$9 \cdot 10^{-5}$	$1.1 \cdot 10^{-3}$	$4 \cdot 10^{-4}$
57°	$3 \cdot 10^{-9}$	—	$3 \cdot 10^{-9}$	$3 \cdot 10^{-9}$	$3 \cdot 10^{-9}$	$3 \cdot 10^{-9}$

At the liquid helium temperature spin-lattice relaxation time is inversely proportional to the temperature and impurities concentration. At higher temperature its temperature dependence becomes stronger and in the region $20 \div 77°K$, $T_1 \sim T^{-7}$. The complete range of results for the sample with Yb^{3+} concentration 0.05% are given in Figure 1. At the upper end of temperature T_1 is independent of the concentration.

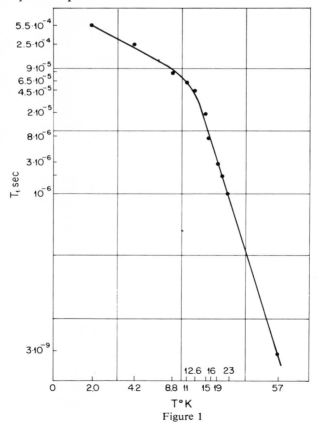

Figure 1

The frequency dependence of the spin-lattice relaxation time is strikingly different from those predicted by the theory. At the frequency 3200 Mc/s at liquid helium temperatures T_1 is approximately three times shorter than at 9100 Mc/s. However this dependence weakens when the temperature increases and at liquid nitrogen temperature T_1 is equal for both the frequencies. This abnormal behavior of T_1 with frequency at temperatures where the direct processes are predominant cannot be interpreted in terms of the present theory of spin-lattice relaxation for rare earth ions.

It is likely that some new mechanisms should be pointed out that would permit to account for the results.

The authors wish to express their gratitude to L. M. Belay'ev, H. S. Bagdasarov and W. Y. Haymov-Mal'kov for the growing the crystals. The authors take this opportunity to record their sincere thanks to L. S. Kornienko, G. M. Zverev and A. I. Smirnov for providing the possibility to carry out some experiments and for assistance with some of the measurements.

REFERENCES

[1] W. Low, *Phys. Rev.* **118**, 1608 (1960).

[2] W. K. Konukhov, P. P. Pashinin and A. M. Prokhorov, *Solid State Physics* **4**, 246 (1962).

[3] C. Kittel and I. M. Luttinger, *Phys. Rev.* **73**, 162 (1948).

[4] W. Low, *Phys. Rev.* **109**, 265 (1958).

[5] W. Low, *Advances in Quantum Electronics*, Columbia University Press, New York, 1961, p. 138.

[6] P. P. Pashinin and A. M. Prokhorov, *JETP* **40**, 49 (1961).

Electron Nuclear Double Resonance in Calcium Fluoride Containing Divalent Europium

J. M. BAKER, J. P. HURRELL AND F. I. B. WILLIAMS

Oxford University

ABSTRACT

Single crystals of CaF_2 containing about 0.01% of Eu^{++} exhibit ENDOR transitions in both the europium and fluorine nuclear resonances. The very narrow lines, ~ 10 kc/s, enable very precise measurements to be made of both hyperfine structure due to interaction between the electrons and the two europium isotopes and also the interaction with the ligand and more distant fluorine nuclei.

We have used the technique of ENDOR in calcium fluoride containing about $10^{-2}\%$ Eu^{++}. The europium electron spin resonance has been used to detect nuclear resonances of both the europium nuclei [1] and the fluorine nuclei. These both have maximum intensity at around $13°K$.

As the lines of the europium nuclear resonance are only about 10 kc/s wide the values of the parameters of the spin-Hamiltonian are obtained with high precision (some of the values obtained are given in the table). In order to fit such accurate measurements with a spin-Hamiltonian it has been necessary to introduce a number of small terms of the type suggested by Koster and Statz [2] and even then the best fit obtained is accurate only to about 10 kc/s, whereas by repeating readings one can obtain line positions to about 1 kc/s. Even though the symmetry of the site of the Eu^{++} ion is cubic, with $J=7/2$ and $I=7/2$ a large number of such small terms are allowed, and there are not enough measured lines to make it feasible to include all possible terms in a trial spin-Hamiltonian. As these small terms may be regarded as arising from high order effects of the various contributions to the full Hamiltonian, and one has a rough idea of the order of magnitude of those various contributions, one can make very rough estimates of the size of the small terms in the spin-Hamiltonian. We have not yet found one empirically which improves the prediction of our line positions. The possibility that there are systematic experimental errors in the measured line positions has been investigated by varying many of the experimental conditions, but only at very high microwave powers is there any effect (this takes the form of a splitting of the line into two, but the center of gravity of the doublet remains in the same place).

The precision with which we obtain the parameters of the spin-Hamiltonian is comparable with that with which Woodgate and his group [3] has been able to measure the same parameters in the free europium atom in an atomic beam (see Table). As the electronic configuration of the atom is identical with that of the ion except for an additional completely filled $6s$ shell, one can

TABLE

Quantity	$^{151}\text{Eu}^{++}$	^{151}Eu
A (Mc/s)	-102.9069 ± 0.0013	-20.0523 ± 0.0003
B (Mc/s)	$-\ 0.7855 \pm 0.0052$	$-\ 0.7012 \pm 0.0035$
g_I (Bohs mags)	$(-\ 7.4969 \pm 0.0020) \times 10^{-4}$	$(-\ 7.369\ \pm 0.010) \times 10^{-4}$
Δ	$-\ 0.63\ \pm 0.07\%$	$-\ 0.10\ \pm 0.07\%$

earn a good deal by a comparison of the results on the ion with those on the atom. In order to do this unambiguously one has to make one or two assumptions which are not strictly valid, but which are probably sufficiently close to the truth to make the conclusions from the comparison of some value. Firstly we have assumed that the hyperfine structure comes entirely from either unpaired f-electrons or from s-electrons which have been unpaired by interaction with the aligned f-electrons, and the hyperfine structure anomaly comes entirely from s-electrons.

We have interpreted the departure of the measured g-value from that one would expect for the $^8S_{7/2}$ state as being due to an admixture by the spin orbit coupling of a small quantity α of the $^6P_{7/2}$ state. This gives $\alpha^2 = 0.029 \pm 0.001$. That this admixture is so small justifies the omission of a contribution from higher order in the spin orbit coupling from $^6D_{7/2}$. The value of α^2 is given by $14\ \zeta^2/E^2$ where ζ is the spin orbit coupling parameter and E is the energy of the $^6P_{7/2}$ state; unfortunately no estimate of these quantities has been made theoretically, and no data is yet avialable from optical measurements. The admixture is very close to that found in the atom, where $\alpha^2 = 0.025$, and is slightly larger because of the larger value of $\langle 1/r^3 \rangle$.

The $^8S_{7/2}$ state should exhibit neither magnetic dipolar, nor electric quadrupolar hyperfine structure. The admixture of the $^6P_{7/2}$ and the $^6D_{7/2}$ states will give rise to a dipolar interaction and the latter to a quadrupole interaction. However, Sandars (unpublished) has shown that these effects alone cannot explain either the magnitude or the sign of the measured interactions in the atom. He has done a calculation of the relativistic effects in the f^7 configuration and concludes that, within the uncertainties of our knowledge of the correct wave functions, the observed interactions in the atom can be adequately explained as due to f-electrons alone, although the finite value of Δ indicates that there is probably some s-electron contribution. Although there is considerable uncertainty about the calculations of absolute values of the interactions from first principles, one might imagine that one ought to be able to extrapolate fron the atom to the ion using Sandars theory. This one can in fact do quite well.

The quadrupole interaction is similar in both cases, as one might expect, because it is due to field gradients from the f-electrons. The slightly larger value in the ion corresponds to the slightly larger value of $\langle 1/r^3 \rangle$.

The f-electron contribution to the value of A is proportional to α so that as $\alpha^2_{ion} = 1.15\ \alpha^2_{atom}$ we assume that $A(f)_{ion} = 1.15\ A(f)_{atom}$. Further one can write

$$A_{ion} = A(s)_{ion} + A(f)_{ion} \quad \text{and} \quad A_{ion}\,\Delta_{ion} = A(s)_{ion}\,\Delta(s)$$

where $\Delta(s)$ is the anomaly for a single s-electron. There will also be a similar pair of equations for the atom. These four equations may be solved giving

$$A(s)_{ion} = -83\,\text{Mc/s} \qquad\qquad A(f)_{ion} = -20\,\text{Mc/s}$$

$$A(s)_{atom} = -3\,\text{Mc/s} \qquad\qquad A(f)_{atom} = -17\,\text{Mc/s}$$

This confirms the suggestion that the bulk of the hfs in the atom is due to f-electrons, but shows that in the ion the bulk of it is due to s-electrons.

Several different nuclear resonances have been observed from fluorine nuclei with the external field along a cube edge. Some of these occur in positions close to those expected for next nearest neighbor nuclei if their interaction with the Eu^{++} ion is purely dipolar. There remain, for each value of S_z or Eu^{++}, either one or two lines which are attributed to the nearest neighbors, which are all equivalent in this direction. These lines do not fall in the positions predicted by a purely dipolar interaction but appear to fit roughly an interaction spin-Hamiltonian $\sum A_s \mathbf{I}\cdot\mathbf{S} + A_p(3I_z\cdot S_z - \mathbf{I}\cdot\mathbf{S})$, the z axis joining the nucleus with the ion and the sum being over the the eight nearest neighbors, with a unique value of the two constants.

The best fit to the data so far obtained is given by

$$A_s = -2.23 \pm 0.01\,\text{Mc/s} \quad \text{and} \quad |A_p| = 4.01 \pm 0.01\,\text{Mc/s}$$

These parameters give the frequencies of the transitions to an accuracy of about 50Mc/s, which is comparable with the line width (considerably greater for F endor than for Eu endor). The value of A_p expected from dipolar interaction is $-$ 5.6 Mc/s, so there is a considerable anisotropic contribution from the unpaired electrons of the fluorine ion as well as an isotropic contribution; both contributions have about the same magnitude but opposite signs. The size of the isotropic contribution is considerably smaller than the value calculated by Watson and Freeman [4] for the isoelectronic Gd^{+++}, where $A_s \approx +8$Mc/s, and with a smaller nuclear charge one would expect the wavefunctions of the electrons of the Eu^{++} ion to be more spread out and to give a larger interaction, (the separation of the F nucleus from the Eu nucleus is about the same as that taken by Watson and Freeman). Also the sign of the measured A_s is opposite to that predicated by Watson and Freeman (the same sign as their contribution from f-electrons) which possibly indicates that the polarisation of the F^- wavefunctions, not included in the calculation, is important.

REFERENCES

[1]   J. M. BAKER AND F. I. B. WILLIAMS, *Proc. Roy. Soc.* **A 267,** 283 (1962).
[2]   G. F. KOSTER AND H. STATZ, *Phys. Rev.* **113,** 445 (1959).
[3]   P. G. H. SANDARS AND G. K. WOODGATE, *Proc. Roy. Sec.* **A 257,** 260 (1960);
      F. M. PICHANICK, P. G. H. SANDARS AND G. K. WOODGATE, *Proc. Roy. Soc.*
      A 257, 277 (1960).
[4]   R. E. WATSON AND A. J. FREEMAN, *Phys. Rev. Letters* **6,** 277 (1961).

Electron Spin Resonance of Interstitial Hydrogen Atoms in CaF_2*

J. L. HALL** AND R. T. SCHUMACHER***

Carnegie Institute of Technology, Pittsburgh 13, *Pennsylvania*

ABSTRACT

The electron spin resonance spectra of hydrogen atoms in suitably prepared CaF_2 show the strong hyperfine interaction of the electron with a spin 1/2 nucleus (proton) and a somewhat weaker, though well resolved hyperfine interaction with 8 equivalent spin 1/2 nuclei (fluorines). All of the experimental results are consistent with the model in which an electrically neutral hydrogen atom is located at one of the body centers of the simple cubic sublattice formed by the fluorines of CaF_2. A simple spin-Hamiltonian exhibiting the symmetry of this model contains four adjustable parameters and is found to describe very accurately all the ESR spectra. The results of a novel type of electron nuclear double resonance experiment are used to show that essentially all of the ESR line width is due to unresolved hyperfine interactions with distant fluorine nuclei. The angular dependence of the double resonance spectra serves further to substantiate the model proposed for the observed paramagnetic center. The analogous center consisting of interstitial deuterium atoms has also been investigated and the results are compared with those for the interstitial hydrogen atom. The origin of some of the interesting differences will be discussed. The results of some recent a priori calculations of the hyperfine splitting constants will be presented.

We report here some of the results of a detailed investigation of the electron spin resonance of interstitial atomic hydrogen in suitably-prepared CaF_2. The following aspects of the problem are to be discussed: 1) the resonance spectra and the physical model of the paramagnetic center; 2) a simple spin-Hamiltonian which accurately describes the spectra; 3) the results of some ENDOR experiments which allow calculation of the ESR line width; 4) the results of a standard a priori calculation of the hyperfine coupling parameters; 5) sample preparation.

I. Spectra and model

In CaF_2, the fluorine system forms a simple cubic lattice with the F^- ions at the corners. The Ca^{++} occupy alternate body centers. We find all the

* Supported by a grant from the National Science Foundation.
Taken in part from a thesis submitted by J. L. Hall in partial fullfillment of the requirements for the PhD degree from Carnegie Institute of Technology.
** National Carbon Predoctoral Fellow. Now at the Joint Institute for Laboratory Astrophysics, Boulder, Colorado.
*** Alfred P. Sloan Foundation Fellow.

experimental results to be consistent with the model in which an electrically neutral hydrogen atom is located at a body center position of the fluorine sublattice. The hydrogen atom interacts but weakly with the eight nearest fluorine ions, and may well be considered to be a "free" atom. The lattice is probably essentially undilated by its presence, and in any event, is locally perfectly cubic. There are no vacancies in the first fluorine shell, and probably none in the second.

The ESR spectra of interstitial atomic hydrogen consist of two similar groups of lines, separated by about 525 gauss by the hyperfine interaction with the proton. Each group, extending over a range of about 300 gauss, arises from electron-fluorine super-hyperfine interaction and in general consists of 81 lines. For simple orientations of the magnetic field, the number is greatly reduced by symmetry. For example, as seen in Figure 1, there are

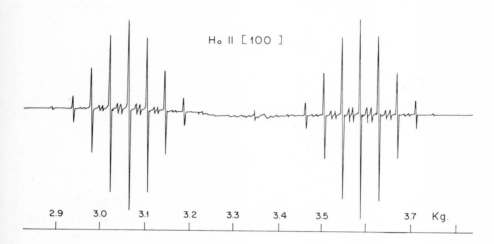

Figure 1

nine main lines when the external field is parallel to a [100] crystal axis. The intensity ratios between these nine lines establish the equivalence of the eight spin 1/2 fluorine nuclei.

The well-resolved doublet structure observed between each pair of the main lines arises from "forbidden" transitions in which a fluorine nuclear spin as well as the electronic spin reorient in the external field.

The energies of the pair of fluorine nuclei which share a given body diagonal can be characterized by the angle between their body diagonal and the external field. For example, at [100], all four pairs of nuclei make the same angle ~ 55°, giving the nine lines previously discussed. With [110] parallel to H_0, we have two pairs at the angle 90°, two pairs at the angle ~ 35°. As expected, the [110] spectrum (Figure 2) shows evidence of two distinct values of hyperfine splitting. The expected number of transitions, 25, is observed.

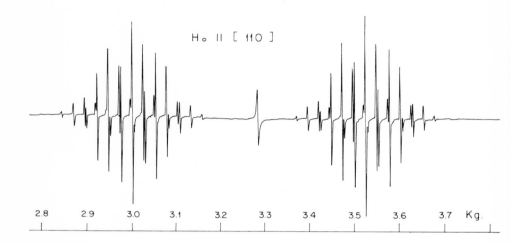

Figure 2

For H_0 aligned parallel to [111], there are three pairs of fluorine nuclei at ~ 71° and one pair at 0°. This spectrum Figure 3, consists of 11 principal lines. There are actually 21 transitions, but an approximate factor-of two relationship between the two splittings results in the "simpler" spectrum. Our arguments give 11 lines with the observed intensity ratios. The "forbidden transition" doublet structure is prominent at this alignment also.

The fourth case which has been analyzed in detail is for H_0 parallel to [11$\bar{2}$], This produces two pairs of fluorines at ~ 65° and one pair each at 90° and 19°. This spectrum contains 45 transitions. Since the [110] spectrum also contains a 90° pair, the observed 25 lines of the [11$\bar{2}$] spectrum can be easily identified.

Before summarizing the experimental results, it is convenient to make a few remarks about the spin-Hamiltonian which is appropriate to this problem.

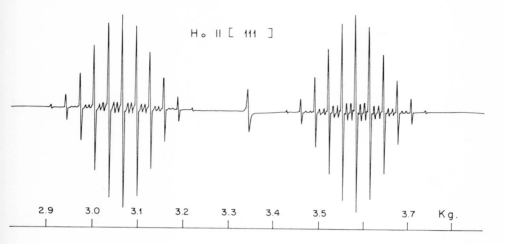

Figure 3

II. Spin-Hamiltonian

We find all ESR spectra are accurately described by the following simple spin-Hamiltonian:

$$\mathcal{H} = g\beta H_0 S_z + B\,\mathbf{I}^p \cdot \mathbf{S} - g_p\beta_n H_0 I_z^p + \sum_{\alpha=1}^{8} \mathbf{S}\cdot\mathbf{T}^{\alpha}\cdot\mathbf{I}^{\alpha} - g_F\beta_n H_0 \sum_{\alpha=1}^{8} I_z^a$$

The first three terms form the spin-Hamiltonian of a hydrogen atom in an external field H_0. The next term is the tensor "superhypefine" interaction between the electron and the eight nearest neighbor fluorine nuclei. The last term is the Zeeman energy of the eight fluorine nuclei. It might be emphasized that the full cubic symmetry of the model is explicitly built into this Hamiltonian. Using symmetry arguments only, one can show that the superhyperfine interaction is axially symmetric and that the angular dependence of the splitting has the form of a straight line in the plot of Figure 5.

The experimental data fit this functional form. We obtain directly preliminary values for the parameters $T_{\parallel}$ and $T_{\perp}$ from the intercepts at zero and 90°. In the precise fitting of the data, the exact Breit-Rabi hydrogen atom energies have been used. The superhyperfine energies have been done to

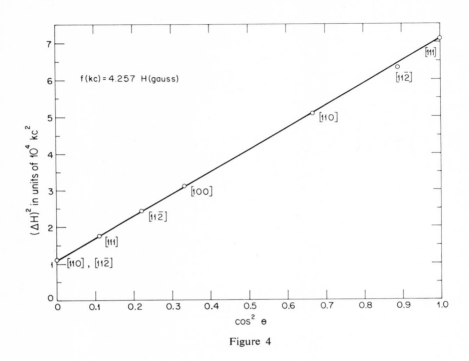

Figure 4

second order in perturbation theory. We find the following values for the four parameters on the spin-Hamiltonian:

TABLE I

$g/g_0 = 1.00011$ $\pm .00003$	$T_\parallel = \begin{pmatrix} 173.83 \\ \pm 0.30 \end{pmatrix}$ Mc.
$B = \begin{pmatrix} 1460.2 \\ \pm 0.1 \end{pmatrix}$ Mc.	$T_\perp = \begin{pmatrix} 69.02 \\ \pm 0.30 \end{pmatrix}$ Mc.

(g_0 is the free hydrogen atom g-value.) The spin-Hamiltonian also accounts in detail for the "forbidden transitions." Analysis of these "forbidden" resonances leads to the conclusion that $T_\parallel$ and $T_\perp$ are of the same algebraic sign.

Finally, it should be remarked that the values of g, B, $T_\parallel$ and $T_\perp$ quoted fit the data at all angles to within 1/10 of the resonance line width at both 9 and 18 kmc.

3. ENDOR and the ESR line width

Thus far, we have been concerned with the magnetic interactions between the hydrogen atom and the eight surroundin g fluorine nuclei. Essentially all of the structure compatible with the symmetry requirements is actually resolved in the experiments. To understand the resonance line widths, it is necessary to consider the interaction of the unpaired electron with more distant fluorine nuclei. The next shell contains 24 fluorine nuclei, each distant from the proton by $1/2 \sqrt{11}$ in units of the fluorine lattice constant. It is convenient to write the relevant interactions in the form

$$\mathcal{H}_E = -g_F \beta_n H_0 \sum_{\alpha=1}^{24} I_z^{\alpha} + a \, \mathbf{S} \cdot \sum_{\alpha=1}^{24} \mathbf{I}^{\alpha}$$

$$+ \frac{b}{2} \sum_{\alpha=1}^{24} (3I_z^{\alpha} S_z - \mathbf{I}^{\alpha} \cdot \mathbf{S}) (3\cos^2\theta - 1)$$

The first term is the Zeeman energy of the 24 fluorine nuclei, the second term is the isotropic contact interaction with the electron, the last term is the dipolar interaction. Here θ^{α} is the angle between $\mathbf{H}_0$ and the vector $\mathbf{r}^{\alpha}$ from the proton to the α th fluorine in the second shell.

Using the detailed physical model discussed earlier and the known alignment of the crystal in the waveguide, it turns out that we expect seven different types of angular variation of the ENDOR lines as the electromagnet is rotated. These seven angular functions are the solid curves of Figure 5; the normalized experimental points are plotted as the circles. Since the angular dependence of the ENDOR lines is determined by the symmetry of the paramagnetic center, this excellent fit constitutes an important corroboration of the proposed model.

In the ENDOR results of Table II, we include for comparison the ESR results on the first shell, expressed in the present notation.

TABLE II

fluorine shell	number equiv. nuclei	distance to H atom	a_j	b_j	b_j dipolar
1	8	$\frac{1}{2}\sqrt{3}$	104 Mc	35 Mc	5.6 Mc
2	24	$\frac{1}{2}\sqrt{11}$	$\left(\begin{array}{c} 415 \\ \pm 15 \end{array}\right)$ kc	$\left(\begin{array}{c} 872 \\ \pm 15 \end{array}\right)$ kc	804 kc
3	12	$\frac{1}{2}\sqrt{19}$	$\left(\begin{array}{c} 20 \\ \pm 25 \end{array}\right)$ kc	$\left(\begin{array}{c} 360 \\ \pm 25 \end{array}\right)$ kc	354 kc

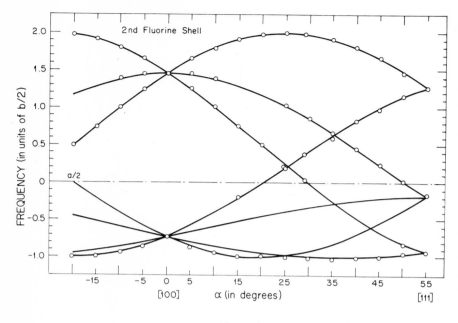

Figure 5

Comparison of the experimental and calculated second moments of the resonances of a powdered sample is slightly complicated by second order effects within the first fluorine shell, but in any event, the width is given within, say 10%, by the Van Vleck formalism.

It may be remarked that this ENDOR data was obtained with good signal to noise at liquid nitrogen temperature using a repetitive form of Feher's "transient, spin-packet shifting" type of double resonance effect [1]. The nuclear probing oscillator is squarewave amplitude modulated at a suitable frequency and the resulting ripple on the static electron absorption signal is synchronously detected. An important advantage of this variant is that the recorder displays directly the nuclear resonance lineshape.

IV. A priori calculation of hfs

In all of the previous discussion, we have taken the four constants of the spin-Hamiltonian to be parameters to be adjusted to fit the experiments. Of course, these constants are entirely derivable in principle on an a priori basis. We here briefly summarize the simplest treatment that contains the essential points and quote numerical results obtained by Professor Schumacher.

The arguments which lead in the ionic limit to the usual one-electron expressions for the hyperfine energies are given by Gourary and Adrian [2]. The wavefunction of the interstitial atom is required to be orthogonal to the core electron wavefunctions of the eight surrounding fluorine ions. The experimental results strongly suggest that the most reasonable procedure is to start with a free hydrogen atom wavefunction and modify it slightly by the Schmidt procedure to achieve the required orthogonality. The resulting function then contains a weak admixture of $1S$, $2S$, and $2P$ fluorine orbitals centered on each of the eight ions. Only components with the same spin orientation as the H atom are admixed. The fluorine wavefunctions used were the free ion Hartree-Foch numerical functions of Miss Froese [3]. The several overlap integrals were evaluated using a Bendix G-20 computer.

The results of the calculation are shown in Figure 10. Here "a" is the isotropic Fermi contact term, "b" is the anisotropic dipolar constant. (Since a and b are actually the calculated quantities, it is preferable to compare them — rather than the equivalent tensor components with experiment.)

TABLE III

Hyperfine constant		Experimental value	Static model calculation
Hydrogen	B	$\left(\begin{array}{c}1460.2\\ \pm\ 0.1\end{array}\right)$ Mc	1660 Mc
	B/B_0	$\left(\begin{array}{c}1.0280\\ \pm\ .0001\end{array}\right)$	1.169
	a	$\left(\begin{array}{c}103.96\\ \pm 0.25\end{array}\right)$ Mc	129.3 Mc
	b	$\left(\begin{array}{c}34.93\\ \pm 0.16\end{array}\right)$ Mc	33.3 Mc
Deuterium	C	$\left(\begin{array}{c}224.93\\ \pm\ .30\end{array}\right)$ Mc	255 Mc
	C/C_0	$\left(\begin{array}{c}1.0306\\ \pm .0014\end{array}\right)$	1.169
	a	$\left(\begin{array}{c}102.44\\ \pm 0.25\end{array}\right)$ Mc	129.3 Mc
	b	$\left(\begin{array}{c}34.75\\ \pm 0.25\end{array}\right)$ Mc	33.3 Mc

Considering the simplicity of the calculation, the agreement of *a* and especially of *b* with experiment is surprising. The large value of the proton hyperfine constant *B*, however, must be counted a serious discrepancy, since it is relevant to compare deviations from the free atom value of 1420 Mc: + 240 Mc calculated vs. + 40 Mc experimental. The sign of this discrepancy illuminates the incompleteness of our calculation. The only crystalline modification of the free atom hydrogen wavefunction has been in response to the Pauli Exclusion Principle. This repulsive interaction acts to increase the charge density at the proton. Neglected interactions with the crystalline environment, such as Vander Waals forces, attractive interactions with nearby calcium ions, and dielectric constant effects, all have the effect of spreading on the wavefunction and decreasing the charge density at the proton.

Comparison of the hydrogen and deuterium results suggests that local vibrations probably are not of qualitative importance. Professor Schumacher has shown, that if one were to take this whole calculation seriously and try to account for the proton denteron differences by allowing vibratory motions of the interstitial atom, the difference in RMS excursions of protons and deuterons would have to be about 0.15Å. This magnitude is perhaps reasonable, but the deuterons have the larger excursions.

V. Sample preparation

A remark about sample preparation is perhaps not inappropriate. The recipe is as follows: pure CaF_2 and aluminum metal are outgassed just below the melting point of the metal. After a few cm Hg of hydrogen or deuterium is cautiously admitted, the temperature is increased to $\sim 900°C$ and maintained for several hours. After removal of the excess aluminum, the crystals are X-rayed at room temperature for a few hours. With this technique we have obtained densities of interstitial *atomic* hydrogen as high as 10^{19}/cc. The samples are thermally stable at room temperature, but appear to deteriorate slowly in a few months' time.

VI. Conclusions

In this paper we have described the magnetic interactions of a hydrogen atom with its surroundings when it is placed in an interstitial position in a CaF_2 lattice. We have shown that the hydrogen atom remains very much as it is in free space. The relatively weak magnetic interactions with the surrounding fluorine nuclei have, however, a profound effect on the paramagnetic resonance spectrum. We have measured the resolved interaction with the eight nearest neighbor fluorine nuclei, determined by ENDOR techniques the interactions with the 24 next nearest neighbor fluorines, and seen some indication of the interaction of the hydrogen electron with the third shell. These measurements provide a quantitative measure of the density of the electron on 33 nuclei. Our sample preparation technique has allowed us to deuterate the specimen and observe the small mass dependence of the interactions. We have also observed the small changes in the magnetic interactions after the crystal is cooled to 77°K.

Questions which remain to be examined and which have not been seriously studied in this investigation include the mechanism for production of the hydrogen interstitial atom and for its thermal bleaching. Nor have we been able to correlate uniquely any well-defined optical absorption effects with the presence of the hydrogen.

We presented the results of an a priori calculation of the parameter describing the magnetic interactions of the electron with the proton and surrounding eight nuclei. The calculation is presented in the spirit of an inquiry into the results one obtains with the standard theoretical techniques which have been used previously in more difficult problems, such as the F-center or Mn^{++} in ZnF_2. The agreement of this calculation with experiment was found to be only fair—the calculated parameters were up to 25 % too large. The calculation was somewhat optimistically extended to a dynamic model in an attempt to understand the small proton deuteron differences and temperature effects. It should also be emphasized that a "standard" calculation is inadequate to explain even qualitatively the observed g-shifts, which are positive.

We conclude by emphasizing our belief that we have studied an impurity center which provides unique opportunities for theorists to calculate from basic principles the measured interactions. We have shown that the wave function is quite close in its main features to that of a free hydrogen atom. At the same time the solid state effects are well defined and susceptible to very accurate measurement. The substitution of the deuteron for the proton allows an additional check on those aspects of the theory which involve local lattice dynamics.

REFERENCES

[1]   G. FEHER, *Phys. Rev.* **114**, 1219 (1959)

[2]   B. S. GOURARY AND F. J. ADRIAN, *Solid State Physics*, F. SEITZ AND D. TURNBULL, eds., Academic Press, NY, 1960, vol. 10, p 127.

[3]   C. FROESE, *Proc. Cambridge Phil. Soc.* **53**, 206 (1957).

DISCUSSION

A. KASTER, France: Have you observed the hydrogen hyperfine lines in a zero external field?

J. L. HALL, U.S.A.: No, but I understand that Prof. Schumacher is intending to do this.

A. ABRAGAM, France: At what concentration would you expect to see clusters of 2 (or more) atoms?

J.L. HALL, U.S.A.: The concentration would have to be very high because we have a minimum of 18 lines. For a pair interaction to be important, all 9 of these nuclei would have to be in the same spin state.

Angular Spectra of $\Delta M = \pm 2$ and ± 3 Transitions in $(0.999 \text{ La}, 0.001 \text{ Gd}) \cdot (C_2H_5SO_4)_3 \cdot 9H_2O$

H. A. BUCKMASTER

Physics Department, University of Alberta, Calgary, Alberta, Canada

ABSTRACT

The spin-Hamiltonian for Gd^{3+} $(S = 7/2)$ in a crystalline electric field of C_{3v} symmetry is transformed from "crystal" to "magnetic" coordinates by

$$D(\alpha,\beta,\gamma)\tilde{O}_{l,m} = \sum_{m' = -l}^{l} \tilde{O}_{l,m'} \mathscr{D}_{m',m}^{(l)} (\alpha, \beta, \gamma)$$

The magnetic resonance angular spectra for the $\Delta M = \pm 2$ and ± 3 transitions has been computed using the published values of the adjustable parameters. Comparison of the calculated spectra with that obtained at frequency of $24 GH_z$ and a temperature of $90°K$ shows good agreement at all orientations within ± 2 gauss. The only exception is the $+ 3/2 \leftrightarrow - 3/2$ transition which has a periodicity of $90°$ instead of $180°$ and a larger amplitude. No explanation is offered. These measurements indicate that $g_{\parallel} = 1.9910 \pm 0.0005$, $g_{\perp} = 1.9910 \pm 0.0005$ and $a_2^0 = (204.7 \pm 0.5) \times 10^{-4}$ cm^{-1} are improved limits of error on these parameters.

Introduction

The paramagnetic resonance spectra of the $\Delta M = \pm 1$ transitions of dilute gadolinium (Gd^{3+}) in the diamagnetic lattice of hydrated lanthanum ethyl sulphate has been studied by Bleaney, Scovil and Trenam [1] at temperatures of $20°K$ and $90°K$ and at wavelengths of 1.2 and 3 cm. The external magnetic field was oriented parallel and perpendicular to the crystal symmetry axis. Measurements were also made when the magnetic field is small compared with the crystalline electric field splittings. Buckmaster [2] reported measurements at $90°K$ and 1.2 cm of the forbidden transitions where $\Delta M = \pm 2$ in the parallel and perpendicular directions and $\Delta M = \pm 3$ transitions in the perpendicular direction. These experimental measurements have been fitted to a spin-Hamiltonian proposed by Elliott and Stevens [3] on the assumption that the crystalline electric field had the same C_{3h} symmetry as the hydrated ethyl sulphate lattice. The spin-Hamiltonian is

$$\mathscr{H} = g\beta\mathbf{H} \cdot \mathbf{S} + A_2^0 O_2^0 + A_4^0 O_4^0 + A_6^0 O_6^0 + A_6^6 O_6^{-6} \tag{1}$$

where $O_l^{-m} = 1/2(O_l^{+m} + O_l^{-m})$ is an angular momentum operator which has the same transformation properties as the corresponding spherical harmonic $Y_l^m(\theta,\phi)$. These operators and tables of their matrix elements have been given by Stevens [4], Elliott and Stevens [3], Judd [5], Baker, Bleaney and Hayes [6], Jones, Baker and Pope [7], Baker and Williams [8], Orbach [9] and Buckmaster [10]. When the external magnetic field is arbitrarily orientated with respect to the crystal symmetry axis (z axis), it is convenient to transform the spin-Hamiltonian into a coordinate system with a new z axis parallel to the applied magnetic field, i.e. "magnetic" instead of "crystal" coordinates. The eigenvectors of the transformed spin-Hamiltonian are useful when transition probabilities are calculated for the design of 3LSSM [11].

Transformation of spin-Hamiltonian

Buckmaster [10] has shown that if modified angular momentum operator equivalents $\tilde{O}_{l \pm m}$ are defined and related to $O_l^{\pm m}$ by rational factors then the matrix elements for the finite rotations, defined by Edmonds [12], can be employed. This is an alternative method of transforming the spin-Hamiltonian from "crystal" to "magnetic" coordinated to that suggested by Baker and Williams [8] and has the advantage that the extensive literature on the transformation properties of angular momentum eigenfunctions and operators is directly applicable.

It can be shown that in "magnetic" coordinates the spin-Hamiltonian (1) becomes

$$
\begin{aligned}
\mathscr{H}^T = {}& (g_\parallel \cos^2\theta + g_\perp \sin^2\theta)\beta H S_z + A_2^0 \left[P_2^0(\cos\theta)O_2^0 \right. \\
& + 2P_2^1(\cos\theta)\bar{O}_2^1 + \left. \frac{1}{2}P_2^2(\cos\theta)\bar{O}_2^2 \right] \\
& + A_4^0 \left[P_4^0(\cos\theta)O_4^0 + 2P_4^1(\cos\theta)\bar{O}_4^1 + \frac{1}{3}P_4^2(\cos\theta)\bar{O}_4^2 \right. \\
& + \left. \frac{1}{3}P_4^3(\cos\theta)\bar{O}_4^3 + \frac{1}{24}P_4^4(\cos\theta)\bar{O}_4^4 \right] \\
& + A_6^0 \left[P_6^0(\cos\theta)O_6^0 + 2P_6^1(\cos\theta)\bar{O}_6^1 + \frac{1}{4}P_6^2(\cos\theta)\bar{O}_6^2 \right. \\
& + \frac{1}{12}P_6^3(\cos\theta)\bar{O}_6^3 + \frac{1}{120}P_6^4(\cos\theta)\bar{O}_6^4 \\
& + \left. \frac{1}{120}P_6^5(\cos\theta)\bar{O}_6^5 + \frac{1}{1440}P_6^6(\cos\theta)\bar{O}_6^6 \right]
\end{aligned}
$$

$$+ A_6^6 \left[4\cos^6 \frac{\theta}{2} \sin^6 \frac{\theta}{2} O_6^0 - 4\cos^5 \frac{\theta}{2} \left(\sin^2 \frac{\theta}{2} - \cos^2 \frac{\theta}{2} \right) \bar{O}_6^1 \right.$$

$$+ \frac{15}{1} \cos^4 \frac{\theta}{2} \sin^4 \frac{\theta}{2} \left(\sin^4 \frac{\theta}{2} + \cos^4 \frac{\theta}{2} \right) \bar{O}_6^2$$

$$- 10\cos^3 \frac{\theta}{2} \left(\sin^3 \frac{\theta}{2} - \cos^6 \frac{\theta}{2} \right) \bar{O}_6^3$$

$$+ 6 \cos^2 \frac{\theta}{2} \sin^2 \frac{\theta}{2} \left(\sin^8 \frac{\theta}{2} + \cos^8 \frac{\theta}{2} \right) \bar{O}_6^4$$

$$- 12\cos \frac{\theta}{2} \sin \frac{\theta}{2} \left(\sin^{10} \frac{\theta}{2} - \cos^{10} \frac{\theta}{2} \right) \bar{O}_6^5$$

$$\left. + \left(\sin^{12} \frac{\theta}{2} + \cos^{12} \frac{\theta}{2} \right) \bar{O}_6^6 \right] \qquad (2)$$

The rotation θ is in plane for which $\cos 6\phi = +1$ and θ is the angle which the magnetic field makes with the crystal symmetry axis. The diagonal terms in (2) are

$$\mathcal{H}^T = (g_{\parallel} \cos^2\theta + g_{\perp} \sin^2\theta)\beta H S_z + A_2^0 P_2^0(\cos \theta) O_2^0 \qquad (3)$$

$$+ A_4^0 P_4^0(\cos \theta) O_4^0 + A_6^0 P_6^0(\cos \theta) O_6^0 + A_6^6 \, 4 \, \cos^6 \frac{\theta}{2} \sin^6 \frac{\theta}{2} O_6^0.$$

The associated Legendre polynomials are defined by

$$P_n^m(\cos \theta) = (\sin \theta)^m \left(\frac{d}{d \cos \theta} \right)^m P_n(\cos \theta)$$

$$= \frac{(\sin \theta)^m}{2^n n!} \left(\frac{d}{d \cos \theta} \right)^{n+m} (\cos^2\theta - 1)^n \qquad (4)$$

(Jahnke and Emde [13]).

Experimental results

The angular spectra of the $\Delta M = \pm 2$ and ± 3 transitions are shown in Figures 1 and 2. The curves connecting the experimental points are the best fit curves. On this scale, these curves approximate to the calculated ones. The transitions are labeled according to Bleaney, Scovil and Trenam (1954) by the high field magnetic quantum numbers. These measurements were made with a double field modulation spectrometer with oscilloscope display. They are currently being repeated at wavelengths of 0.8 and 3 cm with higher sensitivity, narrow band superheterodyne

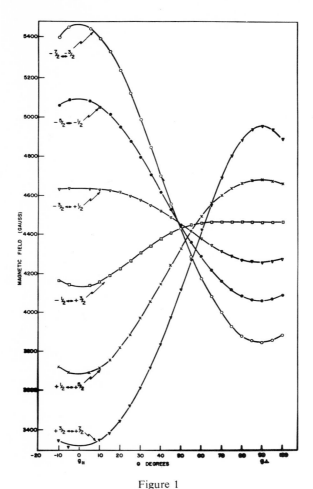

Figure 1

$\Lambda M \pm 2$ Transition in gadolinium ethyl sulphate as a function of the angle with symmetry axis of the crystal. $T = 90°K$ $\gamma = 24.455\,GHz$

spectrometers. The individual measurements are accurate to ± 0.5 gauss. The greatest error in the shape of the spectrum of a given transition is due to inaccuracies in the alignment of the plane for which $\cos 6\phi = +1$ with respect to the rotation axis of the magnetic field and may be as large as ± 5 gauss.

The energy levels for the transformed spin-Hamiltonian have been cal-

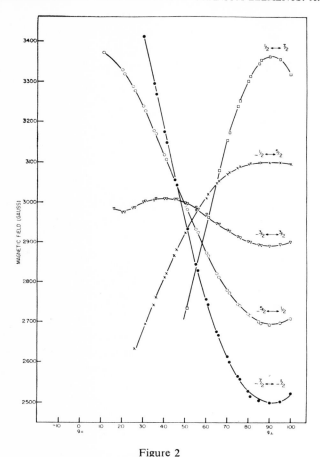

Figure 2

$\Delta = \pm 3$ Transition in gadolinium ethyl sulphate as a funcion of the angle with symmetry axis of the crystal. $T = 90\,^{\circ}\text{K}$. $\gamma = 24\cdot520\text{GHz}$.

culated using the values for the adjustable parameters given by Bleaney, Scovil and Trenam (1954) and shown in Table I.

The agreement between the measured and calculated spectra is within ± 2 gauss at all orientations, with one exception, indicating that the limits of error given by Bleaney, Scovil and Trenam [1] are generous. The following values of the spin-Hamiltonian parameters are consistent with these measurements

$$g_{\parallel} = 1.9110 \pm 0.0005; \; g_{\perp} = 1.9910 \pm 0.0005; \; a_2^0 = (204.7 \pm 0.5)10^{-4}\text{cm}^{-1}.$$

TABLE I

Spin-Hamiltonian parameters for gadolinium ethyl sulphate

$$T = 90°K$$

$g_{\parallel} = 1.991 \pm 0.001$	$g_{\perp} = 1.991 \pm 0.001$
$a_2^0 = (204.7 \pm 2) \cdot 10^{-4} \, \text{cm}^{-1}$	$a_2^0 = 3A_2^0$
$a_4^0 = (-3.96 \pm 0.3) \cdot 10^{-4} \, \text{cm}^{-1}$	$a_4^0 = 60A_4^0$
$a_6^0 = (+0.63 \pm 0.1) \cdot 10^{-4} \, \text{cm}^{-1}$	$a_6^0 = 1260A_6^0$
$a_6^6 = (+3.5 \pm 0.5) \cdot 10^{-4} \, \text{cm}^{-1}$	$a_6^6 = 1260A_6^6$

The measured angular spectrum of the $+3/2 \leftrightarrow -3/2$ transition is not in agreement with that calculated. The measured periodicity is approximately 90° rather than 180°. The amplitude is about twice the calculated value. No satisfactory explanation can be offered. Third order perturbation corrections do not have the measured periodicity and do not decrease the deviation. Second order perturbation corrections due to terms of the form $A_4^3\bar{O}_4^3$ and $A_6^3\bar{O}_6^3$ were calculated to fit the deviation between the calculated and measured $+3/2 \leftrightarrow -3/2$ spectrum. These corrections decreased the deviation between the measured and calculated spectra of the $+3/2 \leftrightarrow -3/2$ to ± 10 gauss by increasing the deviation for the other $\Delta M = \pm 2$ and ± 3 transitions to ± 15 gauss. A calculation of the spin-Hamiltonian parameters, assuming C_{3v} symmetry, for each orientation could yield significant values for A_4^3 and A_6^3 and minimized deviations. The actual symmetry at the site of the Gd^{3+} ions could be lower than that of the last lattice because it is larger than the La^{3+} ion that it replaces. The next lower symmetry to C_{3h} is C_{3v} and this can only be determined experimentally by considering the angular spectra [5].

Conclusion

The fitting of the angular spectra of higher order transitions provides a sensitive test of the correctness of the assumed crystalline electric field symmetry in the spin-Hamiltonian. The measurements presented corroborate the assumption that the crystalline electric field in dilute gadolinium ethyl sulphate has C_{3h} symmetry. There is a possibility that it is C_{3v} but this is not yet substantiated. These measurements do not help to resolve the large discrepancy between the measured and calculated values of the $\pm 3/2 \leftrightarrow \pm 1/2$ transition in zero magnetic field observed by Bleaney, Scovil and Trenam [1].

REFERENCES

[1] B. BLEANEY, H. E. D. SCOVIL AND R. S. TRENAM, *Proc. Roy. Soc.* **A223**, 15 (1954).

[2] H. A. BUCKMASTER, *Can. J. Phys.* **34**, 150, 341 (1956).

[3] R. J. ELLIOT AND K. W. H. STEVENS, *Proc. Roy. Soc.* **A219** 387 (1953).

[4] K. W. H. STEVENS, *Proc. Phys. Soc.* **A65**, 209 (1952).

[5] B. R. JUDD, *Proc. Roy. Soc.* **A227**, 552 (1955).

[6] J. M. BAKER, BLEANEY, B., AND HAYES, W., *Proc. Roy. Soc.* **A247**, 141 (1958).

[7] D. A. JONES, J. M. BAKER, AND D. F. D. POPE, *Proc. Phys. Soc.* **74**, 249 (1959).

[8] J. M. BAKER AND F. I. B. WILLIAMS, *Proc. Phys. Soc.* **78**, 1340 (1961).

[9] R. ORBACH, *Proc. Roy. Soc.* **A264**, 458 (1961).

[10] H. A. BUCKMASTER, In preparation (1962).

[11] E. O. SCHULZ-DU BOIS, *Bell System Tech. J.* **38**, 271 (1959).

[12] EDMONDS, A. R., *Angular Momentum in Quantum Mechanics*, Princeton University Press, Princeton, N.J (1957).

[13] E. JAHNKE AND F. EMDE, *Tables of Functions with Formulae and Curves*, Dover Publications, New York (1945).

Paramagnetic Resonance of Gd^{3+} in Garnet Crystals and its Relation to the Anisotropy of GdIG

J. Overmeyer, E. A. Giess, M. J. Freiser and B. A. Calhoun

International Business Machines Corporation
Thomas J. Watson Research Center, Yorktown Heights, New York

ABSTRACT

The resonance spectra of Gd^{3+} have been examined at 36 kMc in flux-grown crystals of yttrium gallium garnet, lutecium gallium garnet and lutecium aluminum garnet. The spectra, which are similar in all three crystals, reveal the presence of six differently oriented rare sites per earth unit cell. The angular variation of the spectra are described by nine splitting parameters appropriate for the orthorhombic (222) symmetry of the rare earth sites in the garnet lattice. One of the symmetry axes of each site is parallel to a cube edge and the other two are parallel to the perpendicular [110] directions. The anisotropy contribution of Gd in gadolinium iron garnet is due to two effects: (1) the angular variation of the energy levels, determined by the appropriate b_n^m's and (2) dipolar interactions which are unusually important because of the large Gd moment and the weak exchange field. Both contributions have been calculated. The small discrepancy between the calculated and the experimentally observed anisotropy can reasonably be attributed to the difference between the crystal field in the iron garnet and the fields in the diamagnetic garnets used for the calculations.

There has recently been much interest in the effects of crystalline electric fields on the magnetic properties of ferrites, garnets and other ionic compounds. The case of Gd^{3+} in garnets is especially significant because the magnetic behavior of the Gd^{3+} is described unusually well by a "single ion" theory. The dependence of its magnetic moment in gadolinium iron garnet (GdIG) on temperature and applied magnetic field can be described quite accurately by a simple molecular field treatment [1]. The iron–gadolinium exchange interaction magnetizes the gadolinium ions but is sufficiently weak compared to the iron–iron exchange interactions that the "back reaction" on the iron magnetization is negligible. The gadolinium-gadolinium exchange is also very weak and can usually be neglected. Thus, the calculation of the anisotropy of gadolinium iron garnet from the crystal field splitting parameters for Gd in non-magnetic garnets should provide a significant test of the theory.

In an earlier study [2], we determined the magnitude and sign of the second degree splitting parameters b_2^0 and b_2^2 of Gd^{3+} in yttrium gallium garnet. The line widths in that crystal were sufficiently large and the second order terms sufficiently large because of the frequency used (24 kMc) that the fourth and sixth degree parameters could not be accurately determined. Since it is these parameters which mainly determine the anisotropy, we have examined the spectra of more dilute concentrations of Gd in several non-magnetic garnet crystals at 36 kMc. Following the analysis of the spectrum to determine the crystal field splitting parameters, we discuss the information these parameters yield about the anisotropy of iron garnets.

Theory of the spectrum

In the interpretation of our results two features of the crystal structure are very important. The local symmetry of a rare earth site determines the appropriate form of the spin-Hamiltonian for the garnet. X-ray studies [3] of the isostructural iron garnets have established the space group as O_h^{10}-$Ia3d$ and showed that the rare earth ions occupy the special positions $24(c)$. For our purposes, the usual crystallographic coordinate system is not very convenient and we transform to a local system. The origin of the new system is at a rare earth site and the axes are the three two-fold axes which are the only symmetry elements at the $24(c)$ positions. Two of these axes are parallel to crystal [110] directions and the third to a [100] direction. There are six different orientations of this local frame relative to the crystal lattice. We call the axis parallel to a cube edge, x, and the axis which is nearly four-fold (as far as the neighboring oxygens are concerned), z. In this local frame, the eight oxygen neighbors of the rare earth ion at the origin have the positions: $x_1 y_1 z_1$; $x_1 \bar{y}_1 \bar{z}_1$; $\bar{x}_1 y_1 \bar{z}_1$; $\bar{x}_1 \bar{y}_1 z_1$; $x_2 y_2 z_2$; $x_2 \bar{y}_2 \bar{z}_2$; $\bar{x}_2 y_2 \bar{z}_2$ and $\bar{x}_2 \bar{y}_2 z_2$. While the oxygen coordinates in YGaG have not been determined yet, they have been measured in both YIG [4] and GdIG [5]. The differences in oxygen coordinates in these two crystals is slight. The coordinates for YIG were found to be $x = -0274$, $y = .0572$, $z = .1492$. Transforming to our local frame, we obtain $x_1 = -.1524$, $y_1 = -.0308$, $z_1 = -.1117$, $x_2 = .0242$, $y_2 = .1557$, $z_2 = .1170$. It is sometimes useful to consider the oxygen neighbors of a rare earth ion as being on the corners of a (badly) distorted cube. The conditions $|x_1| = |y_2| = \sqrt{2}|z_1| = \sqrt{2}|z_2|$; $y_1 = x_2 = 0$ would correspond to the corners of a cube. Our z axis coincides with one edge of the cube, the x and y axes are rotated $45°$ from the cube edges.

The spin-Hamiltonian for a Gd^{3+} ion in a site with orthorhombic symmetry is [6]

$$\mathscr{H} = g\beta \mathbf{H} \cdot \mathbf{S} + B_2^0 O_2^0 + B_2^2 O_2^2 + B_4^0 O_4^0 + B_4^2 O_4^2$$
$$+ B_4^4 O_4^4 + B_6^0 O_6^0 + B_6^2 O_6^2 + B_6^4 O_6^4 + B_6^6 O_6^6 \qquad (1)$$

where the O_n^m's are the usual spin operators, expressed in terms of the components of S along the local symmetry axes, x, y, z. To determine the nine B_n^m parameters in Eq. (1), we must measure the spectra for four orientations of H relative to the local axes. The most convenient orientations of H are: (1) parallel to z, (2) parallel to y, (3) in the x–z plane at $54°\,44'$ from x, and (4) in the x–y plane at $54°\,44'$ from x. For the perturbation calculation, it is desirable to keep the term $g\beta H \cdot S$ diagonal. Thus we select new coordinates $X\,Y\,Z$ for each of the orientations 2 to 4 so that H is parallel to Z. For convenience, we also introduce a new set of parameters

$$b_2^0 = 3B_2^0, \quad b_2^1 = B_2^1, \quad b_2^2 = B_2^2$$

$$b_4^0 = 60B_4^0, \quad b_4^1 = 6B_4^1, \quad b_4^2 = 6B_4^2, \quad b_4^3 = 6B_4^3, \quad b_4^4 = 12B_4^4$$

$$b_6^0 = 1260B_6^0, \quad b_6^2 = 60B_6^2, \quad b_6^4 = 60B_6^4, \quad b_6^6 = 360B_6^6.$$

Then, in the ith frame $X\,Y\,Z$, Eq. (1) becomes

$$
\begin{aligned}
\mathscr{H} = \; & g\beta H S_{zi} + b_{2i}^0 O_2^0 + b_{2i}^1 O_2^1 + b_{2i}^2 O_2^2 \\
& + b_{4i}^0 O_4^0 + b_{4i}^1 O_4^1 + b_{4i}^2 O_4^2 + b_{4i}^3 O_4^3 \\
& + b_{4i}^4 O_4^4 + b_{6i}^0 O_6^0 \; . \;.
\end{aligned}
\tag{2}
$$

The transformations of the operators and the relations between the b_l^m 's in different coordinate systems are discussed in the Appendix.

The formulas for the fields for resonance are cumbersome and the general form is well known. Two points only should be noted. The diagonal parts of the crystal field, i.e., b_2^0 etc., should be included in the unperturbed energies [7]. It is very important to carry the perturbation to second order in the b_4's because some cross-terms of the form $b_2 b_4$ enter with large coefficients.

Experimental

The crystals, of nominal compositions $Gd_{.002}Y_{2.998}Ga_5O_{12}$, $Gd_{.002}Lu_{2.998}Ga_5O_{12}$ and $Gd_{.002}Lu_{2.998}Al_5O_{12}$, were grown from a lead oxide-fluoride flux [8]. Small crystals were selected and mounted on a quartz post so that a [110] direction was parallel to the axis of a cylindrical cavity which resonated at approximately 36 kMc in the TE 013 mode. The resonant frequency of the cavity was measured using the fourth harmonic of an X-band klystron. The fundamental of this X-band klystron was measured with a transfer oscillator and electronic counter. The spectrometer consisted of a conventional magic tee bridge with the klystron stabilized on the experimental cavity. Magnetic field modulation at 210 cps was used to record the derivatives of the absorption lines. The magnetic fields were measured with a rotating coil gauss meter which was calibrated, in situ, using a Li^7 nmr probe.

The spectrum in the [111] direction, Figure 1, consists of two superposed spectra in which the intensities vary approximately as expected. The spectrum in the [110] direction consists of two axial spectra and a third, incompletely resolved spectrum which is closely bunched around the $\pm 1/2$

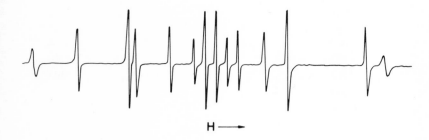

Figure 1

The spectrum of Gd^{3+} in the [111] direction in YGaG. The relative amplitude of the central six lines was reduced by a factor of 3. The abscissa is magnet current, not field, so that the elongation of the high current end of the spectrum is due to the non-linearity of the magnet.

transitions. This spectrum is due to those ions in which H makes oblique angles with the local symmetry axes. One of the two axial spectra consists of seven nearly equally spaced lines and can be approximately represented by only a b_2^0 term. The other axial spectrum shows the influence of an appreciable b_4^0 term, since the 7/2, 5/2 transitions occur closer to the $+1/2$, $-1/2$ transition than do the 5/2, 3/2 transitions. We identify this spectrum with the z axis. The identification of the [111] spectra was made from plots of field for resonance at intermediate angles.

The absolute sign of the b's was determined from the temperature dependence of the intensities [2]. Line width measurements were made only on those lines of the [110] spectra of YGaG due to H parallel to y and z axes. At 36 kMc and room temperature, the width between derivative peaks varied from 5.5 g for $+1/2$, $-1/2$ transitions to 22 g for $\pm 7/2$, $\pm 5/2$ transitions. At 9.4 kMc, room temperature line widths varied from 5 to 16 g. Measurements at 77° and 4.2°K at 9 kMc indicated that the line width was independent of temperature. These results indicate that the observed broadening is due to various residual effects [9] such as variations in the crystal field parameters.

The parameters are listed in Table I.

TABLE I

The splitting parameters of Gd^{3+} in non-magnetic garnets and the calculated anisotropy contributions of Gd^{3+} in GdIG.

	YGaG $T = 300°K$	LuGaG $T = 300°K$	LuGaG $T = 4.2°K$	LuAlG $T = 300°K$
g	1.991	1.99	1.99	1.989
b_2^0	+ 440.7	+ 275	+ 279	+ 571.5
b_2^2	+ 216.1	+ 228	+ 238	+ 112.4
b_4^0	−43.2	−44.9	−47.3	−50.2
b_4^2	+ 0.3			
b_4^4	+ 36.1	+ 39.2	+ 43.3	+ 40.4
b_6^0	+ 0.3			
b_6^2	+ 0.04			
b_6^4	−0.7			
b_6^6	+ 3.9			
$\Delta K'$	−611	−658	−715	−699
$\Delta K''$	−23	−20	−21	−25
ΔK_{Gd}	−778	−822	−880	−868

Anisotropy of gadolinium iron garnet

In gadolinium iron garnet, the Gd ions are subject to exchange interactions as well as a crystal field. The exchange interactions can be treated as an effective field which has a value of approximately 2.5×10^5 oersteds [1; 10]. Thus the behavior of the Gd ions in GdIG should be described by the spin-Hamiltonian, Eq. (1). The calculation of the anisotropy of ferrites and garnets, from this model, has been described by Wolf [11] and by Yosida and Tachiki [12].

We restrict our interest to the value of the anisotropy constant K_1 at very low temperature so that we need to consider only the lowest energy level of the Gd ions. For this level, the terms which depend on the fourth power of the direction cosines of the exchange field (magnetization) are

$$7b_4^{0'} - \frac{63}{4} \frac{(b_2^{1'})^2}{g\beta H_{ex}} - \frac{21}{3} \frac{(b_2^{2'})^2}{g\beta H_{ex}} \tag{3}$$

The contribution to K_1 from each ion will be given by three times the difference in this energy for the field in the crystal [111] and [100] directions, i.e.,

$$\Delta K_1 \text{ per ion} = (3/6) \sum_{\text{sites}} (E_{111} - E_{100}). \tag{4}$$

The appropriate expressions for the b''s are readily obtained, following the method in the Appendix. Substituting these expressions, we obtain, for the first order contribution,

$$\Delta K' \text{ per ion} = \frac{35}{24} \left(\frac{7}{2} b_4^0 + 13\, b_4^2 - \frac{15}{2} b_4^4 \right) \tag{5}$$

and, for the second order contribution

$$\Delta K'' \text{per ion} = - \frac{21}{g\beta\, H_{ex}} \left((b_2^0)^2 - 2b_2^0 b_2^2 + 5(b_2^2)^2 \right)$$

$$- \frac{21}{48g\beta H_{ex}} \left((b_2^0)^2 + 10b_2^0 b_2^2 - 7(b_2^2)^2 \right) \tag{6}$$

The values of $\Delta K'$ and $\Delta K''$ for each garnet are given in Table I.

We now consider the dipolar contribution to the anisotropy. Because of the over-all cubic symmetry of the garnet structure, dipole-dipole interactions of the Gd with other magnetic ions will contribute to the anisotropy only in second order, i.e., in terms of the form $(\mu_{Gd} H_{dipole})^2 / g\beta H_{ex}$. The relatively large magnetic moments of the iron and gadolinium ions and the small exchange field combine to yield an appreciable dipolar contribution to the anisotropy. Yosida and Tachiki [12] have made similar calculations for ferrites. In GdIG, the dominant contribution to the dipolar anisotropy comes from the interactions between the Gd ions and the iron sublattices. This contribution is opposite in sign to and about twice the magnitude of the sum of the contributions arising from the Gd-Gd interactions and the cross terms between the Gd-Gd and Gd-Fe interactions. The resulting dipolar anisotropy is, with $H_{ex} = 2.5 \times 10^5$ oe,

$$\Delta K_d = -3.54 \times 10^4 \text{ ergs/cc.}$$

The lattice sums involved in this calculation were carried out within a sphere of radius 4 unit cell edges and included about 17,000 neighbors. The lattice sums were also calculated for spheres of radii 3.0, 3.98 and 3.99 cell edges. The variations of ΔK_d were less than one per cent.

Discussion

The contribution of the Gd^{3+} ions to the anisotropy of GdIG can be determined by subtracting the anisotropy of YIG from that of GdIG. Resonance measurements by Roderique et al. [13] and torque measurements by Pearson [14] both yield

$$\Delta K_1 = -2.2 \times 10^5 \text{ergs/cc} = -910 \times 10^{-4} \text{cm}^{-1} \text{ per ion.}$$

Calculated values of ΔK_1 range from $-740 \times 10^{-4} \text{cm}^{-1}$ to -900×10^{-4} cm^{-1} depending on the parameters used. This good agreement both provides confirmation of the correctness of the theory [11; 12] and indicates that all the mechanisms responsible for anisotropic behavior of the Gd ions have been included.

Wolf [11] considered the temperature dependence of the anisotropy and found different results for the terms $\Delta K_1'$ and $\Delta K_1''$. Roderique et al. [13] tried to obtain values for these individual contributions from the observed temperature dependence of the Gd anisotropy. There is no agreement between their values and ours, probably for two reasons. Over much of the applicable temperature range, the calculated temperature dependences of the two terms are quite similar. Also, the temperature dependence of the dipolar anisotropy will be somewhat different from either of these functions.

Rimai and de Mars [15] have recently reported EPR measurements of Gd^{3+} in YGaG and YAlG. Aside from trivial differences due to choices of coordinates and proportionality constants, their values for b_2^2 and b_4^4 for YGdG are approximately 20% larger than ours. The most likely explanation for this difference is that they didn't include the fourth degree terms in the second order perturbation calculation. As we noted above, these terms should be kept because the cross-terms ($b_2^m b_4^m$) enter the calculation with large coefficients. Rimai and de Mars also calculated the anisotropy but there are errors in their relation between anisotropy and splitting parameters, so their calculated anisotropies and the apparent agreement with Roderique are meaningless. Their results on YAlG, which we have not measured, indicate that it is similar to the others.

Finally it is of interest to consider the relation between the fourth degree splitting parameters and the crystal field. The nearest neighboring oxygens can be described as being at the corners of a (badly) distorted cube with its edges rotated by 45° about the local z axis. Thus the "cubic" splitting parameter for Gd in the garnets is negative. It has the same sign as the cubic term in the electrostatic potential at the Gd site. In CaF_2, the Gd ion has a similar environment (eight anions at the corners of a cube) but the splitting parameter is positive [16].

Acknowledgments

We wish to thank J. W. Mitchell for his valuable help with the experimental measurements.

Appendix

The transformation of the crystal field operators

The transformation of the spin operators for the crystal field energy under a rotation of the coordinate system is facilitated by the fact that these operators are linear combinations of the components of spherical tensors. Thus, so far as the transformation laws are concerned, it makes no difference whether one transforms a classical potential function or its operator equivalent. Suppose, for example, that we have a spin operator

$$V(S) = \sum_{l,m} c_{lm} Y_l^m(S) \tag{A.1}$$

where $Y_l^m(S)$ is the operator equivalent of the function $r^l Y_l^m(r)$, with S_x S_y, S_z being the spin components along the local symmetry axes of the ion in question. We wish to transform to a new frame of reference and express the operator in Eq. (A.1) as a function of the components of spin along the new axes, $S_{x'}$, $S_{y'}$, $S_{z'}$,

Instead of Eq. (A.1) we consider the potential function

$$V(r) = \sum_{l,m} c_{lm} r^l Y_l^m(r) \tag{A.2}$$

In the new frame of reference the potential becomes [17]

$$\begin{aligned} V'(r') &= \sum_{l,m} c_{lm} r^l \sum_{m'} Y_l^{m'}(r') D_{mm'}^{(l)*}(\alpha, \beta, \gamma) \\ &= \sum_{l,m'} \left[\sum_m c_{lm} D_{mm'}^{(l)*}(\alpha, \beta, \gamma) \right] r^l Y_l^{m'}(r') \end{aligned} \tag{A.3}$$

where α, β, γ are the Euler angles as defined by Rose, [17] for carrying the original frame into the new frame of reference. If the spin operator in the new frame is written as

$$V'(S') = \sum_{l,m'} c'_{lm'} Y_l^{m'}(S') \tag{A.4}$$

then from Eq. (A.3) we obtain

$$c'_{l,m'} = \sum_m c_{lm} D_{mm'}^{(l)*}(\alpha, \beta, \gamma) \tag{A.5}$$

Eq. (A.5) is the transformation law for the coefficients of the crystal field operator. For the lower order terms it may be more convenient to make a direct coordinate substitution in Eq. (A.2) than the calculate the $D_{mm'}^{(l)}$. The significant fact is that one works with classical functions and not with the non-commuting spin operators.

One interesting point concerns the diagonal matrix elements of $V'(S')$. These diagonal elements are given by the term with $m' = 0$. However

$$D_{m0}^{(l)}(\alpha, \beta, \gamma) = \left(\frac{4\pi}{2l+1}\right)^{1/2} Y_l^{m*}(\beta, \alpha) \qquad (A.6)$$

and so

$$c'_{l0} = \left(\frac{4\pi}{2l+1}\right)^{1/2} \sum_m c_{lm} Y_l^m(\beta, \alpha), \qquad (A.7)$$

Thus the coefficient of the lth order diagonal elements of the crystal field operator in the rotated frame is proportional to the lth order part of the potential, Eq. (A.2), with argument given by the polar and azimuthal angles (β and α respectively) of the new z axis in the original frame.

As an example of the application of this method, suppose that we wish to find the energy levels of Gd^{3+} with a magnetic field applied at an arbitrary direction in the local $x-z$ plane. We choose the Euler angles $\alpha = 0$, $\beta = $ angle between H and the local z axis, and $\gamma = 0$. The values of $D^{(l)}$ (α, β, γ) for substitution into Eq. (A.5) can be calculated [17] straightforwardly. It must be remembered, in using this equation, that the b_l^m's which we now wish to transform, differ from the c_{lm}'s by factors which depend on both l and m. After a substantial amount of algebraic manipulation, one obtains

$$b_2^{0'} = \frac{1}{2}(3\cos^2\beta - 1)\,b_2^0 + \frac{3}{2}\sin^2\beta\,b_2^2$$

$$b_2^{1'} = -\sin 2\beta\,b_2^0 + \sin 2\beta\,b_2^2$$

$$b_2^{2'} = \frac{1}{2}\sin^2\beta\,b_2^0 + \frac{1}{2}(\cos^2\beta + 1)\,b_2^2$$

$$b_4^{0'} = \frac{1}{8}(35\cos^4\beta - 30\cos^2\beta + 3)\,b_4^0$$
$$+ \frac{5}{4}\sin^2\beta(7\cos^2\beta - 1)\,b_4^2 + \frac{5}{8}\sin^4\beta\,b_4^4$$

$$b_4^{1'} = \frac{1}{4}\sin 2\beta(3 - 7\cos^2\beta)\,b_4^0 + \frac{1}{2}\sin 2\beta$$
$$(7\cos^2\beta - 4)\,b_4^2 + \frac{1}{4}\sin 2\beta\sin^2\beta\,b_4^4$$

$$b_4^{2'} = \frac{1}{4}\sin^2\beta(7\cos^2\beta - 1)\,b_4^0 + (\cos^4\beta + \frac{1}{2}\sin^4\beta$$
$$- 2\cos^2\beta\sin^2\beta)\,b_4^2 + \frac{1}{4}\sin^2\beta(\cos^2\beta - 1)\,b_4^4$$

$$b_4^{3'} = -\frac{7}{4}\sin 2\beta \sin^2\beta \, b_4^0 - \frac{7}{2}\sin 2\beta \cos^2\beta \, b_4^2$$

$$+ \frac{1}{4}\sin 2\beta (\cos^2\beta + 3) \, b_4^4$$

$$b_4^{4'} = \frac{7}{8}\sin^4\beta \, b_4^0 + \frac{7}{4}\sin^2\beta (\cos^2\beta + 1) \, b_4^2$$

$$+ (\cos^4\beta + \cos^2\beta \sin^2\beta + \frac{1}{8}\sin^4\beta) \, b_4^4.$$

These expressions can then be substituted into Eq. (2) in order to obtain the energy levels.

REFERENCES

[1]   R. PAUTHENET, Thesis, University of Grenoble (1958).
[2]   B. A. CALHOUN, J. OVERMEYER AND M. J. FREISER, *Bull. A.P.S.* **4**, 416 (1959).
[3]   F. BERTAUT AND G. FORRAT, *Compt. rend.* **242**, 382 (1956); S. GELLER AND M. A. GILLEO, *Acta Cryst.* **10**, 239 (1957).
[4]   S. GELLER AND M. A. GILLEO, *J. Phys. Chem. Solids* **3**, 30 (1957).
[5]   J. E. WEIDENBORNER, *Acta Cryst.* **14**, 1051 (1961).
[6]   D. A. JONES, J. M. BAKER AND D. F. D. POPE, *Proc. Phys. Soc.* (*London*) **74**, 249 (1959).
[7]   S. GESCHWIND AND J. P. REMEIKA, *Phys. Rev.* **122**, 757 (1961).
[8]   J. W. NIELSEN AND E. F. DEARBORN, *J. Phys. Chem. Solids* **5**, 202 (1958).
[9]   W. LOW, *Paramagnetic Resonance in Solids*, Academic Press, Inc., New York, 1960 p. 159-60.
[10] V. L. MORUZZI, Thesis, Syracuse University (1962).
[11] W. P. WOLF, *Phys. Rev.* **108**, 1152 (1957).
[12] K. YOSIDA AND M. TACHIKI, *Prog. Theor. Phys.* **17**, 331 (1957).
[13] G. P. RODERIQUE, H. MEYER AND R. V. JONES, *J. Appl. Phys.* **31**, 376S (1960).
[14] R. F. PEARSON, *J. Appl. Phys.* **33**, 1236 (1962).
[15] L. RIMAI AND G. A. DEMARS, *J. Appl. Phys.* **33**, 1254 (1962).
[16] W. LOW, *Phys. Rev.* **109**, 265 (1958).
[17] M. E. ROSE, *Elementary Theory of Angular Momentum*, Chapter IV, John Wiley and Sons, Inc., New York, 1957.

ESR SPECTRA OF RARE EARTH AND URANIUM ELEMENTS

B. Theoretical aspects of ESR in rare earth ions

Energy Levels of and Energy Transfer in Rare Earth Salts*

G. H. DIEKE

The Johns Hopkins University, Baltimore, Maryland

ABSTRACT

Very detailed empirical energy level diagrams of rare earth ions in crystals can be obtained from the analysis of the absorption and fluorescence spectra of these ions. These levels are often essential for a proper interpretation of the paramagnetic resonance data. For the analysis of the energy diagram, theoretical calculations of the free ion energies of the Stark splittings are required which have now been made for all rare earths. The electrostatic crystal field model appears to give a satisfactory account of the splittings. Discrepancies between calculated and observed Stark components can mostly be attributed to inadequacies of the free ion wavefunctions. The breakdown of the electrostatic model accounts for the width of the lines, the appearance of supernumerary lines and relaxation times. The latter can be studied qualitatively through the analysis of the fluorescence spectra with monochromatic excitation. Different lattices behave very differently. For Er^{3+} the ion interacts least with the $LaCl_3$ lattice, most with the hydrated salts, and the garnets and oxides in between.

1. Introduction

During the past few years a basic understanding has been reached on the structure of the spectra of the rare earth ions in crystal lattices. This has been brought about by a combination of experimental and theoretical efforts. The former have consisted in obtaining accurate and complete data on the absorption and fluorescence spectra of the rare earth ions in a number of different crystal lattices which provide the energy levels with high accuracy. Zeeman effect data have greatly contributed to the understanding of the nature of the states, and paramagnetic resonance data have had an important part among these, because of their high accuracy even though they are, in general, restricted to the ground state of the ion.

For the interpretation of the experimental data two fundamental steps are necessary. In the first place it is necessary to know the energy levels of the various $4f^3$ configurations of the free ions. For this two ways are open. One might say that the most direct and logical approach would be to obtain the empirical energy levels from the emission spectra of these ions. This has been undertaken at Johns Hopkins University [1] but because of the complexity of the spectra, the large number of lines involved,

---

* Work carried out with partial support of U.S. Atomic Energy Commission.

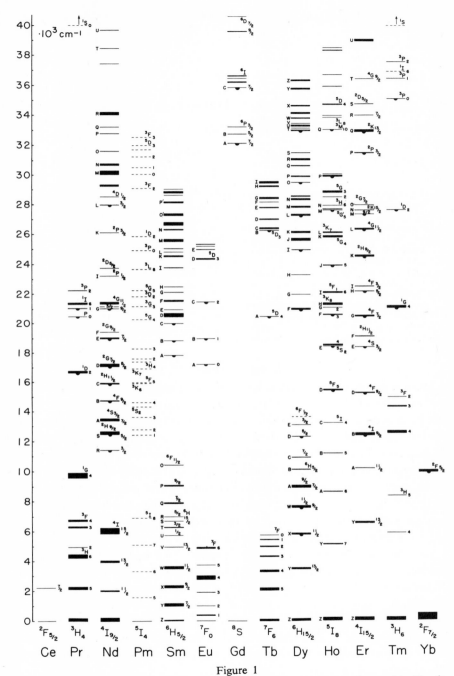

Figure 1

The low lying energy levels of the trivalent rare earth ions. Shown are the empirical levels and their classification where known. The diagram is complete up to about 25000 cm⁻¹ for all ions, up to the energies shown for most others. The width of a level gives the total Stark splitting in $LaCl_3$. The pendant semicircles indicate stable levels from which fluorescence is observed in $LaCl_3$.

and the fact that most of the strength of the fourth rare earth spectra lies in the vacuum ultraviolet, progress is necessarily slow. In the absence of the empirical energy levels it is necessary to rely on calculated levels. Even though such calculations can give only approximate values, they have been amazingly successful. Such calculations first initiated systematically by Elliott, Judd and Runciman [2] after more restricted calculations by others with the Russell Saunders coupling approximation and then carried out for more general coupling schemes by a number of investigators are now available for all trivalent ions. They not only give approximate values of the energies but also give the wavefunctions which are necessary for the crystal field calculations and cannot be obtained in any other way.

In comparing the empirical levels with the calculated ones in general a clear correlation can be found for the lower levels of all the rare earths so that their interpretation can now be regarded as firmly established. The present status is summarized in Figure 1 while Figures 2–4 give some typical examples of the actual spectra from which the data are extracted. For these comparisons the nature of the crystal field is of little importance, except for the fact that often the important low lying levels cannot be obtained for some crystals that show no fluorescence.

The next step is the evaluation of the influence of the crystal field. For this the wavefunctions of the free ion are necessary. The calculations are made in first order with the assumption that the electric field acting on the

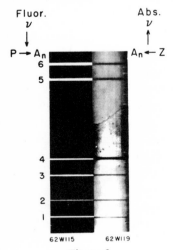

Figure 2

The $^4I_{11/2}$(A) group of Er^{3+} in Y_2O_3, right in absorption near 9800Å, left in fluorescence from the P level near 4740Å. Note that all six expected Stark components are present and no spurious lines occur.

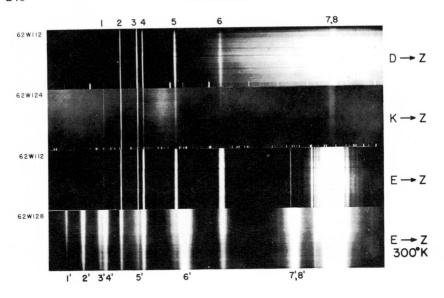

Figure 3

Fluorescence to the ground state of Er^{3+} in Y_2O_3 from three excited levels providing the structure of the ground state. D—Z near 6600Å, K—Z near 4100Å, and E—Z near 5480Å. The upper three spectra are at 4°K. The lower one at room temperature shows also fluorescence from the second component of E 87 cm^{-1} above the first which is in thermal equilibrium with it. The extra lines at the right of the E—Z group belong to the K—Y transition.

ion is a purely electrostatic field with the symmetry of the crystal site. The calculations are simplest for lattices with high symmetry. Pure rare-earth salts of cubic symmetry are unfortunately not available. The hexagonal anhydrous chlorides and the ethyl sulfates furnish the best examples and a number of successful calculations have been made which give a reasonable agreement between calculated and observed crystal field splittings. It is the author's belief, based on some empirical evidence, that the major cause for the discrepancies that remain lies in the inadequacies of the free ion wavefunctions rather than in major shortcomings of the electrostatic field model.

The results obtained with the electrostatic field model can, of course, represent only an approximation, and a rather crude approximation at that. The results that have been obtained with this model form, however, an absolutely necessary foundation for further progress as they have brought order into what seemed chaos only a few years ago. We shall now discuss a few items where the electrostatic model is no longer adequate.

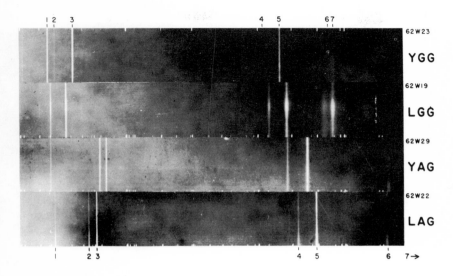

Figure 4

The Stark components of the $^4I_{13/2}(Y)$ state of Er^{3+} in four related garnets obtained from fluorescence.

2. Position of the centers of the Stark patterns

The crystal field calculations have been usually carried out for expediency in the approximation that only interactions between the magnetic components of one free ion level are taken into consideration. In this approximation the positions of the centers of the Stark patterns are independent of the crystal field and coincide with the free ion levels. The restriction to this approximation is due to no fundamental difficulties but simply makes the computations less laborious. The interaction of different free ion levels through the crystal field, often called J-mixing, has been taken into consideration in several cases, perhaps most thoroughly for the two lowest multiplets [3] of Sm^{3+} and Dy^{3+}. Shifts of the order of 10 cm^{-1}, going up to 40 cm^{-1} when interacting levels are close together, have been found in the LaCl$_3$ lattice.

One way of analyzing the extent to which the electrostatic model can account for the properties of the crystal levels is to compare the same ion in many different lattices. Er^{3+} is very suitable for this as its level structure is well understood and many different levels are available which are quite distinct. Figure 5 shows the level structure. Table I gives the centers of the various Stark groups for a number of different lattices. Only those

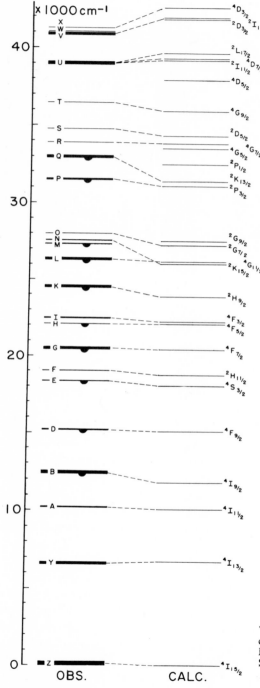

Figure 5

The observed and calculated levels of Er^{3+} in $LaCl_3$. Same remarks as for Figure 1.

are given where all Stark components are empirically known with a reasonable degree of certainty. In the absence of J-mixing the differences between any two levels in Table I should be independent of the lattice.

We see easily from Table I that this is not the case and that there are discrepancies of more than 200 cm^{-1} (compare e.g. E–A for LaCl$_3$ (8179) and YCl$_3$. 6H$_2$O (7935)). Even lattices with similar structure have considerable differences.

Although, in order to come to a clear decision whether the discrepancies cannot be due to simple J-mixing in the electrostatic model, the calculations would have to be carried through in detail which would be quite difficult for the lattices with relatively low symmetry, comparison with those cases that have been carried out indicates that the discrepancies are too large.

While the data in Table I support the approximate nature of the electrostatic model they indicate at the same time that forces act on the ion which cannot be accounted for by the simple electrostatic forces [4]. It is premature to attribute the non-electrostatic forces to a particular one of the possible models.

3. Interactions with the crystal lattice

The electrostatic field model when properly handled may yield the position of energy levels with good approximation but will of course not be able to give an account of many other important features.

In perfect crystals the lines should be almost ideally sharp. The relaxation time of all the levels should be determined by the radiation life times, which is of the order of several milliseconds. Fluorescence should be observed from every excited level.

We know that what is observed in actual crystals is usually quite different, often radically so. The reason for the departures from the electrostatic model are mainly the interactions of neighboring ions which often manifest themselves as a coupling between the ion and the lattice which sometimes is expressed as electron-phonon interaction.

The theory of these interactions which is based on the ordinary electrostatic and magnetic forces between the charged particles in a crystal has made some notable progress in recent years [5]. Another approach is to study experimentally the interactions in the crystal which manifest themselves by line broadening, line shifts, extra lines, shortened relaxation times and other phenomena. One particularly direct method is through the study of the appearance of fluorescence with monochromatic excitation.

The details of the method have been perfected by F. Varsanyi at Johns

TABLE I

Centers of observed Stark patterns for Er^{3+} in various lattices

		$LaCl_3$	$LaBr_3$	YCl_3	YGG	LGG	YAG	LAG	Y_2O_3	WO_3	$ErCl_3 \cdot 6H_2O$	$Er_2(SO_4)_3 \cdot 8H_2O$	$Er(NO_3)_3 \cdot 6H_2O$
Z	$^4I_{15/2}$	108.04			254.73	270.51			206.65	114.46			
Y	$^4I_{13/2}$	6589.61	564.38	593.71	721.08	736.14		745.49	663.15				
A	$^4I_{11/2}$	10219.42			344.59	358.86	350.57	360.58	276.39		256.38	236.10	339.49
B	$^4I_{9/2}$	12459.61							489.04		496.44		
D	$^4F_{9/2}$	15283.61						398.23	274.23	398.21	329.36		
E	$^4S_{3/2}$	18398.72	349.99	282.31	432.66	442.27	424.13	429.42	273.94	391.50	431.24		
F	$^2H_{11/2}$	19		103.61		219.50		219.50	133.11		202.92		
G	$^4F_{7/2}$	20							466.73		563.64		
H	$^4F_{5/2}$	22175.66	110.80					253.53	102.04		225.59		
I	$^4F_{3/2}$	22517.38											
K	$^2H_{9/2}$	24502.93							506.68				
L	$^4G_{11/2}$	26350.76							277.41				
P	$^2P_{3/2}$	31492.96											

Hopkins University [6]. Figure 6 gives an illustration. The heavy diagonal lines represent the exciting monochromatic radiation in two orders of the grating. Its wavelength is changed to shorter values as the time proceeds from bottom to top. Each horizontal line represents thus the fluorescence spectrum with the excitation at a particular wavelength which is at the

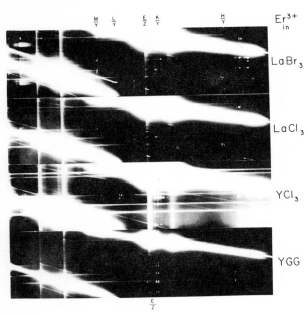

Figure 6
Survey of fluorescence by monochromatic excitation. For explanation see text.

intersection of the horizontal with the excitation diagonal. We see that for Er^{3+} in $LaCl_3$ and $LaBr_3$ most fluorescence groups appear only at very distinct excitation frequencies. This however, depends greatly on the particular ion and on the lattice. We shall restrict ourselves here mainly to Er^{3+} which has been most thoroughly studied. The case of YCl_3 and yttrium gallium garnet (YGG) shows that the same fluorescence group is excited by many different wavelengths. This means much less isolation of the ion from the lattice. Once the information presented by these survey plates has been obtained, further details can be obtained by taking separate spectra at the various excitation frequencies and comparing the resulting fluorescence spectra. Such data are presented in Figure 7 for Er^{3+} in $LaCl_3$. One observes that the fluorescence groups are almost entirely different for each excitation. Some of the transitions are indicated at the top of the figure.

The rest can be inferred from Table III which lists all existing fluorescence groups between 3000 and 12000Å. Almost all of those below 9000Å have actually been observed although their relative intensity naturally depends very much on the method of excitation.

One way to study the energy transfer is to compare one ion in different lattices. Er^{3+} is particularly favorable for this as its energy level scheme is well known and the ion behaves very differently in different lattices. The fluorescence in the following lattices has been examined in some detail. They are arranged so that the lattices in which the Er^{3+} is most isolated comes first and the lattices where it interacts most strongly at the end, with those with intermediate properties in between.

$LaCl_3$, $LaBr_3$, YCl_3, $ErCl_3$, Y_2O_3 $CaWO_4$, 4 garnets: YGG, LGG, YAG, LAG hydrated salts like $ErCl_3 \cdot 6H_2O$, $Er_2(SO_2)_3 \cdot 8H_2O$, etc. CaF_2.

In the first place, as has been known for a long time, Er^{3+} in the hydrated salts is so strongly linked to the lattice that the relaxation times are very short and all the excitation energy is transferred to the lattice. No trace of line fluorescence is observed. This in our experience is also true for CaF_2, although in this case the behavior may very well depend on the manner in which the crystal was grown.

At the other extreme Er^{3+} in $LaCl_3$ shows pronounced fluorescence from the excited states $B, D, E, G, H, K, L, M, P, Q$ (see Figure 5). It will be seen that all these states have an interval of at least 900 cm^{-1} between them and the next lower state (Table II). If one of the states not listed above is excited, fluorescence will in general appear from the stable level below it, indicating that the energy difference is dissipated in the crystal as phonons. For important exceptions see below.

The distance between the stable levels of Er^{3+} in $LaCl_3$ and the crystal level immediately below it is given in Table II.

In $LaCl_3$ and $LaBr_3$ the M level with a clearance of 928 cm^{-1} definitely fluoresces whereas the F level with a clearance of 724 cm^{-1} definitely does not. It is thus evident that between 724 and 928 is the limit of energy that can be transferred to the lattice. This is not intended to imply that there are not other properties of the state which contribute to the coupling to the lattice besides the energy gap. It is evident, however, that the lattice is the predominant factor.

Note: Fluorescence is present from all levels below those indicated but it is not always observed from the B level because it falls in an inconvenient wavelength region. It is absent from the levels above the first one indicated.

TABLE II

Energy interval (ΔE) between levels of Er^{3+} and the level immediately below them and the fluorescence observed from these levels

Levels	ΔE	$LaCl_3$	YCl_3	Y_3O_3	WO_3	Garnets
$F - E$	724	absent				
$M - L$	928	present				
$G - F$	1302	,,				
$Q - P$	1388	,,				
$H - G$	1616	,,	weak			
$L - K$	1728	,,	present	weak		
$K - I$	1971	,,	,,	present	present	very weak
$B - A$	2152	,,				
$D - B$	2704	,,	,,	,,	,,	present
$E - D$	3070	,,	,,	,,	,,	,,
$P - O$	3480	,,	,,	,,	,,	*

* Fluorescence from the P-level is not observed in the garnets, because the excitation region is opaque through iron impurities.

TABLE III

Approximate position of the fluorescence groups of Er^{3+} in $LaCl_3$

Group	λ	ν	Group	λ	ν
$Q-Z$	3039	32900	$H-Y$	6401	15619
$P-Z$	3176	31474	$D-Z$	6555	15252
$M-Z$	3656	27346	$M-B$	6686	14953
$Q-Y$	3792	26367	$Q-E$	6888	14513
$L-Z$	3802	26293	$K-A$	6993	14296
$P-Y$	4025	24836	$L-B$	7178	13927
$K-Z$	4091	24436	$G-Y$	7185	13915
$Q-A$	4406	22692	$P-E$	7638	13088
$H-Z$	4510	22168	$B-Z$	8067	12393
$P-A$	4718	21190	$P-F$	8102	12339
$M-Y$	4804	20812	$M-D$	8231	12146
$Q-B$	4875	20507	$K-B$	8255	12110
$G-Z$	4881	20481	$H-A$	8358	11961
$L-Y$	5058	19765	$E-Y$	8446	11837
$P-B$	5239	19081	$L-D$	8981	11131
$E-Z$	5452	18336	$G-A$	9730	10274
$K-Y$	5574	17937	$A-Z$	9795	10207
$Q-D$	5670	17631	$H-B$	10226	9776
$M-A$	5833	17139	$K-D$	10807	9251
$P-D$	6183	16168	$D-Y$	11462	8722
$L-A$	6205	16112	$E-A$	12223	8179

For other lattices the position is not significantly different.

For Er^{3+} in YCl_3 the limit lies near H which fluoresces very weakly. The greater splitting of the levels shows that the crystal field is stronger, and this somewhat lowers the clearances but we see that what couples the levels to the crystal field is not merely determined by the clearances but by other properties of the lattice. This becomes evident when we consider the hydrated crystals some of which have Stark splittings of the order of those in $LaCl_3$ and nevertheless have no fluorescence whatsoever.

Er^{3+} in Y_2O_3 is a very well studied case. For it fluorescence from the L level occurs very weakly showing that its relaxation time is considerably reduced. Fluorescence from the levels below it in Table II is strong and distinct. $CaWO_3$ behaves similarly except that no fluorescence from L has been found. This is true also for the garnets where emission from K is very weak and entirely absent in some of the garnets.

In the electrostatic model where the lattice is held together by purely electrostatic forces between the ions no energy transfer of any kind can take place between the excited electron and the lattice, as in this approximation the possibility of the lattice to vibrate has been excluded. This model also represents the extreme of polar binding, the ion being considered as rigid immovable spheres. When we introduce some of the real properties of the lattice, coupling between the lattice vibrations and the excited electron becomes inevitable. We might say that this increases as the nature of the bond becomes more covalent and the interaction becomes very large when we have a case like UO_2^{++} where coupling to the molecular vibrations is very pronounced.

When small amounts of energy are to be transferred this is given to the lattice as single or multiple phonons, when more energy is available it is transferred to vibrations of molecular complexes. The more complex the lattice is, the more vibrational frequencies are available. The probability of transfer becomes especially large when there is a close resonance between a pure electronic level and another level which contains one or several quanta of vibration superimposed on the same or another, lower electronic level. There is strong experimental evidence that the relaxation time for a transfer of energies of the order of a few hundred cm^{-1} is extremely short and is the chief cause for the broadening of the higher Stark components observed for practically every electronic level. If the relaxation time becomes of the order of 10^{-8} seconds, the line broadening caused by it will usually be unobservable, but the effect on the quenching of fluorescence from that level will be very large as long as the transfer relaxation times are short compared to the radiation times which ordinarily are of the order of between one and ten milliseconds.

When the energy to be transferred to the lattice becomes too large so that the processes referred to above become too inefficient, the transfer relaxation times become of the order of the radiation time or larger, and we have again a stable state from which fluorescence can be observed. For Er^{3+} in the $LaCl_3$ lattice this limit lies evidently near 800 cm^{-1}. When this limit is passed we observe two things. Fluorescence from this excited state is observable and at the same time fluorescence from the state below it ceases. We saw that for the E state in Er^{3+} the F state (724 cm^{-1} above E) falls below this limit whereas the G state (1300 above F) is above it.

Evidently this limit depends very strongly on the nature of the lattice. For the hydrated erbium salts energy can be probably transferred first to the many vibrational modes of the H_2O complex and from it to the lattice. When this possibility exists the complete gap between any two levels is filled up and energy transfer always takes place so that there are no excited states capable of emitting fluorescence.

There is, however, one additional mechanism of energy transfer [7] which also can be observed very clearly for Er^{3+} in $LaCl_3$. Let us again concentrate on the fluorescence from the E level. It is observed when the E or F levels are excited but not for excitation of G, H or K. However, when L is excited we observe not only strong fluorescence from L but fluorescence from E reappears (see Figure 7). We note that $K_1 - E_2 = 6116$ cm^{-1} but $L - E$ $= 8920$ and $L - F = 7165$. The latter value is not much above the 6644 cm^{-1}, the highest Stark component of the Y state. This has suggested that here an ion pair is involved in the energy transfer. The ion in the L state excites a neighboring ion to the Y state, goes itself to the F state and transfers the remaining energy of 500 cm^{-1} directly to the lattice. The F state immediately changes to the E state with a transfer of 724 cm^{-1} to the lattice.

There is considerable evidence that this two ion process actually takes place. When the M state is excited no fluorescence from E is observed but pronounced E fluorescence is again observed for excitation of P and Q. We have $P - E = 13063$, only 515 above B and $Q - F = 13722$ which appears somewhat too high for effective pair resonance but $Q - G = 12419$ is only 26 cm^{-1} above B and the fluorescence from G is definitely present; and so it is from P excitation as $P - G = 10922$ which is 680 cm^{-1} above A.

There is thus ample evidence that the ion pair resonance is real in Er^{3+}. At the present time this evidence is from purely qualitative experiments based on the appearance or non-appearance of certain fluorescence transition with the monochromatic excitation of a single level. One should of course like to have quantitative data about the probabilities of the various

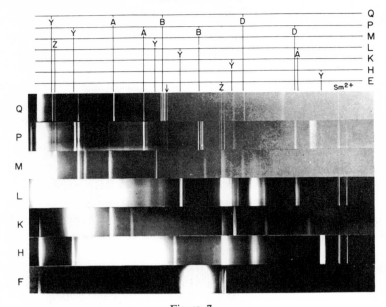

Figure 7

The fluorescence spectrum of Er^{3+} in $LaCl_3$ with monochromatic excitation. The level excited is indicated at the right. The diffuse features are scattered mercury lines.

transitions. This requires much more sophisticated experiments which, however, are well within the realm of present possibilities and have been started. It would not be prudent to draw too detailed conclusions from the present data, which were obtained with a single grating monochromater. Even though it is a very good one, some scattered light of different wavelength cannot be entirely avoided and this will produce spurious excitation.

It should not be forgotten that the results given here apply to Er^{3+} and should not be generalized to other ions without a careful analysis. Data on most other ions are available but less extensive. It is clear that the individual properties of the ions, that is the wavefunctions of the free ions, play an important role. This can be judged qualitatively from the behavior of the hydrated ions, which do not fluoresce at all for the ions at both ends of the rare earth group but fluoresce strongly in the middle (Gd^{3+}) and progressively less strongly as one goes from the middle to either end [8]. At a first glance this seems to be paralleled by the free interval below fluorescing levels which is 32100 cm^{-1} for Gd^{3+}, 14800 for Tb^{3+}, 12300 for Er^{3+}, 7500 for Sm^{3+} and Dy^{3+} whereas free intervals of this size occur rarely or not at all in the other ions. The size of these intervals is undoubtedly a contributing factor to the efficiency of fluorescence, but that it cannot be the whole story is seen from the fact that both the D_0 and D_1 levels of $EuCl_3 \cdot 6H_2O$ fluoresce. D_1 is only 1800 cm^{-1} above D_0 and even with free intervals much larger than this no fluorescence is observed for instance in $ErCl_3 \cdot 6H_2O$.

It is generally observed that when a particular single level is excited, fluorescence is observed also from one or several lower levels. This cascading down of the excitation is, however, very different in degree for different cases. It occurs least when the electrostatic model is most closely approximated as for this model no energy transfer of any kind should occur. Er^{3+} in $LaCl_3$ discussed in detail above is a good example for this, where the fluorescent levels can in most cases be isolated and cascading over a considerable distance seems to occur chiefly through the ion pair resonance process.

The chances for energy transfer to occur by this process are greatest when the low levels of an ion are closely spaced and a look at Figure 1 shows that this is the case in the left half of the rare earth group rather than in the right half. This is probably the explanation for the fact that for Nd^{3+}, for example, the energy cascades down much more freely and it is only rarely found that one particular level is excited only by one narrow wavelength band.

If the ion pair resonance plays a significant part in the energy transfer in a crystal, this should be effective particularly at high concentrations. So far this point has not been examined closely. There are, however, a few observations on the anhydrous chlorides with the absorbing ion in high concentration. $PrCl_3$ has the same crystal structure as $LaCl_3$. It fluoresces strongly and it was shown that an ion pair mechanism plays an important part in the excitation [7]. On the other hand, Nd^{3+} in $LaCl_3$ does not fluoresce at all in concentrations* of about 50%. For the heavier rare earth the pure anhydrous chlorides have a different crystal structure which is isomorphous with that of YCl_3. Pure $ErCl_3$ fluoresces strongly as does pure $TbCl_3$ which has a third and unknown structure. The study of the concentration effect of Er^{3+} in $LaCl_3$ is difficult because the $LaCl_3$ lattice accepts Er only in small concentrations. For higher concentrations we have the YCl_3 structure.

It is evident that even simple experiments can give important information on the energy transfer in crystal lattices, but that much more work must be done before the subject is thoroughly understood. It is equally evident that without complete knowledge of the energy level system at least for the low levels, an interpretation of the observed phenomena would be entirely impossible. The progress that can be reported now is largely due to the

---

* Note. Later experiments have shown that concentrated Nd Cl$_3$ fluoresces.

fact that our knowledge of this energy level system is now very much advanced while only a few years ago such knowledge was very insecure.

The present paper does not pretend to give a general review of the subject which would be impossible in the allotted space. In such a review the work of many other laboratories would require a prominent part. The intention is merely to report some recent contributions made at Johns Hopkins University. These are based on the work of many students and collaborators. For the purpose of this discussion the results of F. Varsanyi and B. Pandey, some of them as yet unpublished, are particularly pertinent.

REFERENCES

[1] G. H. DIEKE, H. M. CROSSWHITE AND B. DUNN, *J. Opt. Soc. Am.* **51**, 820 (1961).
[2] J. P. ELLIOTT, B. R. JUDD AND W. A. RUNCIMAN, *Proc. Roy. Soc.* A240, 509 (1957).
[3] J. AXE AND G. H. DIEKE, in process of publication.
[4] These remarks agree with the conclusions of Wong and Richman (*J. Chem. Phys.* **36**, 1889 (1962)) who compared Pr^{3+} in $LaCl_3$ and $LaBr_3$ and found the shifts in the centers too large to be accounted for by J-mixing. They discuss possible mechanisms for the observed shifts. We have analyzed the same spectrum and find some discrepancies with the results of Wong and Richman.
[5] See e.g. R. ORBACH, *Proc. Roy. Soc.* A264, 458, 485 (1961). A. KIEL, *Dissertation*, Johns Hopkins University, 1962. Report.
[6] F. VARSANYI, *Dissertation*, Johns Hopkins University, 1961,
[7] F. VARSANYI AND G. H. DIEKE, *Phys. Rev. Letters* **7**, 442 (1961).
[8] K. W. HELLWEGE, *Ann. Physik* **40**, 529 (1941). G. H. DIEKE AND L. H. HALL, *J. Chem. Phys.* **27**, 465 (1957).

DISCUSSION

W. Low, Israel: In the crystals of CaF_2 doped with rare earths, which we have investigated, there are hundreds of satellite lines. Are there any explanations of these?

G. H. DIEKE, U. S. A.: We have looked at CaF_2 and were horrified by those lines and, therefore, dropped CaF_2. The situation is better in $CaWO_4$. Probably the satellite lines arise from the fact that when you force trivalent ions where they do not belong, you have charge compensation. The details are still obscure.

W. Low, Israel: The amazing aspect is that the satellite structure is sometimes as sharp as the main line.

G. H. DIEKE, U. S. A.: Yes, that can happen and they may have the same Zeeman effect.

The Validity of Crystal Field Theory as Applied to Rare Earth Ions: An Analysis of the Spectrum of Praseodymium Trichloride

J. C. EISENSTEIN

National Bureau of Standards, Washington, D.C.

ABSTRACT

The spectrum of PrCl$_3$ below 25000 cm^{-1} is analyzed from the point of view of crystal field theory. Coulomb, spin-orbit and crystal field interactions are taken into account. The Coulomb integrals, the spin-orbitcoupling constant and the quantities $A_l^m \langle r^l \rangle$ which characterize the crystal field are treated as parameters. The eigenvalue problem for the f^2 configuration is solved by diagonalization of the complete interaction matrices.

The calculated positions of the enrrgy levels are compared with the experimental results. This comparison indicates the existence of appreciable interaction between the f^2 and higher configurations. Also it appears that no single set of crystal field parameters will give good agreement between calculated and observed levels for all multiplets. This difficulty may also be ascribable to neglect of configuration interaction.

Introduction

Crystal field theory has been a useful part of physics for more than thirty years. However, its many qualitative successes have caused the problem of its quantitative adequacy to be neglected; it is not known just how good an approximation it really is. When the predictions of simple crystal field theory do not quite agree with experimental results it is customary to make additional assumptions such as that covalent bonding occurs; or that small fields of low symmetry are present; or to say that neglected interactions will acount for the discrepancy between theory and experiment. Refinement of the theory requires the introduction of additional adjustable parameters. One usually reaches a situation where the total number of parameters is barely larger than the number of data to be fitted, and the data themselves often have large limits of error. The agreement between theory and experiment may be regarded as satisfactory but one is left wondering what has really been established.

For the purpose of critical appraisal of the simple crystal field theory the transition element and actinide compounds can quickly be eliminated from consideration. The reasons, in both cases, are that covalent effects are important and that there is very appreciable interaction between the ion of interest and its surroundings. The covalent effects can be treated in a phenomenological way at the expense of adding parameters to the theory but the interaction with the surroundings negates the basic premise of crystal field theory; namely, that the ion of interest is in an electrostatic field produced by neighboring ions and molecules.

Consequently, for the critical appraisal, one must use data on rare earth compounds. The easiest compounds to study for which adequate amounts of data exist are praseodymium trichloride and thulium ethyl sulphate. The ground state electron configurations of the lanthanide ions are f^2 for Pr^{3+} and f^{12} for Tm^{3+}. Only $PrCl_3$ will be discussed in this paper.

Spectrum of $PrCl_3$

The spectrum of $PrCl_3$ has been extensively studied, both experimentally and theoretically. Sayre, Sancier and Freed [1] have observed the absorption spectrum. Dieke and Sarup [2] have observed the absorption and the fluorescence spectra. Many of the same energy levels have been found in both absorption and fluorescence and, very nearly, at the same positions. It follows that the action of the Pr^{3+} ion on its surroundings is small; if the interaction were large the fluorescence quanta would not have the same energies as the absorption quanta. The sharpness of the spectral lines also indicates that the interaction of the Pr^{3+} ions with their surroundings is small.

The first detailed theoretical study of $PrCl_3$ was made by Judd [3]. He correctly identified all the levels known at the time his paper was written, and obtained values for the crystal field parameters, the Coulomb integrals and the spin-orbit coupling constant. To determine the crystal field effects Judd resorted to a perturbation calculation. Margolis [4] has recently made a complete calculation of the energy levels in which the Coulomb, spin-orbit and crystal field interactions are simultaneously diagonalized. Independently of Margolis I made a similar calculation.

One interesting result which comes out of these calculations is that it is impossible to put all the multiplets which arise from the f^2 configuration in their observed positions. There are twelve observed multiplets and four adjustable parameters—three Coulomb integrals and the spin-orbit coupling constant. My parameters were chosen so that all the multiplets except $^1I_6$ were in approximately the correct positions. Margolis chose his parameters to minimize the r.m.s. deviation of the centers of gravity of calculated and observed multiplets. By including orbit-orbit interaction in his calculations he was able to reduce this r.m.s. deviation to 105 cm^{-1}. One can argue that if interactions between the f^2 and higher configurations were taken into account the terms would occur in the right places. This argument is unsatisfactory because there is no way to establish its correctness. However, since the existence of configuration interaction is undeniable one must regard the "best" values of the Coulomb integrals and spin-orbit coupling constant as subject to appreciable error.

It is no defect of the crystal field theory that one cannot put the terms in the right positions. Therefore it is reasonable to compare theory and experiment by using the positions of the calculated and observed levels relative to their respective centers of gravity in each term. This procedure has been used by Judd and Margolis and will be used here.

The point symmetry about the Pr^{3+} ion is C_{3h}. In the calculations it has always been assumed that there is D_{3h} symmetry. The difference between the potential functions for C_{3h} and D_{3h} symmetries is an imaginary term which connects the $m_l = \pm 3$ and the $m_l = \mp 3$ states. By calculating the potential for a point charge model one can show that this imaginary term is quite small; it probably does not affect the separations of the levels appreciably.

The potential for D_{3h} symmetry has four adjustable constants. By giving appropriate values to these parameters Margolis was able to reduce the r. m. s. deviation between the experimental and calculated positions of 40 energy levels to 7 cm^{-1}. The parameters I used are not the same as Margolis' but the results are the same; the r.m.s. deviation between my calculated crystal field energy levels and the 35 levels observed by Dieke and Sarup is 7 cm^{-1}.

Although this 7 cm^{-1} seems to indicate that the agreement between theory and experiment is good, it is actually very puzzling that the r. m. s. deviation is so large.

Let us consider first the levels for which the crystal quantum number is 3. These levels have a twofold degeneracy in a purely axial field; this degeneracy is removed by the term in the potential which has sixfold symmetry about the molecular axis:

$$V_6^6 = \{ 32\, A_6^6 r^6\, \Theta_6^6/(6006)^{\frac{1}{2}} \} \{ e^{i6\phi} + e^{-i6\phi} \}.$$

The approximate splitting due to the action of V_6^6 between two states of the same term can easily be calculated, and the exact splitting can be obtained from machine calculations. The results for $A_6^6 \langle r^6 \rangle = 429$ cm^{-1} are as follows:

Separations

Levels	First order cm⁻¹	Exact cm⁻¹	Experimental cm⁻¹
$^3F_4(3)$	26.7	37.5	51.0
$^3F_3(3)$	80.0	67.3	58.4
$^3H_5(3)$	64.0	69.3	67.2

The differences between columns 2 and 3 represent the effects of perturbations which act between terms. Since all the terms except $^1I_6$ (which is 14,000 cm⁻¹ above $^3F_4$) are nearly in their correct positions, changes in these positions cannot substantially affect the contributions to the results of the perturbations which act between terms. It is apparent that no value of $A_6^6\langle r^6\rangle$ exists which will enable one to fit the three separations listed above.

Secondly, let us consider the $^1D_2$ term. Values of the parameters which work moderately well for the other terms are not at all appropriate to $^1D_2$, as one can see from the following table.

$^1D_2$ *level shifts and separations*

| Level | Eisenstein | | | Margolis | |
	First order cm⁻¹	Exact cm⁻¹	Separation cm⁻¹	Exact cm⁻¹	Experiment cm⁻¹
$^1D_2(\pm1)$	147.60	139.55			
			23.58	15.9	48.3
$^1D_2(\pm2)$	123.06	115.97			
			86.21	90.8	100.7
$^1D_2(0)$	25.93	29.76			

One can see from the second and third columns that the effects of perturbations which act between terms are 4 to 8 cm⁻¹. For any reasonable values of these inter-term separations the effects of these perturbations will remain about the same. To bring the calculated and the experimental separations into agreement it is necessary to use values of the crystal field parameters which differ by about 50 % from the values required to minimize the r. m. s. deviation for the totality of the levels.

For the remaining terms the evidence that the crystal field parameters must be adjusted for the individual terms is not as clear cut, but nevertheless exists. The required changes in the parameters from the set which minimizes the r. m. s. deviation are of the order of 20 % or less.

There are several physical effects that might be invoked to account for the apparent variation of the crystal field parameters from term to term. For example, covalent effects might be important. However, these possible covalent effects can be regarded as already included in the theory. Covalency will alter the values of all crystal field matrix elements, but the matrix elements are treated as parameters to be determined from the experimental data.

Secondly, small fields of low symmetry might be present. The observed transitions follow the selection rules for a crystal field of C_{3h} symmetry so one can probably rule out the existence of fields of lower symmetry. In any case, the required additional fields are large, rather than small.

Thirdly, one might argue that the Jahn-Teller theorem requires the existence of some kind of configurational instability. However, there is no spectroscopic evidence for the existence of any Jahn-Teller splitting of the degenerate energy levels of $PrCl_3$.

It seems most likely that the apparent variation of the crystal field parameters from term to term is due to neglect of interactions with higher configurations. It has already been pointed out that configuration interaction is necessary for the correct positioning of the terms. The crystal field, like the Coulomb interaction, has matrix elements between states in different configurations. Because of the large number of possible excited configurations, and lack of knowledge of the matrix elements, it is difficult to estimate the shifts of the levels of the f^2 configuration which will be produced, but an effect surely exists.

Magnetic properties of $PrCl_3$

Dieke and Sarup have measured the Zeeman splitting factors for eight levels. They state that some of their results were obtained from unsatisfactory plates. The experimental results are not in close agreement with the values I calculated from the eigenvectors. In view of the uncertainty about the data the only significant comparison one can make is for the ground state. The ground state $g_\parallel$-value as measured spectroscopically by Dieke and Sarup is 0.96. Hutchison and Wong's[5] microwave resonance experiments yielded 1.03 for $g_\parallel$. My calculated value is about 1.5. The calculated value can be reduced by using a larger value of $A_6^6 \langle r^6 \rangle$ or by assuming some chlorine orbitals are mixed with the Pr^{3+} wave functions. A larger value of $A_6^6 \langle r^6 \rangle$ is not compatible with the spacings of the levels in the ground term, unless other crystal field parameters are also changed. It is possible also that the calculated g-value would be reduced if configuration interaction were taken into account.

The situation is similar for $CeCl_3$ where the calculated $g_\parallel$-value is larger than the measured one. To reduce $g_\parallel$ it is necessary to assume an unreasonably large value for $A_6^6\langle r^6\rangle$, or that there is some mixing of Ce^{3+} and Cl^- orbitals, or that configuration interaction occurs.

Conclusion

The accuracy of both the experiments and the theory seems sufficient fully to justify the conclusion that the crystal field parameters vary from term to term in $PrCl_3$. However the sharpness of the absorption and fluorescence lines strongly indicates that the Pr^{3+} ion is passive in its physical environment, and that the crystal field does not change from term to term. A possible explanation of this apparent dilemma is that the neglected interactions with higher configurations displace the Stark levels by as much as 20 cm^{-1}. It follows that the "best" crystal field parameters (as obtained from a least squares analysis) are not necessarily the correct crystal field parameters. If this explanation is right it also enables one to understand why the "best" parameters for, say, Pr in $LaCl_3$ are not the same as the "best" parameters for Nd in $LaCl_3$.

REFERENCES

[1] E. V. SAYRE, K. M. SANCIER AND S. FREED, *J. Chem. Phys.* **23**, 2060 (1955).
[2] G. H. DIEKE AND R. SARUP, *J. Chem. Phys.* **29**, 741 (1958).
[3] B. R. JUDD, *Proc. Roy. Soc.* (*London*) **A241**, 414 (1957).
[4] J. S. MARGOLIS, *J. Chem. Phys.* **35**, 1367 (1961).
[5] C. A. HUTCHISON JR. AND E. WONG, *J. Chem. Phys.* **29**, 754 (1958).

Discussion

W. MARSHALL, ENGLAND: M. Blume and R. Watson have performed calculations on free ions taking proper account of the contribution to the effective spin orbit coupling parameter coming from electron-electron interactions. They find almost exact agreement with the observed spectra and this is a considerable improvement over the fit possible using a single empirical spin orbit parameter. Probably a similar calculation would remove the discrepancies in your free ion fit but this, of course, may not be important for the crystal field terms you have mainly discussed here.

G. H. DIEKE, U.S.A.: There is strong experimental evidence in other rare earths e. g. Er^{3+} that the discrepancies between observed and calculated crystal field levels must be attributed to inadequacies of the free ion wavefunctions rather than to faults of the electrostatic model. That this cannot be the complete solution of the problem is shown by the large differences in the centers of the stack patterns for the same ion in different lattices (see preceding paper)

J. C. Eisenstein, U.S.A.: In many crystals there are large deviations of the bary centers of a pattern from that calculated from electrostatic parameters. Apparently, configuration interaction is very important.

A. Abragam, France: Is not the real problem with crystalline fields, to understand why this model does work well, when it agrees with experiment, rather than to explain its failure since after all this model is a gross oversimplification of the real Hamiltonian?

Shielding and Crystal Fields at Rare Earth Ions

GERALD BURNS

International Business Machines Corporation, Thomas J. Watson Research Center
Yorktown Heights, New York

Several aspects of the crystal field problem of rare earth ions in ionic solids are discussed. In particular, three problems are considered.

1. A calculation is performed to determine to what extent the $5\,s^2 p^6$ electrons shield the $4f$ electrons from the crystal field. The shielding is small ($< 10\%$) and unimportant compared to the many other uncertainties in crystal field calculations. The calculation was carried out by considering the crystal field, $\sum B_n^m r^n Y_n^m$, as a perturbation on the $5\,s^2$ and $5\,p^6$ state. The excited state wavefunctions are calculated by solving the first perturbed Schrödinger, $(H_0 - E_0)\psi_1 = -(H_1 - E_1)\psi_0$, for ψ_1. The extra potential, $\sum B_n^m Y_n^m F_{n,m}(r)$, due to the distorted charge distribution is compared to crystal potential by taking its expectation value over the $4f$ electrons and comparing it to the relevant $\langle r^n \rangle$ for the $4f$ electrons.

2. The reason as to why the rare earth ions effectively see smaller crystal fields than the iron series ions is considered by performing the lattice sums in several typical lattices so that the B_n^m coefficients could be compared. One observes that the crystal field to spin orbit coupling ratio is considerably larger in the iron series ions than for the rare earth ions for straightforward reasons (the iron series ions have $B_n^m \approx 3$ to 10 times larger, $\langle r^n \rangle \approx 2$ times larger (for positive n) and spin orbit coupling constants $\approx 1/2$ times as large as the rare earth ions). Thus, the difference in behavior between these two groups of ions comes about for straightforward reasons without resorting to shielding.

3. The calculated crystal field parameters, $\langle r^n \rangle B_n^m = V_n^m$, for the rare earth ions are compared with those obtained by fitting optical levels. A discussion of the problems involved in calculating the lattice sums (B_n^m) is given and one can see why detailed agreement is not expected. The calculated V_n^m for $n = 4$ and 6 are reasonable but smaller than those obtained from the optical data. Little can be said for the $n = 2$ terms because of the uncertainties involved in the lattice sums. (A detailed paper has been submitted to the *Physical Review*.)

Crystalline Field Splittings in Cerium Magnesium Nitrate

M. J. Leask
Clarendon Laboratory, Oxford, England

R. Orbach
Division of Engineering and Applied Physics, Harvard University, U.S.A.

M. J. D. Powell
U.K. Atomic Energy Research Establishment, Harwell, England
and
W. P. Wolf
Clarendon Laboratory, Oxford, England

ABSTRACT

An analysis of experimental susceptibility and paramagnetic resonance data on cerium magnesium nitrate has been made, in terms of an ionic $4f^1$ configuration and a crystalline potential of C_{3v} symmetry. The results are qualitatively similar to Judd's earlier analysis on other rare earth double nitrates, but they indicate even larger sixth degree terms. Possible reasons for this apparent trend are discussed.

Introduction

The rare earth double nitrates have for some time been one of the principal series of materials in which the magnetic properties of rare earth ions have been studied, and it therefore seems strange that the one containing the simplest ion of all, Ce^{3+}, has so far been almost neglected from a theoretical point of view. The reason for this lies in the experimental fact that the ionic energy levels are such that spectroscopic data are difficult to obtain and interpret, so that until recently the only data available were paramagnetic resonance g-factors for the Ce^{3+} ion ground state doublet. By themselves these are insufficient to allow the determination of the various parameters contained in the usual crystal field theory, but if they are combined with other data such as susceptibility measurements, it should be possible to fit the theory to the experimental observations. In principle this is an attractively simple problem, since in the usual theory the free Ce^{3+} ion is uniquely specified by the configuration $4f^1$, ^2F, with no possibility of intermediate coupling effects. The only constants to be fitted, therefore, are the parameters characterising the crystal field.

The experiments

To provide the additional data, precise susceptibility measurements were made on single crystals, both parallel and perpendicular to the crystallographic c axis, at temperatures in the range 1.5°–36°K. Since this work was started, similar measurements have also been reported by Hellwege [1], whose results are in essential agreement with ours, though there are some small systematic differences which can be explained.

At the lowest temperatures only one Kramers doublet is populated and the Curie constant $(Ng^2\beta^2/4K)$ in the susceptibility yields a value for the g-factor which may be compared with that obtained from paramagnetic resonance measurements. Table I, which summarises all the available results

TABLE I

Ground satte properties obtained from experiment

$g_\parallel$	$a_\parallel$	$g_\perp$	$a_\perp$	Ref.
≤ 0.05	0.00467	1.832	0.02235	a
—	—	—	0.02237	b
0.032 ± 0.068	—	1.828	—	c
0.025 ± 0.005	—	—	—	d
$0.25 \ \pm 0.05$	—	1.84 ± 0.01	0.024	e
0.07	—	—	—	f
0.025 ± 0.025	0.00467	1.835	0.02235	g

a   This work.
b   R. P. HUDSON AND W. R. HOSLER, *Phys. Rev.* **122**, 1417.
c   H. J. STAPLETON AND T.J. SCHMUGGE, priv. comm. (1962).
d   J. C. WHEATLEY AND T. L. ESTLE, *Phys. Rev.* **104**, 264.
e   A. H. COOKE, H. J. DUFFUS AND W. P. WOLF, *Phil. Mag.* **44**, 623.
f   R. P. HUDSON, R. S. KAESER AND H. E. RADFORD, *Proc. 7th Int. Conf. Low Temp. Physics*, Toronto (1960).
g   Values chosen as input data for our analysis.

for the ground state properties, shows that the agreement between the results of susceptibility and resonance experiments is very good. The factor α is the temperature independent contribution to the susceptibility and is not observable with paramagnetic resonance techniques. All these results have been reduced to one best set (Table I, last line) to be used as input data for theoretical analysis, and since four parameters alone are still insufficient to define the problem, we supplement these with susceptibility measurements

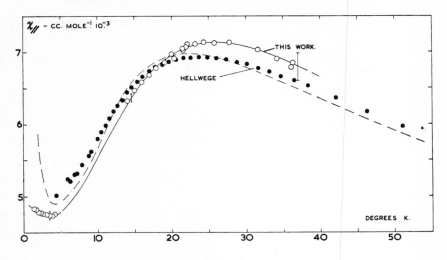

Figure 1

$\chi_\parallel$ against T between 2° and 50°K showing the results of this work and that of Hellwege et al. The solid and dashed lines represent the best computed fit to the respective sets of data.

at higher temperatures where the excited states are becoming populated (see for example, Figure 1, which shows $\chi_\parallel$, between 4° and 36°K).

Theory

From a theoretical standpoint [2], the problem is completely specified by the Hamiltonian

$$\mathscr{H} = A_2^0 \langle r^2 \rangle V_2^0 + A_4^0 \langle r^4 \rangle V_4^0 + A_6^0 \langle r^6 \rangle V_6^0 + A_4^3 \langle r^4 \rangle V_4^3 + A_6^3 \langle r^6 \rangle V_6^3$$
$$+ A_6^6 \langle r^6 \rangle V_6^6 + \tau \mathbf{L} \cdot \mathbf{S} + \beta H \cdot (\mathbf{L} + 2\mathbf{S}),$$

subject to $\mathbf{L}$ and $\mathbf{S}$ being good quantum numbers. Here τ is the spin-orbit coupling constant, taken to be 643 cm^{-1} [3], and the terms $A_n^m \langle r^n \rangle V_n^m$ are those appropriate to the most general crystal field with C_{3v} symmetry. The eigenvalues of $\mathscr{H}$ give the energy levels as a function of H, and from these we may compute the susceptibility:

$$\chi = \sum_i \left(\frac{(W_i^{(1)})^2}{kT} - 2(W_i^{(2)}) \right) e^{-W_i^{(0)}/kT} / \sum_i e^{-W_i^{(0)}/kT} \qquad (1)$$

where $W_i = W_i^{(0)} + W_i^{(1)}H + W_i^{(2)}H^2...$

The susceptibility is thus an implicit function of the six $A_n^m \langle r^n \rangle$ which may be treated as adjustable parameters and fitted to the experimental data using numerical methods. This was done using both our own experimental data and those of Hellwege et al. which included measurements extending to higher temperatures. In both cases a good fit was obtained (see Figure 1), and the $A_n^m \langle r^n \rangle$ show generally reasonable agreement, as may be seen in Table II. The small discrepancies may be due partly to experimental errors, and partly to the fact that the results of Hellwege et al. extended over a wider temperature region, for which thermal expansion effects could introduce a variation in the A_n^m not taken into account here.

TABLE II

Values of $A_n^m \langle r^n \rangle$ and the energy of the first excited state in cerium magnesium nitrate

$A_n^m \langle r^n \rangle$	$A_2^0 \langle r^2 \rangle$	$A_4^0 \langle r^4 \rangle$	$A_6^0 \langle r^6 \rangle$	$A_3^4 \langle r^4 \rangle$	$A_6^3 \langle r^6 \rangle$	$A_6^6 \langle r^6 \rangle$	Δ (k°)
This work	-155 ± 34	5.8 ± 7.7	-43 ± 9	-1780 ± 133	4963 ± 128	2393 ± 201	37.6 ± 2.5
Hellwege et al.	-57.4	1.6	-17.6	-1676	4420	1471	$(33(41.5*$

* Hellwege's best fit to equation 1 in terms of $W_i^{(r)}$ rather than $A_n^m \langle r^n \rangle$.

Discussion

The striking features shown by both sets of $A_n^m \langle r^n \rangle$ are the large values of $A_6^3 \langle r^6 \rangle$ and $A_6^6 \langle r^6 \rangle$ compared with the more usual magnitudes of the $A_n^0 \langle r^n \rangle$. These large values result from the necessity of modifying the magnetic properties of the free-ion $J = 5/2$ state to account for the observations, and within the framework of ionic crystal field model this can only be achieved by crystal fields comparable with the spin-orbit interaction. On the other hand the crystal fields operating *within* the $J = 5/2$ manifold must be quite small, since the temperature variation of χ indicates small splittings. (~ 40K°). Both qualitatively and quantitatively these conclusions can be reached without any uncertainty arising from approximations in the calculations themselves, since the problem is sufficiently simple and well-defined to permit exact numerical solutions.

While there is nothing to rule out crystal fields of the required orders of magnitude, it may nevertheless be worthwhile to consider other effects, normally omitted from the theory, which could influence the ground term in a qualitatively similar way to a crystal field off-diagonal in J. There appear to be four possibilities:

i) Distortion of the closed $5s^2 5p^6$ shells by the crystal field, resulting in an interaction with the 4-f electron through intra-ionic exchange.

ii) Covalency of the magnetic 4-f electron, resulting in reduction of its effective orbital angular momentum.

iii) Configurational interaction with 5d states through crystal field terms of odd parity [4].

iv) Time-dependent effects arising from low-frequency vibrations of the ionic environment.

Each of these effects will probably be small, but the inclusion of one or more of them could result in an appreciable reduction of the large $A_6^3 \langle r^6 \rangle$ and $A_6^6 \langle r^6 \rangle$ values. As it is, the crystal field parameters are not too unreasonable compared with Judd's values for Pr^{3+} and Nd^{3+}, which were deduced with much more certainty from spectroscopic data, the general trend being quite consistent with the variation of the $\langle r^n \rangle$ [5]. It is clear that more information on the splittings of the excited $J = 7/2$ term would greatly clarify the situation.

One unambiguous result of the present analysis is an estimate of the energy of first excited state relative to the ground state. As may be seen from Table II, the magnetic data indicate a value 38K° with an uncertainty of about 3K°, in very reasonable agreement with the temperature dependence of the spin-lattice relaxation time [6;7].

Acknowledgment

We wish to thank Dr. W. Marshall and Dr. R. E. Watson for stimulating discussions. This work was carried out during the tenure of an N.S.F. Postdoctoral Fellowship by R.O., and a Pressed Steel Postdoctoral Fellowship by M.J.M.L., and it was supported in part by the Electronics Research Directorate, A.F.C.R.L., through the European Office, Aerospace Research, U.S. Air Force.

REFERENCES

[1]   K. H. Hellwege, Int. Conf. on Mag. and Cryst.; Paper 152, Kyoto (1961): see also Hellwege, Schembs and Schneider, to be published.
[2]   B. R. Judd, *Proc. Roy. Soc.* **A241**, 122.
[3]   R. J. Lang, *Canad. J. Res.* 14/127 (1936).
[4]   R. J. Elliott and K. W. H. Stevens, *Proc. Roy. Soc.* **A215**, 439.
[5]   A. J. Freeman and R. E. Watson, *Phys. Rev.* 1962 — to be published.
[6]   C. B. P. Finn, R. Orbach and W. P. Wolf, *Proc. Phys. Soc.* **77**, 261.
[7]   O. S. Leifson and C. D. Jeffries, *Phys. Rev.* **122**, 1781.

DISCUSSION

R. P. HUDSON, USA: The energy separation to the first excited state is always found to be 34°K by relaxation measurements and about 38°K in various susceptibility determinations. Although you tended to dismiss this discrepancy in your paper, it seems to me that it is, in fact, significant and lies outside the estimated experimental uncertainties. Can you offer any comment on this?

W. P. WOLF, England: The accuracy of these calculations is 38 ± 2.5°K. There may be another relaxation effect from a higher excited level which may contribute somewhat to the measurement.

Quelques Propriétés des Niveaux Cristallins Γ_8 en Symétrie Cubique

Y. Ayant

Institut Fourier, Grenoble

SOMMAIRE

On étudie l'effet Zeeman sur un niveau Γ_8 pour une orientation quelconque du champ magnétique. On précise les règles de sélection pour les cas où le champ magnétique est parallèle à un axe quaternaire, ternaire ou binaire. On discute le cas ou il existe une distorsion tétragonale ou trigonale.

1.

Il est fréquent de rencontrer des niveaux appartenant à la représentation Γ_8 (selon les notations de Bethe) lorsqu'on a affaire à un ion possédant un nombre impair d'électrons plongé dans un champ cristallin de symétrie cubique. Nous rappelons qu'il y a 8 représentations irréductibles (de Γ_1 à Γ_8) du groupe du cube, et que la représentation Γ_8 est celle de multiplicité la plus élevée 4.

En vue du but concret d'évaluer un effet Zeeman, éventuellement sura-jouté à une distorsion non cubique, sur un tel niveau, il faut donc résoudre le problème d'obtenir des matrices 4×4 représentatives d'un vecteur sur ce niveau. La table des caractères du groupe du cube fournit l'équation suivante entre représentations:

$$(\Gamma_8)^2 = \Gamma_1 + \Gamma_2 + \Gamma_3 + 2\Gamma_4 + 2\Gamma_5, \tag{1}$$

il est bien connu que les vecteurs engendrent la représentation $\mathcal{D}_1$ s'il s'agit du groupe complet des rotations et que l'on a:

$$\mathcal{D}_1 = \Gamma_4$$

en se restreignant au groupe du cube, sous-groupe du précédent. Donc, (1) démontre "qu'il y a deux vecteurs", c'est-à-dire plus précisément que les matrices cherchées dépendent linéairement de deux paramètres arbitraires (à fixer dans chaque cas concret).

2. Choix tétragonal des axes

Nous prenons d'abord comme axes $Oxyz$ les 3 axes quaternaires du cube. Choisissons comme base quantique de l'espace associé à Γ_8, 4 états tels qu'une rotation d'angle $\omega = \pm \Pi/2$ ou Π autour de Oz les multiplie simplement par

$$\exp(-i\,\omega\,M)$$

M étant un nombre quantique analogue à un nombre quantique magnétique usuel, mais prenant ici seulement les valeurs $3/2$, $1/2$, $-1/2$, $-3/2$.

La composante A_z d'un vecteur $\mathbf{A}$, invariante dans les transformations précédentes, sera ainsi representée par une matrice diagonale, que nous écrirons provisoirement:

$$\begin{vmatrix} P & & & \\ & Q & & \\ & & Q' & \\ & & & P' \end{vmatrix}$$

Si l'on considère une rotation R d'angle π autour de Ox il est clair que l'on a:

$$\Gamma_8(R)^{-1}\,A_z\,\Gamma_8(R) = -A_z \tag{2}$$

Or, $\Gamma_8(R) = \mathscr{D}_{3/2}(R)$, l'équivalence des deux représentations peut être ramenée à une identité simplement en choisissant convenablement les phases des états $|M\rangle$, ce qui est loisible. $\mathscr{D}_{3/2}(R)$ est connue, dans le cas actuel, par exemple en utilisant la formule de Majorana, et l'on obtient ainsi:

$$\Gamma_8(R) = -1 \begin{vmatrix} & & & 1 \\ & & 1 & \\ & 1 & & \\ 1 & & & \end{vmatrix}$$

On peut ainsi déduire de (2) que:

$$-\langle M\,|\,A_z\,|\,M\rangle = \langle -M\,|\,A_z\,|-M\rangle$$

ce qui donne pour A_z une forme mettant en évidence les deux seuls paramètres libres du problème:

$$A_z = \begin{vmatrix} P & & & \\ & Q & & \\ & & -Q & \\ & & & -P \end{vmatrix} \tag{3}$$

A ce stade, il est intéressant d'introduire un spin fictif $3/2$, soit $\mathbf{S}$, dont les composantes sont les matrices usuelles. (3) peut alors visiblement mis sous la forme:

avec:

$$A_z = aS_z + bS_z^3$$

$$P = 3a/2 + 27b/8$$

(4)

et

$$Q = a/2 + b/8$$

$$a = -P/12 + 9Q/4$$

$$b = P/3 - Q$$

La relation (4) s'étend aux autres composantes x, y. En effet, soit une rotation R du groupe du cube amenant par exemple Oz sur Ox, nous avons d'une part:

$$A_x = \Gamma_8^{-1}(R) \quad A_z \Gamma_8(R)$$

par définition même de la représentation associée au niveau étudié; or:

$$S_x = \mathscr{D}_{3/2}(R)^{-1} \quad S_z \mathscr{D}_{3/2}(R)$$

Vu l'identité de Γ_8 et $\mathscr{D}_{3/2}$, on voit donc que l'on passe de S_z, S_z^3 et A_z à S_x, S_x^3 et A_x par la même transformation canonique, ce qui établit donc la relation cherchée:

$$A_\alpha = aS_\alpha + bS_\alpha^3 \quad (\alpha = x, y, z)$$

Cela permet donc d'écrire explicitement les matrices des composantes de **A** à l'aide soit de a et b, soit de P et Q; nous les donnons ci-dessous avec ce dernier choix:

$$A_x = \begin{vmatrix} \cdot & \frac{\sqrt{3}}{4}(P+Q) & & \frac{1}{4}(P-3Q) \\ \frac{\sqrt{3}}{4}(P+Q) & \cdot & \frac{3P-Q}{4} & \\ & \frac{3P-Q}{4} & \cdot & \frac{\sqrt{3}}{4}P(+Q) \\ \frac{1}{4}(P-3Q) & & \frac{\sqrt{3}}{4}(P+Q) & \cdot \end{vmatrix}$$

$$A_y = \begin{vmatrix} \cdot & -\frac{\sqrt{3}}{4}(P+Q)i & & \frac{1}{4}(P-3Q)i \\ \frac{\sqrt{3}}{4}(P+Q)i & \cdot & -\frac{3P-Q}{4}i & \\ & \frac{3P-Q}{4}i & \cdot & -\frac{\sqrt{3}}{4}(P+Q)i \\ -\frac{1}{4}(P-3Q)i & & \frac{\sqrt{3}}{4}(P+Q)i & \cdot \end{vmatrix}$$

$$A_z = \begin{vmatrix} P & & & \\ & Q & & \\ & & -Q & \\ & & & -P \end{vmatrix} \tag{5}$$

3. Choix trigonal des axes

La pratique montre qu'il est très important de reprendre le même problème, l'axe privilégié étant un des axes ternaires du cube, soit 0ζ. Nous définirons un nouveau trière, dit "trigonal", par les cosinus directeurs:

$$0\xi : \qquad -1/\sqrt{6} \qquad -1/\sqrt{6} \qquad 2/\sqrt{6}$$

$$0\eta : \qquad 1/\sqrt{2} \qquad -1/\sqrt{2} \qquad 0$$

$$0\zeta : \qquad 1/\sqrt{3} \qquad 1/\sqrt{3} \qquad 1/\sqrt{3}$$

Il est aisé, évidemment de ramener les composantes $A\xi, \eta, \zeta$ aux anciennes composantes $A_{x,y,z}$, donc à S_x, S_y, S_z et leurs cubes. Arrivé à ce stade, on change la base quantique de l'espace associé à Γ_8 pour rendre diagonal S_ζ; soit $|M'\rangle$ cette nouvelle base, nous aurons évidemment:

$$\langle M' | S_\zeta | M' \rangle = M'$$

$$\langle M' + 1 | (S_\xi + iS_\eta) | M' \rangle = \sqrt{15/4 - M'(M'+1)}$$

Il est alors aisé d'exprimer S_x, S_y, S_z à l'aide de S_ξ, S_η, S_ζ et d'en déduire les expressions matricielles explicites suivantes:

$$S_z = \begin{vmatrix} \dfrac{\sqrt{3}}{2} & \dfrac{1}{\sqrt{2}} & \cdot & \cdot \\[2mm] \dfrac{1}{\sqrt{2}} & \dfrac{1}{2\sqrt{3}} & \dfrac{2}{\sqrt{6}} & \cdot \\[2mm] \cdot & \dfrac{2}{\sqrt{6}} & -\dfrac{1}{2\sqrt{3}} & \dfrac{1}{\sqrt{2}} \\[2mm] \cdot & \cdot & \dfrac{1}{\sqrt{2}} & -\dfrac{\sqrt{3}}{2} \end{vmatrix}$$

$$S_z^3 = \begin{vmatrix} \dfrac{23}{8\sqrt{3}} & \dfrac{9}{4\sqrt{2}} & \dfrac{1}{2} & \dfrac{1}{\sqrt{6}} \\[2ex] \dfrac{9}{4\sqrt{2}} & \dfrac{13}{8\sqrt{3}} & \dfrac{7}{2\sqrt{6}} & -\dfrac{1}{2} \\[2ex] \dfrac{1}{2} & \dfrac{7}{2\sqrt{6}} & -\dfrac{13}{8\sqrt{3}} & \dfrac{9}{4\sqrt{2}} \\[2ex] \dfrac{1}{\sqrt{6}} & -\dfrac{1}{2} & \dfrac{9}{4\sqrt{2}} & -\dfrac{23}{8\sqrt{3}} \end{vmatrix}$$

Quant aux matrices S_x et S_x^3, S_y et S_y^3, on note qu'on les obtient à partir de S_z et S_z^3 par une rotation de $\pm 2\pi/3$ autour de 0ζ; la nouvelle base choisie est telle qu'une rotation d'angle $\pm 2\pi/3$ multiplie $|M'\rangle$ par exp. $(\mp iM'2\pi/3)$, il est aisé d'en déduire que:

$$\langle M'|S_x|M\rangle = \langle M'|S_z|M\rangle \cdot \exp(-i(M'-M)2\pi/3)$$

j et j^2 étant les racines cubiques de l'unité, on multiplie donc les éléments de matrice de A_z par 1 ou j ou j^2 pour en déduire ceux de A_x; résultats analogues pour A_y; en définitive, on obtient les matrices:

$$A_\xi = aS_\xi + b \begin{vmatrix} \cdot & \dfrac{9\sqrt{3}}{8} & \dfrac{\sqrt{6}}{4} & \cdot \\[2ex] \dfrac{9\sqrt{3}}{8} & \cdot & \dfrac{7}{4} & -\dfrac{\sqrt{6}}{4} \\[2ex] \dfrac{\sqrt{6}}{4} & \dfrac{7}{4} & \cdot & \dfrac{9\sqrt{3}}{8} \\[2ex] \cdot & \dfrac{\sqrt{6}}{4} & \dfrac{9\sqrt{3}}{8} & \cdot \end{vmatrix}$$

$$A_\eta = aS_\eta + bi \begin{vmatrix} \cdot & -\dfrac{9\sqrt{3}}{8} & \dfrac{\sqrt{6}}{4} & \cdot \\[2ex] \dfrac{9\sqrt{3}}{8} & \cdot & -\dfrac{7}{4} & -\dfrac{\sqrt{6}}{4} \\[2ex] -\dfrac{\sqrt{6}}{4} & \dfrac{7}{4} & \cdot & -\dfrac{9\sqrt{3}}{8} \\[2ex] \cdot & \dfrac{\sqrt{6}}{4} & \dfrac{9\sqrt{3}}{8} & \cdot \end{vmatrix} \; ; \; A_\zeta = aS_\zeta + b \begin{vmatrix} \dfrac{23}{8} & \cdot & \cdot & \dfrac{1}{\sqrt{2}} \\[2ex] \cdot & \dfrac{13}{8} & & \\[2ex] \cdot & & -\dfrac{13}{8} & \\[2ex] \dfrac{1}{\sqrt{2}} & & & -\dfrac{23}{8} \end{vmatrix}$$

$$A_\xi = \begin{vmatrix} \cdot & \dfrac{P}{\sqrt{3}} & \dfrac{\sqrt{6}}{4}\left(\dfrac{P}{3}-Q\right) & \cdot \\ \dfrac{P}{\sqrt{3}} & \cdot & \dfrac{P+Q}{2} & -\dfrac{\sqrt{6}}{4}\left(\dfrac{P}{3}-Q\right) \\ & \cdot & & \dfrac{P}{\sqrt{3}} \end{vmatrix} \quad A_\eta = i \begin{vmatrix} \cdot & -\dfrac{P}{\sqrt{3}} & \dfrac{\sqrt{6}}{4}\left(\dfrac{P}{3}-Q\right) & \cdot \\ \cdot & & -\dfrac{P+Q}{2} & -\dfrac{\sqrt{6}}{4}\left(\dfrac{P}{3}-Q\right) \\ & & & -\dfrac{P}{\sqrt{3}} \end{vmatrix}$$

$$A_\zeta = \begin{vmatrix} \dfrac{5P+3Q}{6} & \cdot & \cdot & \dfrac{a}{\sqrt{2}}\left(\dfrac{P}{3}-Q\right) \\ & \dfrac{P-Q}{2} & & \\ & & -\dfrac{P-Q}{2} & \\ & & & -\dfrac{5P+3Q}{6} \end{vmatrix}$$

4. Effet Zeeman sur un niveau Γ_8

(en l'absence de distorsion non-cubique)

Cette question se traite au mieux en axes tétragonaux; $\mathbf{M}$ étant le moment magnétique, $\mathbf{H}$ étant le champ magnétique, dont l'orientation sera fixée par les cosinus directeurs $\alpha\beta\gamma$, on appliquera la théorie précédente au vecteur $\mathbf{M}/\mu_B$, pour raisonner sur un vecteur $\mathbf{A}$ sans dimension.

L'Hamiltonian de l'effet Zeeman s'écrit ainsi:

$$\mathscr{H} = H\mu_B \begin{vmatrix} \gamma P & \dfrac{\sqrt{3}}{4}(\alpha-\beta i)(P+Q) & & \dfrac{1}{4}(\alpha+\beta i)(P-3Q) \\ \dfrac{\sqrt{3}}{4}(\alpha+\beta i)(P+Q) & \gamma Q & \dfrac{1}{4}(\alpha-\beta i)(3P-Q) & \\ \cdot & \dfrac{1}{4}(\alpha+\beta i)(3P-Q) & -\gamma Q & \dfrac{\sqrt{3}}{4}(\alpha-\beta i)(P+Q) \\ \dfrac{1}{4}(\alpha-\beta i)(P-3Q) & \cdot & \dfrac{\sqrt{3}}{4}(\alpha+\beta i)(P+Q) & -\gamma P \end{vmatrix}$$

Si l'on désigne les sous-niveaux Zeeman par $H\mu_B x$, x obéit à l'équation bicarrée:

$$x^4 - (P^2+Q^2)x^2 + P^2 Q^2$$
$$+ \frac{3}{16}(P-3Q)(3P-Q)(P+Q)^2 \cdot (\alpha^2\beta^2 + \beta^2\gamma^2 + \gamma^2\alpha^2) = 0 \quad (8)$$

Cette équation permet de discuter en général les positions des 4 sous-niveaux Zeeman; insistons sur les cas particuliers suivants:

a) Si **H** est parallèle à un axe quaternaire, on retrouve évidemment:

$$x = \pm P, \quad \pm Q.$$

En ce qui concerne les règles de sélection, en se bornant au cas usuel où l'excitation se fait par un champ radiofréquence magnétique ayant une composante perpendiculaire au champ directeur, on prévoit l'existence de toutes les transitions $\Delta M = \pm 1$ et en plus la transition $3/2 \leftrightarrows -3/2$ (sauf si $b = 0$). (Cf. (5)).

b) Si **H** est parallèle à un axe ternaire, (8) donne:

$$x = \pm \tfrac{1}{2}\sqrt{3(P^2 + Q^2) + 2PQ}$$

$$x = \pm \tfrac{1}{2}(P - Q)$$

ce résultat s'obtiendrait évidemment par un étude directe en axes trigonaux, qui aurait l'intérêt de montrer que les deux premiers sous-niveaux Zeeman trouvés correspondent à $M' = \pm 3/2$, les deux autres à $M' = \pm 1/2$.

Du point de vue des règles de sélection (même remarque que précédemment), on prévoit l'existence des transitions $\Delta M' = \pm 1$, et en outre des transitions $\Delta M' = \pm 2$ (sauf si $b = 0$).

Notons en passant que, dans le cas d'une orientation quelconque, toutes les transitions sont permises, dès que b est non nul (cela tient à ce que toute symétrie est détruite, donc, une base quantique qui diagonaliserait la composante longitudinale de **M** donnerait des matrices "pleines" pour les composantes transversales).

5. Effet Zeeman sur un niveau Γ_8 en présence d'une distorsion tétragonale

Nous supposons que l'hamiltonien cristallin contient un petit terme non cubique tétragonal (petit devant le terme cubique) de telle sorte que le niveau Γ_8 est, en l'absence de champ magnétique, décomposé en deux doublets de Kramers, dont les vecteurs propres sont néanmoins sensiblement les mêmes que ceux de l'hamiltonien purement cubique; il est clair que l'un de ces deux niveaux correspond à $M = \pm 3/2$, l'autre à $\pm 1/2$ (M étant le nombre quantique "magnétique" défini en axes tétragonaux Cf. 2)).

Explicitons ici le cas où l'effet Zeeman est faible devant cette distorsion non-cubique; chacun des niveaux initialement doubles présente un dédoublement commandé par une matrice 2 × 2:

$$H\mu_B \begin{vmatrix} \gamma P & \frac{1}{4}(\alpha + \beta i)(P - 3Q) \\ \frac{1}{4}(\alpha - \beta i)(P - 3Q) & -\gamma P \end{vmatrix} \quad \text{pour } \pm 3/2$$

$$H\mu_B \begin{vmatrix} \gamma Q & \frac{1}{4}(\alpha - \beta i)(3P - Q) \\ \frac{1}{4}(\alpha + \beta i)(3P - Q) & -\gamma Q \end{vmatrix} \quad \text{pour } \pm 1/2$$

Les sous-niveaux Zeeman sont donnés (à partir des niveaux à champ nul, et en facteur de $H\mu_B$, θ étant la colatitude du champ magnétique) respectivement par :

$$x = \pm \sqrt{P^2 \cos^2\theta + \frac{1}{16}\sin^2\theta (P - 3Q)^2}$$

$$x = \pm \sqrt{Q^2 \cos\theta + \frac{1}{16}\sin^2\theta (3P - Q)^2}$$

Lorsque θ a une valeur quelconque ($\neq 0$), on vérifie que toutes les transitions sont permises (pourvu que $b \neq 0$), à la différence de la situation usuelle dans le groupe du Fer pour un ion de spin 3/2, dont le fondamental oribtal est un singulet, et pour lequel on sait que la transition entre les deux sous-niveaux $\pm 3/2$ est interdite, si le couplage Zeeman est faible devant le dédoublement à champ nul.

6. Effet Zeeman sur un niveau en présence d'une distorsion trigonale

Nous supposons une situation analogue à celle du 5., la distorsion non-cubique étant maintenant trigonale; le travail est exactement le même, mais en employant les axes trigonaux, nous nous bornons toujours à l'approximation; couplage Zeeman $\ll$ distorsion trigonale $\ll$ terme cubique. Les sous-niveaux à champ nul présentent un dédoublement Zeeman commandé cette fois par les matrices :

$$H\mu_B \begin{vmatrix} \gamma \dfrac{5P + 3Q}{6} & \dfrac{\gamma}{2}\left(\dfrac{P}{3} - Q\right) \\ \dfrac{\gamma}{\sqrt{2}}\left(\dfrac{P}{3} - Q\right) & -\gamma \dfrac{5P + 3Q}{6} \end{vmatrix} \quad \text{pour } \pm 3/2$$

$$H\mu_B \left| \begin{array}{cc} \gamma\,\dfrac{P-Q}{2} & \dfrac{P+Q}{2}\,(\alpha-\beta i) \\[2ex] \dfrac{P+Q}{2}(\alpha+\beta i) & -\gamma\,\dfrac{P-Q}{2} \end{array} \right| \quad \text{pour } \pm\tfrac{1}{2}$$

Le dédoublement (mêmes définitions qu'au 5.) est donné respectivement par:

$$x = \pm\ \tfrac{1}{2}\cos\theta\ \sqrt{3(P^2+Q^2)+2PQ}$$

$$x = \pm\ \tfrac{1}{2}\ \sqrt{P^2+Q^2-2PQ\cos 2\theta}$$

7. Un exemple d'application: le cas de Er^{3+} en environnement octaèdrique

En ce qui concerne les terres rares, une première approximation souvent suffisante consiste à considérer le couplage spin-orbite comme grand devant le couplage cristallin, ce qui fait de J un bon nombre quantique. Il est alors possible d'appliquer le théorie précédente au moment cinétique $\mathbf{J}$ en écrivant le couplage Zeeman sous la forme $g_j\mu_B\,\mathbf{H}\cdot\mathbf{J}$.

L'Hamiltonien purement cubique est représenté, en axes tétragonaux, par

$$J_x^4 + J_y^4 + J_z^4 - \frac{3}{2J+1}\operatorname{Tr} J_z^4$$

La représentative matricielle de cet opérateur est maintenant bien connue, il est aisé d'en obtenir les vecteurs propres, et de là les valeurs de P et Q (relatives à $\mathbf{J}$ et à un niveau Γ_8 donné, en général le fondamental).

Des expériences sont en cours, concernant Er^{3+} dilué dans MgO, d'où un environnement octaèdrique d'ions O^{--}; l'ion libre Er^{3+} est un système $(4f)^{11}\ {}^4I_{15/2}$, pour lequel $g_J=6/5$; le fondamental cristallin est précisément un niveau Γ_8 et le calcul, mené dans l'approximation donnée ci-dessus, donne:

$$P = 4.5834; \qquad Q = 2.8565$$

Bornons-nous ici à donner le diagramme de niveaux en l'absence de distorsion non cubique (en face des niveaux, sont indiqués les valeurs de x) en multipliant par $6H\mu_B/5$ on obtient les valeurs des niveaux); les transitions permises donnent lieu à des raies Zeeman caractérisées par un facteur $g = \hbar\omega/\mu_B H$ égal à:

2.072;   6.856;   11.000   (H parallèle à une axe quaternaire)

5.361;   2.072;   7.434   (H parallèle à une axe ternaire).

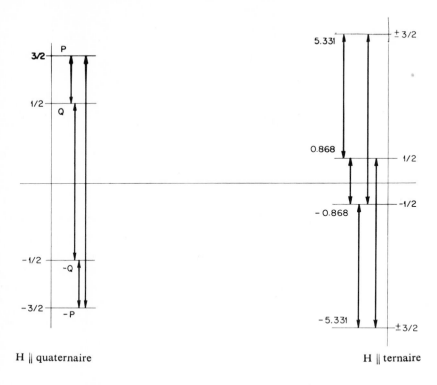

H ∥ quaternaire   H ∥ ternaire

Figure 1

Appendice

Il est intéressant de compléter l'étude précédente de l'effet Zeeman sur le niveau Γ_8 (en l'absence de distorsion non cubique) par l'examen du cas où le champ magnétique est parallèle à un axe binaire du cube; en effet, il y a là une symétrie suffisante pour entraîner l'existence de règles de sélection. Nous utiliserons la même méthode que celle qui a été utilisée plus haut pour passer en axes trigonaux; nous définirons un système d'axes "digonaux" $OXYZ$ définies par leurs cosinus directeurs:

$$
\begin{array}{cccc}
OX: & -1/\sqrt{2} & 1/\sqrt{2} & 0 \\
OY: & 0 & 0 & 1 \\
OZ: & 1/\sqrt{2} & 1/\sqrt{2} & 0
\end{array}
$$

OZ est bien un axe binaire du cube.

Pour un vecteur A et avec les mêmes paramètres P et Q que plus haut, on trouve que:

$$A_z = \frac{1}{8} \begin{vmatrix} 7P + 3Q & \cdot & \sqrt{3}(P - 3Q) & \cdot \\ \cdot & 3P - Q & \cdot & -\sqrt{3}(P - 3Q) \\ \sqrt{3}(P - 3Q) & \cdot & -3P + Q & \cdot \\ \cdot & -\sqrt{3}(P - 3Q) & \cdot & -7P - 3Q \end{vmatrix}$$

Nous appliquerons un champ magnétique parallèle à OZ, donnant des niveaux Zeeman $H\mu_B x$; faisons $\mathbf{A} = \mathbf{M}$, on obtient:

$$x = \frac{P + Q}{4} \pm \frac{1}{4}\sqrt{7P^2 + 7Q^2 - 2PQ}$$

qui appartient aux nombres quantiques $M = 3/2, -1/2$;

$$x = -\frac{P + Q}{4} \pm \frac{1}{4}\sqrt{7P^2 + 7Q^2 - 2PQ}$$

qui appartiennent aux nombres quantiques $-3/2, +1/2$.

Cela est naturel, M est ici defini modulo 2; on peut, si l'on veut, introduire un nombre quantique $M'' = -1/2$ et $+1/2$ respectivement, pour décrire les niveaux obtenus.

On obtient d'autre part:

$$A_x = \frac{1}{8} \begin{vmatrix} \cdot & \sqrt{3}(3P - Q) & \cdot & P - 3Q \\ \sqrt{3}(3P - Q) & \cdot & 3P + 7Q & \cdot \\ \cdot & 3P + 7Q & \cdot & \sqrt{3}(3P - Q) \\ P - 3Q & \cdot & \sqrt{3}(3P - Q) & \cdot \end{vmatrix}$$

$$A_y = \frac{-1}{4} \begin{vmatrix} \cdot & \sqrt{3}(P + Q) & \cdot & -P + 3Q \\ -\sqrt{3}(P + Q) & \cdot & 3P - Q & \cdot \\ \cdot & -3P + Q & \cdot & \sqrt{3}(P + Q) \\ P - 3Q & \cdot & -\sqrt{3}(P + Q) & \cdot \end{vmatrix}$$

qui conduisent à une règle de selection $\Delta M'' = \pm 1$; les transitions $\Delta M'' = 0$ sont interdites.

Nous compléterons cela en donnant en function de P et Q les différentes possibilités concernant les règles de sélection sous la forme d'un diagramme schématique de niveaux avec, à gauche le cas tétragonal (H parallèle à un axe quaternaire, à droite le cas trigonal (H parallèle à un axe ternaire) et au milieu le cas digonal (H parallèle à un axe binaire) (étant entendu qu'on pourrait toujours trouver un "chemin" évitant ce dernier cas). Nous indiquons les nombres quantiques de chaque niveau (respectivement définis modulo 4, 3 et 2) et les transitions interdites); le lecteur vérifie que

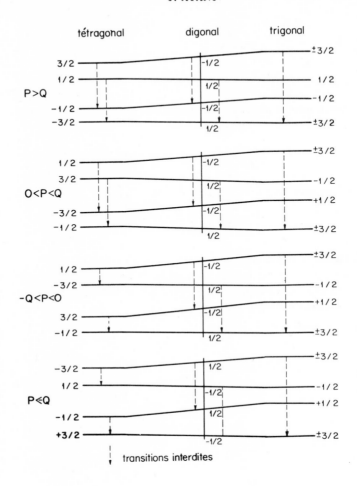

Figure 2

le cas $-P$, $-Q$ "ressemble" beaucoup au cas P, Q (il suffit de renverser tous les niveaux), nous prenons donc $Q > 0$ et discutons en faisant varier P: le cas où $P = 3Q$ est trivial et fixe les nombres quantiques, des considérations évidentes d'intersection des niveaux permettent, par continuité de compléter la discussion.

REFERENCES

[1] B. BLEANEY, *Proc. Phys. Soc.* **73**, 937 (1959).
[2] N. BAKER, *Proc. Phys. Soc.* **73**, 943 (1959).
[3] A. VINCOW, AND W. LOW, *Phys. Rev.* **122**, 1390 (1961).

Etude Théorique du Blocage du Moment Magnétique des Ions Terres Rares dans les Gallates à Structure Grenat

Y. Ayant et J. Thomas

Laboratoire d'Électrostatique et de Physique du Métal, Grenoble

ABSTRACT

L'Hamiltonien de champ cristallin d'un ion terre rare, de J donné, placé dans un site 24 c de la maille grenat dont le voisinage présente une symétrie orthorhombique grossièrement cubique, s'écrit sous la forme:

$$\mathscr{H} = \mathscr{H}_0 + A \left\{ t \ \left[Y_0^2 + K(Y_2^2 + Y_2^2) \right] \right.$$

$$+ \ Y_0^4 + k(Y_4^4 + Y_{-4}^4)$$

$$+ \ s \left[Y_0^6 + k'(Y_4^6 + Y_{-4}^6) \right] \Big\}$$

le terme principal étant le terme Y.

On en déduit les facteurs de Landé théoriques ainsi que, par la théorie de Van Vleck, les propriétés magnétiques en laissant indéterminés des paramètres de la formule (1). On peut ajuster ces derniers en comparant aux résultats expérimentaux.

On a ainsi interprété les propriétés magnétiques (courbes de susceptibilité et d'aimantation aux basses températures, résonance paramagnétique) de l'Yb Er, Tb, Nd, Pr. Les amplitudes relatives des séparations entre sous-niveaux s'en déduisant, ainsi que l'importance relative des différents termes de la formule (1). De bons recoupements sont possibles avec les divers résultats expérimentaux. Les énergies trouvées sont nettement plus fortes que prévues, et dans de nombreux cas l'approximation consistant à prendre un Hamiltonien invariant dans la symétrie du cube est insuffisante.

I. L'étude des ferrites de terres rares, type Grenat, par Pauthenet ayant laissé présager un blocage du moment magnétique des ions terres rares, une étude expérimentale des Gallates, qui ont même structure, fut entreprise par Cohen et Ducloz et nous entreprimes conjointement une étude théorique du blocage.

Le modèle choisi est un modèle électrostatique de charges ponctuelles réparties au centre des ions O^{--} voisins. Ce modèle respecte intégralement la symétrie du champ cristallin vu par l'ion (si on néglige l'action de 2ème, 3ème ··· voisins). Les huit voisins de l'ion magnétique constituent un hexaèdre irrégulier obtenu par déformation d'un cube par torsion autour d'un de ses axes quaternaires, puis légère distorsion des faces. Cette figure présente la symétrie orthorombique, dont le groupe comporte 4 représentations d'ordre 1 et une 5ème représentation d'ordre 2 si on ajoute les rotations spinorielles.

Nous avons développé l'Hamiltonien en série de fonctions sphériques des coordonnées $r\theta\phi$ des électrons 4f. Des considérations élémentaires de théorie des groupes d'une part, et les règles de sélection appliquées aux électrons 4f d'autre part, permettent d'écrire l'Hamiltonien sous la forme

$$\mathcal{H} = \mathcal{H}_0 + a_0^2 Y_0^2 + a_2^2(Y_2^2 + Y_{-2}^2)$$
$$+ a_0^4 Y_0^4 + a_2^4(Y_2^4 + Y_{-2}^4) + a_4^4(Y_4^4 + Y_{-4}^4)$$
$$+ a_0^6 Y_0 + a_2^6(Y_2^6 + Y_{-2}) + a_4^6(Y_4^6 + Y_{-4}^6) + a_6^6(Y_6^6 + Y_{-6}^6).$$

Si on prend le modèle des charges ponctuelles les coefficients a_m^l ont pour expression:

$$a_m^l = \frac{2e^2\sqrt{4\pi\lambda_l\sigma_l\overline{r^l}}}{\sqrt{2l+1}} \sum_{i=l}^{8} \frac{Y_m^l(\theta_i\phi_i)}{d_i^{l+1}}$$

avec e : charge de l'électron

Λ_l : coefficient de normalisation provenant de la composition des Hamiltoniens individuels relatifs à chaque électron f.

σ_l : coefficient d'écran dû aux couches $5s^2 5p^6$

$\overline{r^l}$: l^{ieme} puissance moyenne du rayon de la couche 4f

$d_i\theta_i\phi_i$: coordonnées sphériques du i ion O^{--} voisin

Il est probable que l'étendue dans l'espace des ions O^{--}, ainsi que l'existence d'autres types de liaisons (covalentes par exemple) introduisent un facteur supplémentaire. Nous l'avons groupé avec le facteur $\sigma_l \overline{r^l}$ qui est mal connu et qui détermine l'amplitude de l'effet cristallin. L'autre facteur, d'origine cristallographique, $\sum_{i=l}^{8} \frac{Y_m^l(\theta_i\phi_i)}{d_i^{l+1}}$ présente pour le voisinage considéré la propriété remarquable suivante: les coefficients qui s'annuleraient si la symétrie était la symétrie cubique sont, au facteur $\sigma_l\overline{r^l}$ près, très petits et pratiquement indéterminés: ils se présentent dans les calculs comme la différence de 2 fonctions presque égales des coordonnées des charges ponctuelles envisagées (ces fonctions seraient rigoureusement égales si la symétrie était la symétrie cubique); exemple:

$$a_0^2 = \sum_{i=1}^{8} \frac{3\cos^2\theta_i - 1}{d^3} = 0 \text{ si } \cos^2\theta = \frac{1}{3}, \text{ cas du cube}$$

Par contre, les termes qui ne sont pas nuls dans le cas de la symétrie cubique sont importants et bien déterminés et on peut négliger les premiers devant les seconds s'ils sont en facteur de la même puissance de r (rayon vecteur de l'électron considéré).

Aussi peut-on restreindre l'Hamiltonien à la forme:

$$\mathscr{H} = \mathscr{H}_0 + a_0^2 Y_0^2 + a_2^2(Y_2^2 + Y_{-2}^2)$$

$$+ a_0^4 Y_0^4 + k\sqrt{\frac{5}{14}}(Y_4^4 + Y_{-4}^4)$$

$$+ a_0^6 Y_0^6 + k'\sqrt{\frac{7}{2}}(Y_4 + Y_{-4}^6)$$

Les coefficients k et k' introduits sont égaux à 1 si la symétrie est la symétrie cubique. Ils correspondent à la torsion du cube déjà signalée ($k = \cos \alpha$, α demi-angle de torsion du cube, 4 nombre magnétique quantique) et leur introduction dans les calculs est particulièrement aisée si on a pris comme première approximation l'hypothèse simplificatrice d'une symétrie cubique du voisinage.

Dans le développement de l'Hamiltonien, à cause de la petitesse de a_2^2 le terme principal est le terme $a_0 \left[Y_0^4 + k\sqrt{\frac{5}{14}}(Y_4^4 + Y_{-4}^4) \right]$ les autres termes étant des termes perturbateurs.

Les résultats ultérieurs, sur l'Ytterbium en particulier, nous ont conduit à considérer comme négligeable le terme $a_0^6 Y^6$. Par contre, les termes $a_0^2 Y_0^2$ et $a_2^2(Y_2^2 + Y_{-2}^2)$ peuvent avoir un effet important (en particulier dans le cas du Néodyme). Il est à remarquer que ces termes sont susceptibles de grosses variations d'un grenat à l'autre, car les différences de fonctions des coordonnées des charges qu'ils contiennent en facteur ont une variation relative très grande pour des variations même minimes de ces coordonnées.

Les facteurs $\sigma_l \bar{r}^i$ qui conditionnent l'amplitude de l'énergie du champ cristallin ont été laissés indéterminés. Le facteur principal $\sigma_4 \overline{r^4}$, ainsi que l'ensemble a_0^2 et a_2^2 sont donc les 3 paramètres de cette théorie et nous avons cherché à les ajuster pour justifier les résultats expérimentaux.

Nous avons posé, comme d'habitude dans le cas des terres rares, que l'énergie du couplage avec le champ cristallin était faible devant le couplage de structure fine et que c'était le moment total qui était bloqué. Autrement dit, J est considéré comme "un bon nombre quantique" et l'Hamiltonien de champ cristallin comme une perturbation levant la dégénérescence du niveau fondamental. En fait, cette énergie a été trouvée plus grande que prévue mais suffisamment petite toutefois pour que cette hypothèse reste valable, au moins en première approximation.

Les opérateurs Y_m^t ont été écrits dans la base $|M_J\rangle$ à l'aide d'une technique de polynomes publiée antérieurement (Y.Ayant, J. Rosset, *Ann. Inst. Fourier* **10**(1960), pp. 345–358). On obtient ainsi des matrices avec en facteur un coefficient A directement lié à l'amplitude de la décomposition du niveau due au champ cristallin et qui, dans le modèle des charges ponctuelles, vaut:

$$A = \frac{2e^2\sqrt{4\pi}\lambda_4\sigma_4\,\bar{r}_4}{3} \sum_{=1}^{8} \frac{Y_0^4(\theta\,\phi_i)}{d_i^5} \tag{1}$$

Dans cette formule, tout est connu sauf $\sigma_4\,\overline{r^4}$. L'ajustement du paramètre A pour rendre compte des résultats expérimentaux permet donc de calculer $\sigma_4\overline{r^4}$. On a trouvé en général $\sqrt[4]{\sigma_4\overline{r^4}} = 0,7$ Å à $0,8$ Å, valeur tout à fait acceptable compte tenu des valeurs généralement admises pour la couche $4f$.

II. Les expériences de Cohen et de Ducloz ont montré, d'une façon générale qu'en dessous de la température ambiante il existait un ou plusieurs domaines de température dans lesquels les échantillons suivaient assez bien une loi de la forme:

$$\chi = \frac{C}{T} + \alpha \qquad \text{ou}\ \chi T = C + \alpha T \tag{2}$$

les températures de Curie étant négligeables ($|\theta_c| \langle 2°\text{K})$.

Les constantes de Curie sont plus petites que celles de l'ion libre et, s'il y a plusieurs domaines de températures où on peut les définir, elles décroissent avec la température. Par contre, $\frac{d}{dT}(\chi T)$ décroît systématiquement lorsque la température croît, les paramagnétismes constants étant de l'ordre de 10^{-2} CGS.

L'existence de plusieurs domaines de température où la formule (2) s'applique avec des valeurs différentes des constantes, s'interprète par une disposition particulière des niveaux dans le spectre d'énergie. Ces niveaux seraient rassemblés en "paquets", ces paquets pouvant eux-mêmes être groupés. Ces paquets, dans le domaine de température considéré, jouent le rôle d'un niveau unique, et les limites inférieure et supérieure en température de validité de la loi (2) donne l'ordre de grandeur en énergie de la décomposition de ces "paquets de niveaux" ou de leur regroupement avec d'autres paquets. On a ainsi des estimations de l'énergie de champ cristallin, c'est-à-dire de A, estimations que l'on peut recouper avec les valeurs obtenues à partir des paramagnétismes constants en appliquant la théorie de Van Vleck.

Dans cette théorie, le paramagnétisme constant contient en facteur une somme de termes tels que : $\dfrac{\Sigma \, |\langle i \, | \, M \, | \, j \rangle |^2}{w_i - w_j}$, M: moment magnétique de l'ion $\langle i |$: un état fondamental, $|j\rangle$: un état excité, w_i et w_j: énergies des niveaux correspondants. On voit que A est en facteur dans le dénominateur, alors qu'il n'intervient pas dans les constantes de Curie qui sont de la forme : $\Sigma \, |\langle i \, | \, M \, | \, i \rangle|^2$. Ces estimations sont d'ailleurs en bon accord avec les mesures de spectroscopie infra-rouge. Il est à remarquer qu'un "paquet de niveaux" sera souvent formé par la décomposition d'un niveau lié à une représentation du groupe du cube en sous-niveaux liés aux représentations du groupe orthorombique considéré comme sous-groupe du groupe du cube. Enfin, nous avons tenu compte de certains résultats de résonance paramagnétique récemment publiés. On sait que les ions terres rares sont disposés dans la maille grenat, dans les sites 24 C, tous équivalents, sauf en ce qui concerne l'orientation. Il y a six orientations différentes ce qui, du point de vue magnétisme pur, même sur monocristaux, fait disparaître pratiquement toute anisotropie. Nous avons principalement étudié l'Ytterbium, le Néodyme, l'Erbium, le Terbium et la Praséodyme.

III. Cas de l'Ytterbium

Nous avons, comme dans les autres cas, commencé l'étude en faisant l'hypothèse simplificatrice d'une symétrie cubique du voisinage. La réduction de la $\mathscr{D}_{7/2}$ dans le groupe du cube est $\Gamma_6 + \Gamma_7 + \Gamma_8$ et c'est le doublet de Krammers Γ_7 qui est le sous-niveau fondamental. Il n'est que peu altéré si on revient à la symétrie exacte, et cette hypothèse est suffisante pour une étude magnétique pure. Elle permet de calculer, de façon absolue, la constante de Curie.

$$C = \frac{9}{4} \, \frac{N\mu^2 g^2}{k} = 1{,}08 \text{ cgs}$$

De façon plus précise, l'aimantation δ est, en fonction du champ magnétique H et de la température T:

$$\sigma = \frac{3}{2} N \, g \, \mu \left[th\frac{3}{2} \, \frac{g\mu}{k} \, \frac{H}{T} + \frac{g\mu H}{5A} \right]$$

où N: nombre d'Avogadro

g: facteur de Landé = 8/7

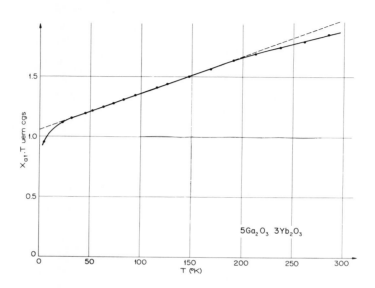

μ: magnéton de Bohr

k: constante de Boltzman

A: constante de la formule (1). Ici Λ_4 vaut $\dfrac{1}{77}$

Autrement dit, la courbe d'aimantation sera celle obtenue avec 1 spin fictif 1/2 et un facteur de Landé $3g = \dfrac{24}{7}$. Ceci est en parfait accord avec les résultats expérimentaux de Pauthenet.

La courbe expérimentale de susceptibilité tracée par Cohen et Ducloz en coordonnée χT, T montre, en accord avec cette théorie, une partie rectiligne en-dessous de 200°K avec un paramagnétisme constant $\alpha = 0,3\ 10^{-2}$. On peut en déduire A d'où l'amplitude totale de la décomposition du niveau $^2F_{7/2}$ par le champ cristallin, soit $32A = 900°K$ environ en bon accord avec les résultats de spectroscopie de Pappalardo. Par ailleurs, au-dessus de 200°K la courbe expérimentale s'écarte de la droite $C + \alpha T$, d'une quantité dont la valeur théorique est, en supposant que seul le 1er niveau excité commence à se peupler:

$$\frac{N\mu^2 g^2}{k}\left(\frac{65}{36} + \alpha' T\right)\exp\frac{20A}{kT}$$

et l'accord avec les valeurs expérimentales est bon.

Cette théorie, pas plus que les mesures de magnétisme, ne met en évidence l'anisotropie créée en chaque site par le fait que l'on a une symétrie orthorombique et non une symétrie cubique. Les expériences de résonance paramagnétique décèlent cette anisotropie. Nous nous sommes servis des résultats expérimentaux publiés par Wolf et ses collaborateurs. Pour interpréter cette anisotropie, il suffit de revenir à la symétrie exacte du voisinage. L'introduction du paramètre k distingue les valeurs $g_\perp$ et g du facteur de Landé.

L'introduction comme Hamiltonien perturbateur des termes: $a_0^2 Y_0^2 + a_2^2(Y_2^2 + Y_{-2}^2)$ provoque une évolution de l'état fondamental et font évoluer $g_x g_y g_z$ et on peut très bien ajuster les 2 paramètres a_0^2 et a_2^2 pour interpréter les 3 quantités $g_x g_y g_z$. Les valeurs trouvées pour a_0^2 et a_2^2 sont acceptables, et les énergies perturbatrices mises en jeu dans ce cas sont de l'ordre de 1/10ème de l'énergie totale du couplage du champ cristallin.

IV. Cas du Néodyme

Si on cherche à faire, pour le Néodyme, une théorie analogue à celle faite à propos de l'Ytterbium, on trouve que les résultats expérimentaux ne sont pas en accord avec les prévisions. La $D_{9/2}$ est décomposée par le groupe du cube en $\Gamma_7 + 2\Gamma_8$; et un des quadruplets Γ_8 est l'état fondamental. On devrait donc avoir une courbe d'aimantation analogue à celle obtenue avec un spin fictif 3/2, ce qui n'est pas en accord avec les résultats expérimentaux et la constante de Curie calculée est de 1,19 cgs, alors qu'expérimentalement elle vaut 1,05 pour $150°$ K $< T < 250°$K et 0,6 pour $T < 80°$K. Dans ces deux zones de température les paramagnétismes constants sont respectivement 0,11 10^{-2} et 0,55 10^{-2}. En effet, un aspect caractéristique de la courbe expérimentale de Cohen et Ducloz est la présence de 2 domaines de températures où la formule (2) est valable.

On peut estimer que pour $150°$K $< T < 250°$K l'hypothèse simplificatrice de la symétrie cubique du voisinage est une 1ère approximation valable. L'amplitude totale de la décomposition Stark du niveau $I_{9/2}$ par le champ cristallin, déduite de la valeur du paramagnétisme constant est de $1000°$K. Remarquons tout de suite à ce sujet que le niveau $^4I_{11/2}$ se trouve à $2000°$ du fondamental. Il faut donc certainement introduire des termes correctifs pour tenir compte de cette proximité.

Pour les températures inférieures, le 2ème blocage est évidemment dû à la décomposition du niveau Γ_8 en 2 doublets de Krammers par l'écart entre la symétrie réelle et la symétrie cubique.

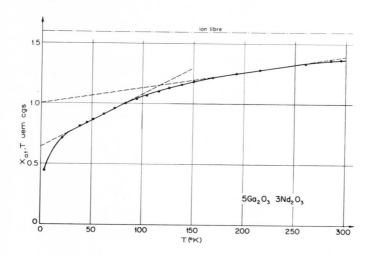

Si on introduit le paramètre k dans les calculs le niveau, Γ_8 est décomposé en 2 doublets, mais l'amplitude de cette décomposition (30°K environ) est en désaccord avec la température de la zone de courbure de la courbe expérimentale $\chi T(T)$: de 100 à 150°K. Les états propres correspondant aux deux précédents doublets de Krammers sont des combinaisons d'états:

$$\left| \pm \frac{9}{2} \right\rangle, \left| \pm \frac{1}{2} \right\rangle \text{ et } \left| \mp \frac{7}{2} \right\rangle \text{ d'une part et } \left| \pm \frac{5}{2} \right\rangle \text{ et } \left| \mp \frac{3}{2} \right\rangle \text{ d'autre part.}$$

L'introduction dans l'Hamiltonien des termes perturbateurs $a_2^2 (Y_2^2 + Y_{-2}^2)$ provoque un mélange de ces états. Le coefficient de mélange dépend essentiellement de a_2^2/a_0^2, et la constante de Curie à très basse température est donnée, si on appelle $\cos \phi$ le coefficient de mélange, par l'expression:

$$C = a \sin^4\phi + 2b \sin^2\phi \cos^2\phi + c \cos^4\phi$$

Si on remplace les constantes a, b, c par leur valeur tirée de la théorie du modèle des charges ponctuelles on trouve que si ϕ varie de 0 à $\frac{\pi}{2}$, C peut osciller entre 0,6 et 0,7, ce qui est en accord avec l'expérience. D'autre part, le rapport des paramagnétismes constants à moyenne et très basse température permet, en faisant appel à la théorie de Van Vleck, d'évaluer grossièrement le paramètre a_0^2 et l'amplitude de la décomposition du niveau Γ_8.

La valeur trouvée, 200°K, est en accord satisfaisant avec la température de la zone de courbure de la courbe expérimentale, compte tenu des approximations grossières que nous avons faites. Les valeurs obtenues pour a_0^2 et a_2^2 en tenant compte des constantes de normalisation, sont comparables à celles obtenues pour l'Ytterbium à partir de l'anisotropie de site.

L'intérêt de ce cas est qu'il montre l'importance que peuvent prendre les termes perturbateurs par rapport à l'approximation couramment faite de la symétrie cubique du voisinage. Un cas analogue est celui du praséodyme. Il est exposé par ailleurs par Bélorizky.

V. Cas de l'Erbium

La valeur élevée de $J = 15/2$ rend, dans ce cas, les calculs très compliqués. La décomposition du niveau $^4I_{15/2}$ par l'Hamiltonien perturbateur de champ cristallin à symétrie cubique fait apparaître comme niveau fondamental un doublet très proche d'un quadruplet, les autres niveaux étant nettement séparés. On peut s'attendre, et c'est ce que l'expérience confirme, à ce qu'a température moyenne ce quasi sextuplet joue le rôle de niveau fondamental. La constante de Curie calculée ainsi est de 10 cgs, alors que la valeur expérimentale est de 8,85 pour 70°K T 300°K. Du paramagnétisme constant expérimental $0,72.10^{-2}$, on déduit la valeur de l'amplitude de la décomposition du niveau $^4I_{15/2}$: 550 $A = 300°K$. Elle est donc nettement plus faible que dans les cas précédents. Cela provient à la fois des constantes de normalisation apparaissant dans les calculs de composition des Hamiltoniens relatifs à chaque électron et d'une variation de la quantité π_4. De la valeur de A on déduit que la différence d'énergie entre le doublet fondamental et le quadruplet voisin serait de 15°K environ, alors que la zone de courbure de la courbe expérimentale laisse présager une amplitude de l'ordre de 50°K. Il est donc nécessaire de tenir compte de la symétrie exacte, et les calculs montrent qu'il est possible d'ajuster les paramètres pour rendre compte des résultats expérimentaux. Les résultats de Wolf et de son équipe montrent que l'anisotropie varie considérablement lorsque l'on passe du gallate à l'aluminate. Cette variation ne peut provenir que de la variation des facteurs:

$$\sum_{i=1}^{8} Y_0^2(\theta_i\phi_i)/d_i^3 \quad \text{et} \quad \sum_{i=1}^{8} Y_2^2(\theta_i\phi_i)/d_i^3$$

Une circonstance particulière intéressante est que, dans toute une zone des valeurs des θ_i ϕ_i d_i, le sous-niveau fondamental est un état $\langle 15/2 \rangle$ presque pur, ce qui justifie la forte anisotropie de site constatée expérimentalement par Wolf, et ce qui nous a permis de donner une bonne approximation de la courbe d'aimantation.

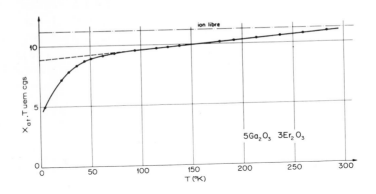

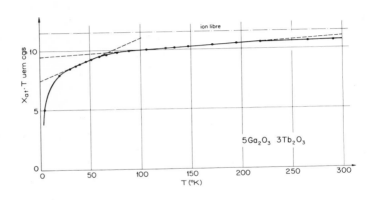

Un cas analogue de regroupement des sous-niveaux liés aux représentations du groupe du cube est celui du Terbium avec cette différence qu'ici, *J* étant entier, les sous-niveaux sont des signulets et non des doublets de Krammers. Quantitativement les résultats théoriques s'accordent assez bien avec les résultats expérimentaux.

VI. De tous ces résultats on peut tirer les conclusions suivantes

Le champ électrostatique dû à des charges ponctuelles disposées au centre des ions électronégatifs voisins de l'ion terre rare donne à un facteur près une bonne représentation du "champ cristallin"

En première approximation on peut disposer ces charges au sommet d'un cube. Cette approximation est valable au-dessus de $150°$K.

L'énergie de couplage est élevée: de 500 à 1500°K selon les cas, mais reste suffisamment petite devant l'énergie de couplage de structure fine: elle varie beaucoup d'un grenat à l'autre: cette variation provient de 2 facteurs:

–un facteur arithmétique provenant des propriétés du groupe du cube considéré comme sous-groupe du groupe des rotations. Ce facteur dépend de J et peut varier du simple au double.

–un facteur $\sigma_4 \overline{\pi^4}$ provenant de la structure électronique de la terre rare considérée. Il semble lui aussi sujet à de grosses variations d'une terre rare à l'autre et il est assez élevé.

L'approximation du voisinage à symétrie cubique n'est plus valable en dessous de 150°K. On trouve, sauf pour l'Ytterbium, ce qui s'interprète très facilement, un blocade plus grand. La correction à apporter fait intervenir des énergies de 100 à 200°K. Elle provient de l'écart entre la symétrie réelle et la symétrie cubique. Comme l'energie principale, elle dépend des facteurs arithmétique et de structure électronique et, en outre, d'un 3ème facteur d'origine cristallographique provenant des variations des paramètres des ions O^{--} dans la maille grenat. Ce facteur peut varier très sensiblement d'un grenat à l'autre (Cf. le cas de Tellium étudié par Wolf) et introduit une forte anisotropie de site. C'est lui qui est à l'origine des grandes variations des propriétés des grenats. Il est malheureusement très difficile à déterminer.

Etude de la Structure Hyperfine de l'Ion Pr³⁺
dans le Gallate de Praséodyme

E. Belorizky et Y. Ayant

Laboratoire d'Electrostatique et de Physique du Métal, Grenoble

SOMMAIRE

Les données paramagnétiques permettent de connaître d'une façon assez précise les niveaux électroniques de l'ion $Pr^{3+}(4f)^2\ ^3H_4$ dans les gallates. Le niveau fondamental électronique, un singulet, donne lieu à une structure hyperfine de l'ordre de quelques dizaines de MHz, entre les niveaux de laquelle on se propose de créer des transitions.

Le niveau fondamental de l'ion Pr^{3+} libre $(4f)^2$ est $^3H_4$. Dans une note précédente [1], nous avions étudié cet ion dans un potentiel cubique pur, et nous avions vu que le fondamental est un niveau triple appartenant à la représentation Γ_5, auquel on peut associer un moment cinétique fictif J' avec $J'=1$, et tel que $\mathbf{J}_{\Gamma_5}=5/2\,\mathbf{J}'(1)$; $\mathbf{J}$ étant le vrai moment cinétique.

En présence d'un champ non parfaitement cubique, on a un terme supplémentaire qui vient s'ajouter à notre Hamiltonien cristallin cubique, et qui, dans le cas des gallates, est totalement dépourvu de symétrie. Nous pouvons l'écrire.

$$H = A J_x'^2 + B J_y'^2 + C J_z'^2$$

Il est loisible par un choix convenable des axes, de supposer que l'on a

$$C < A < B \qquad \text{et} \qquad A + B + C = 0$$

Nous pouvons alors écrire la matrice représentative de H dans la base $|M_{J'}\rangle$, dont les valeurs propres sont $-A$, $-B$, $-C$ et les états propres normés associés:

$$|A\rangle = (1/2)^{\frac{1}{2}}(|1\rangle - |-1\rangle)$$

$$|B\rangle = (1/2)^{\frac{1}{2}}(|1\rangle + |-1\rangle)$$

$$|C\rangle = 0$$

Le niveau initial Γ_5 se décompose ainsi en 3 niveaux; nous allons déterminer les écarts entre ces niveaux, en considérent la courbe expérimentale donnant la susceptibilité paramagnétique χ du gallate de praséodyme en fonction de la température.

Le moment magnétique électronique provenant du niveau Γ_5, s'écrit

$$\mathbf{M} = - g_J \mu_B \mathbf{J}$$

μ_B étant le magnéton de Bohr; $g_J = 4/5$ est le facteur de Landé. En utilisant la relation (1), on peut écrire le moment magnétique sous la forme

$$\mathbf{M} = K \mu_B \mathbf{J'} \quad \text{avec} \quad K = 5/2\, g_J = -2$$

D'autre part, si on applique la formule de Van Vleck, donnant la suscepti-bilité d'un corps paramagnétique, sur les niveaux précédents, on obtient pour N ions de praséodyme:

$$\chi_{\text{observée}} = 1/3\,(\chi_x + \chi_y + \chi_z)$$

observée

$$= \frac{2\,K^2\mu_B^2 N}{3(1 + e^{-\beta A_1} + e^{-\beta C_1})} \left[e^{-\beta A_1}\left(\frac{1}{C_1 - A_1} - \frac{1}{A_1} \right) + \frac{1}{A_1} + \frac{1}{C_1} + e^{-\beta C_1} \right.$$

$$\left. \left(\frac{1}{A_1 - C_1} - \frac{1}{C_1} \right) \right]$$

avec $\beta = 1/kT$ et en posant pour les differences d'énergie entre les ni-vaux: $B - A = A_1$; $B - C = C_1$.

Mais nous n'avons pas tenu compte ici du paramagnétisme constant pro-venant des niveaux supérieurs et, dans tous les cas, il convient d'ajouter à χ une constante α, α étant donné par la pente de la droite (voir courbe). On trouve $\alpha = 1,35 \cdot 10^{-3}$

1. Etude aux hautes températures

On suppose les écarts entre les niveaux faibles devant kT. En faisant un développement en série on obtient:

$$\chi T = \frac{2K^2 \mu_B^2 N}{3k} \left[1 - \frac{\beta^2}{18}\,(A_1^2 + C_1^2 - A_1 C_1) \right] + \alpha T$$

Comme en unités C.G.S. on a $N\mu_B^2/3k = 0,125$ (N nombre d'Avogadro)

$$\chi T = 0,25 K^2 \left[1 - \frac{\beta^2}{18}(A_1^2 + C_1^2 - A_1 C_1) \right] + \alpha T$$

Aux très hautes températures, nous aurons une droite donnée par $\chi T = 0,25 K^2 + \alpha T$; l'ordonnée à l'origine de cette droite est $0,25 K^2$ et l'on trouve expérimentalement $(\chi T)_0 = 0,85$ d'ou $K^2 = 3,4$. Théorique-ment nous avons vu que l'on devrait avoir $K^2 = 4$ soit $(\chi T)_0 = 1$. Cet écart de 15% entre la théorie et l'expérience semble provenir de la présence

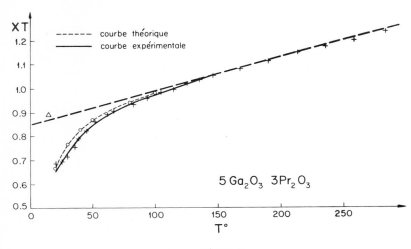

Figure 1

d'impuretés diamagnétiques dans le gallate dont on a étudié expérimentalement la susceptibilité. (On refait actuellement la courbe expérimentale avec un corps plus pur).

D'autre part, l'écart entre la droite et la courbe expérimentale doit être égal, pour des températures suffisamment élevées, à

$$\delta(\chi T) = \frac{0{,}250\,K^2}{18T^2}(A_1^2 + C_1^2 - A_1C_1)$$

A_1 et C_1 étant exprimés en degrés k. On vérifie que le produit $\delta(\chi T)\ T^2 \simeq 176$ reste constant et on a ainsi la relation

$$A_1^2 + C_1^2 - A_1C_1 = 3730 \qquad (2) \qquad ;\ (K^2 = 3{,}4)$$

2. Etude des basses températures

On suppose les écarts entre les niveaux grands devant kT. On peut alors écrire

$$\chi = \frac{2\,K^2\,\mu_B^2\,N}{3}\left(\frac{1}{A_1} + \frac{1}{C_1}\right)$$

D'après la courbe expérimentale, à la température de l'hélium liquide soit $T = 4{,}2°K$, on a $\chi T = 0{,}225$; d'où $1/A_1 + 1/C_1 = 0{,}063$. Par comparaison avec (2), on a $C_1 = 68{,}7°$; $A_1 = 20{,}7°$

Nous avons donc le diagramme de niveaux ci-contre

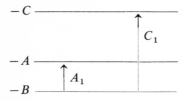

Compte tenu des valeurs de A_1 et de C_1 trouvées précédemment, la formule de Van Vleck s'écrit:

$$\chi T = \frac{0{,}85T\left[0{,}063 - 0{,}028e^{\frac{-20{,}7}{T}} - 0{,}035e^{\frac{-60{,}7}{T}}\right]}{1 + e^{\frac{-68{,}7}{T}} + e^{\frac{-20{,}7}{T}}} + 1{,}35.10^{-3}T$$

Nous voyons que nous obtenons une courbe théorique très voisine de la courbe expérimentale.

Etude de la structure hyperfine

Pour l'ion Pr^{3+}, l'Hamiltonin hyperfin magnétique peut s'écrire $H = A\mathbf{IJ} = A'\mathbf{IJ'}$; A' a été estimé à $0{,}092$ cm^{-1} d'après une étude expérimentale sur le fondamental $^4I_{9/2}$ de Pr $I^{(2)}$. La perturbation du premier ordre est nulle par suite de l'absence d'éléments diagonaux de la matrice $\mathbf{I}\cdot\mathbf{J'}$ dans la base du système non perturbé, c'est-à-dire $|M_I\rangle|B\rangle$

A second ordre du calcul des perturbations, nous aurons à traiter la matrice

$$A^2 \sum_{\substack{A,C \\ m_I''}} \frac{\langle m_I'|\langle B|\mathbf{I}\cdot\mathbf{J'}|A \text{ ou } C\rangle|m_I''\rangle\langle m_I''|\langle A \text{ ou } C|\mathbf{I}\cdot\mathbf{J'}|m_I\rangle|B\rangle}{E_B - E_{A \text{ ou } C}}$$

E_A, E_B, E_C étant les énergies des niveaux A, B, C.

On obtient ainsi: $H^{(2)} = -A'^2\left(\dfrac{I_z^2}{A_1} + \dfrac{I_x^2}{C_1}\right)$

Soit en experimant les énergies en MHz :

$$H^{(2)} = -(17{,}7I_z^2 + 5{,}3I_x^2)\,\text{MHz}$$

Mais nous devons tenir compte également du couplage quadrupolaire noyau-électron au premier ordre. Nous avons vu que ce couplage se traduit par un Hamiltonien effectif

$$H = C\left[\frac{13}{4}(\mathbf{J'}\cdot\mathbf{I}) + \frac{13}{2}(\mathbf{J}.\mathbf{I})^2 - \frac{5}{2}\sum_k \mathbf{J'}_k{}^2 I_k{}^2 + cte\right]$$

La constante C a été estimée à $0{,}21$ MHz $= 7.10^{-6}$ cm^{-1}

Nous devons traiter la matrice: $\langle m'_I | \langle B | H_Q | B \rangle | M_I \rangle$
et nous obtenons $H_Q = -0,8(I_z^2 + I_x^2)$ MHz

En ajoutant ces deux effets, on a un Hamiltonien hyperfin effectif

$$H = -18,5(I_z^2 + \eta I_x^2)\text{MHz avec } \eta = 0,33$$

La représentation de H dans la base $|M_I\rangle$ est une matrice d'ordre 6, symétrique par rapport à son centre, qui se ramène à un problème d'ordre 3. On obtient ainsi les écarts entre les niveaux du multiplet hyperfin.

Notre niveau fondamental (associé à la valeur propre — B de l'Hamiltonien cristallin non cubique) se décompose sous l'action du couplage hyperfin en 3 niveaux comme l'indique le schéma ci-dessous.

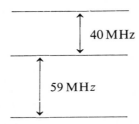

Remarquons que nous avons fait des calculs assez grossiers pour estimer l'influence d'un mélange de configurations faisant intervenir des électrons S; ces calculs semblent montrer que l'influence du terme de contact est négligeable.

Conclusion

Nous avons interprété la susceptibilité magnétique du gallate de praséodyme aux basses températures. L'existence d'impuretés diamagnétiques dans notre composé ne modifie en rien notre théorie puisque nous avons fait intervenir un facteur correctif; la courbe de susceptibilité du corps purifié sera simplement affine de la précédente. Nous attendons les résultats des expériences de résonance magnétique sur ce gallate pour poursuivre nos calculs. Nous allons étudier aussi d'autres composés du praséodyme et notamment le Pr dilué dans la thorine.

BIBLIOGRAPHIE
[1]   Y. AYANT ET E. BELORITZKY. *J. Phys. Rad.* **22,** 461 (1961).
[2]   LEW HIN. *Phys. Rev.* **91,** 619 (1953).

PART III

THEORY RELATED TO ESR

On the Spin-Hamiltonian Description of Energy Levels in Crystals

WALTER HAUSER

Northeastern University, Boston, Mass.

ABSTRACT

The coupling coefficients, $U_{k,ij}$, which appear in the group theoretical approach of Koster and Statz for treating the Zeeman splitting of the ground levels of a paramagnetic ion in a crystalline environment, are shown to be expressible in terms of the matrix elements of spin angular momentum operators such as appear in the conventional "spin-Hamiltonian" description of the energy levels. It is thus possible to construct the most general spin-Hamiltonian, which contains as many linear independent, irreducible tensor spin angular momentum operators, each multiplied by an arbitrary constant, as the number of arbitrary parameters required on the basis of symmetry arguments. The method is also applicable for the construction of spin-Hamiltonians in double or higher representations, as is done in the treatment of hyperfine splitting, where the spin-Hamiltonian contains both spin S and spin I angular momentum operators. We illustrate by constructing the spin-Hamiltonian for an ion in a cubic crystal.

I. Introduction

Paramagnetic resonance experiments concern themselves with the investigation of the lowest group of energy levels of a paramagnetic ion in a crystalline electric field. One approach which permits a rather simple description of the experimental results is the "spin-Hamiltonian" description [1]. The spin-Hamiltonian is an operator, a polynomial in the components of the spin angular momentum operators S_z and $S_{\pm} = S_x \pm iS_y$, whose eigenvalues are the energies of the observed levels, and whose eigenfunctions are linear functions of the fictitious spin eigenfunctions ψ_s^m. The number of such eigenfunctions, $2s + 1$, is chosen equal to the number of energy levels in the lowest group of levels under investigation.

A seemingly different group theoretical approach has been presented by Koster and Statz [2]. In the latter approach, the matrix elements of the Hamiltonian of an ion in a crystal, evaluated between the ground state wavefunctions, are related by means of the Wigner-Eckart theorem for point groups [3] to the coupling coefficients, $C_{\alpha\beta}(\gamma\nu \,|\, \lambda\mu)$, for the coupling of two sets of basis functions ϕ_α^λ and ϕ_β^μ, belonging respectively to the Γ_α and Γ_β irreducible representations of a point group, to form basis functions ϕ_γ^ν of the Γ_γ irreducible representation of the same group.

$$\phi_\gamma^\nu = \sum_{\lambda\mu} C_{\alpha\beta}(\gamma\nu \mid \lambda\mu)^* \phi_\alpha^\lambda \phi_\beta^\mu \tag{1}$$

Our $C_{\alpha\beta}(\gamma\nu \mid \lambda\mu)$ are the $U_{k,ij}$ used by Koster and Statz.

The constants which multiply the coupling coefficients in the Wigner-Eckart theorem are chosen so that the eigenvalues of the Hamiltonian matrix yields the experimentally observed energies of the ground manifold.

One objection to the former method is its use of fictitious spin eigenfunctions which in general do not have the same rotational properties as the actual unperturbed eigenfunctions of the ion in the crystal. We can readily conceive of examples where because of this fact the former method would require more arbitrary constants in the "spin-Hamiltonian" to represent the energy levels of the ground manifold than required on the basis of symmetry arguments by the group theoretical method of Koster and Statz.

We can overcome this objection by utilizing instead of the $2s + 1$ fictitious spin eigenfunctions mentioned above, spin wavefunctions which do have the same rotational symmetry as the energy states in the ground manifold. Such wavefunctions can be constructed from spin s' wavefunctions, which belong to the $D^{s'}$ irreducible representation of the continuous rotation group, if the irreducible representations of the point group in the ground manifold are contained within $D^{s'}$. It is always possible to obtain innumerable irreducible representations, $D^{s'}$, which contain the irreducible representations of the point group contained within the ground manifold. For all of these, $2s' + 1$ is in general larger than the number of levels in the ground manifold. We choose the spin functions belonging to the lowest $D^{s'}$ which contains all the irreducible representations of the point group whose energy levels we wish to represent. From these we form the functions

$$\phi_\beta^\mu(s') = \sum_{m'} a_{\beta\mu,s'm'} \cdot \psi_{s'}^{m'} \tag{2}$$

which are basis functions of the Γ_β irreducible representation. The coefficients $a_{\beta\mu,s'm'}$ are the elements of the matrix which reduces the $D^{s'}$ irreducible representation into the irreducible representations of the point group contained within $D^{s'}$. The coefficients for the cubic group have been tabulated by Griffith [1]. Other tables of the reduction matrices have appeared in the literature [4]. For our application however it is of utmost importance that the $D^{s'}$ be reduced into identical representations. We have computed these coefficients and agree with Griffith except for the phases of several coefficients, some of the Γ_5 coefficients for $s' = 3$, and some of the Γ_8 coefficients for $s' = 7/2$.

We proceed to show that if we proceed as outlined, then the two methods for describing the energy levels of ions in crystals are equivalent. Given the irreducible representations contained within the ground manifold, use of a table of the $a_{\alpha\lambda,s'm'}$ coefficients greatly facilitates the construction of a "spin-Hamiltonian" for the description of the energy levels of the ground manifold. Double and higher representations are also discussed.

II. Wigner-Eckart theorem for point groups

The evaluation of the matrix elements of symmetric operators was considered by Koster [3] who extended the Wigner-Eckart theorem for the full rotation group to such matrix elements. Koster showed that the matrix elements $\langle \gamma v | O_\alpha^\lambda | \beta \mu \rangle$ of the symmetric operator O_α^λ belonging to the Γ_α irreducible representation of a point rotation group G, evaluated between wavefunctions belonging to the Γ_γ and Γ_β irreducible representations of the same group, are related to the coupling coefficients, $C_{\alpha\beta}(\gamma v | \lambda \mu)$ for the coupling of two sets of basis functions ϕ_α^λ and ϕ_β^μ of the Γ_α and Γ_β irreducible representations to form basis functions of the Γ_γ irreducible representation.

$$\phi_{\gamma i}^{v} = \sum_{\lambda\mu} C_{\alpha\beta}^{i}(\gamma v \,|\, \lambda\mu)^* \phi_\alpha^\lambda \phi_\beta^\mu \qquad (3)$$

In the above equation, the symbol i is used to distinguish different sets of basis functions of the same Γ_γ irreducible representation which may be formed from the coupling of the basis functions of the Γ_α and Γ_β irreducible representations. The difference between the Wigner-Eckart theorem for the full rotation group and the point rotation group lies in this fact, that whereas for the full rotation group the $D^l \times D^{l'}$ representation contains the $D^{l''}$ irreducible representation, where $|l - l'| \leqq l'' \leqq |l + l'|$ only once, the $\Gamma_\alpha \times \Gamma_\beta$ representation of a point group may contain the Γ_γ irreducible representation more than once. There may exist therefore more than one coupling coefficient $C_{\alpha\beta}(\gamma v | \lambda \mu)$ which appears in the Wigner-Eckart theorem for point groups. Koster found that for such cases the Wigner-Eckart theorem is expressed by

$$\langle \gamma v | O_\alpha^\lambda | \beta \mu \rangle = \sum_{i=1}^{n_{\gamma,\alpha\beta}} k_i(\alpha, \beta, \gamma) \, C_{\alpha\beta}^{i}(\gamma v \,|\, \lambda\mu) \qquad (4)$$

where $n_{\gamma,\alpha\beta}$ is the number of times the Γ_γ irreducible representation is contained within $\Gamma_\alpha \times \Gamma_\beta$. The $k_i(\alpha,\beta,\gamma)$ are constants independent of λ, μ and v.

To relate the two methods for representing the energy levels of an ion in a crystal, we must be able to express the coupling coefficients $C_{\alpha\beta}^{i}(\gamma v | \lambda\mu)$

in terms of the matrix elements of symmetric spin angular momentum operators. Such operators can readily be constructed from the irreducible tensor operators S_s^m which transform irreducibly under the rotations of the full rotation group, belonging to the D^s irreducible representation. The symmetric spin angular momentum operators, $S_\alpha^\lambda(s)$ which belong to the Γ_α irreducible representation of a point group G are given by

$$S_{\alpha_j}^\lambda(s) = \sum_m a_{\alpha\lambda,sm}^j S_s^m. \tag{5}$$

The $a_{\alpha\lambda,sm}^j$ are the same coefficients which appear in equation (2). The j distinguishes the different $\phi_\alpha^\lambda(s)$ wavefunctions or $S_\alpha^\lambda(s)$ operators which may respectively be formed from spin s wavefunctions or S_s^m irreducible tensor angular momentum operators.

We now apply the Wigner-Eckart theorem for point groups to the matrix elements, $\langle \phi_\gamma^\nu(s') | S_\alpha^\lambda(s) | \phi_\beta^\mu(s') \rangle$ where $\phi_\gamma^\nu(s')$ and $\phi_\beta^\mu(s')$ are wavefunctions belonging to the Γ_γ and Γ_β irreducible representations formed from spin s' wavefunctions,

$$\phi_{\gamma_j}^\nu(s') = \sum_{m'} a_{\gamma\nu,s'm'}^j \cdot \psi_{s'}^{m'} \tag{6}$$

and

$$\phi_{\beta_j}^\mu(s') = \sum_{m'} a_{\beta\mu,s'm'}^j \cdot \psi_{s'}^{m'}$$

It is assumed that the smallest s' was chosen for which the Γ_γ and Γ_β irreducible representations are contained within D'. From Eq. (4) we have that

$$\langle \phi_\gamma^\nu(s') | S_\alpha^\lambda(s) | \phi_\beta^\mu(s') \rangle = \sum_{i=1}^{n_{\gamma,\alpha\beta}} K_i(\alpha,\beta,\gamma,s,s') C_{\alpha\beta}^i(\gamma\nu | \lambda\mu) \tag{7}$$

For $0 \leq s \leq 2s'$ there exist $(2s'+1)^2$ linear independent irreducible tensor operators S_s^m from which we can always construct $n_{\gamma,\alpha\beta}$ $S_\alpha^\lambda(s)$ operators. Numbering these $S_{\alpha,p}^\lambda$, where p goes from 1 to $n_{\gamma,\alpha\beta}$, we have that for those $n_{\gamma,\alpha\beta}$ linear independent operators, the equations

$$\langle \phi_\gamma^\nu(s') | S_{\alpha,p}^\lambda | \phi_\beta^\mu(s') \rangle = \sum_{i=1}^{n_{\gamma,\alpha\beta}} K_{i,p} C_{\alpha\beta}^i(\gamma\nu | \lambda\mu) \tag{8}$$

are $n_{\gamma,\alpha\beta}$ simultaneous equations which may be solved for the $C_{\alpha\beta}^i(\gamma\nu | \lambda\mu)$ in terms of the matrix elements $\langle \phi_\gamma^\nu(s') | S_{\alpha,p}^\lambda | \phi_\beta^\mu(s') \rangle$, if the determinant of the matrix, K, formed by the elements $K_{i,p}$ is not zero. It is readily shown [5] that we can always find $n_{\gamma,\alpha\beta}$ operators $S_{\alpha,p}^\lambda$ such that

$$\det K \neq 0.$$

Since the coupling coefficients are the elements of a unitary transformation such that

$$\sum_{\lambda,\mu} C^i_{\alpha\beta}(\gamma v \mid \lambda\mu) C^j_{\alpha\beta}(\gamma v \mid \lambda\mu)^* = \delta_{ij} \tag{9}$$

it follows from Eq. (8) that

$$\begin{aligned}
K_{i,p} &= \sum_{\lambda,\mu} C^i_{\alpha\beta}(\gamma v \mid \lambda\mu)^* \langle \phi^v_\gamma(s') \mid S^\lambda_{\alpha,p} \mid \phi^\mu_\beta(s') \rangle \\
&= \sum_{\lambda,\mu,v} \frac{1}{l_\gamma} C^i_{\alpha\beta}(\gamma v \mid \lambda\mu)^* \langle \phi^v_\gamma(s') \mid S^\lambda_{\alpha,p} \mid \phi^\mu_\beta(s') \rangle
\end{aligned} \tag{10}$$

Solving Eq. (8) for the coupling coefficients we obtain

$$C^i_{\alpha,\beta}(\gamma v \mid \lambda\mu) = \sum_{p=1}^{n_{\gamma,\alpha\beta}} K^{-1}_{p,i} \langle \phi^v_\gamma(s') \mid S^\lambda_{\alpha,p} \mid \phi^\mu_\beta(s') \rangle, \tag{11}$$

which when inserted into the Wigner-Eckert theorem, Eq. (4), yields

$$\langle \gamma v \mid O^\lambda_\alpha \mid \beta\mu \rangle = \sum_{p=1}^{n_{\gamma,\alpha,\beta}} A_p \langle \phi^v_\gamma(s') \mid S^\lambda_{\alpha,p} \mid \phi^\mu_\beta(s') \rangle \tag{12}$$

where

$$A_p = \sum_{i=1}^{n_{\gamma,\alpha\beta}} k_i K^{-1}_{p,i}$$

III. Application to the spin-Hamiltonian

The application of Eq. (11) to the construction of spin-Hamiltonians for the description of a group of energy levels of an ion in a crystal should be clear. If the unperturbed Hamiltonian, H_0, of an ion in a crystal is invariant to the symmetry transformations of the crystal, then barring any accidental degeneracies, the eigenfunctions belonging to the same energy eigenvalue are basis functions of an irreducible representation of the crystal point group. The manifold under investigation can therefore be decomposed into sets, each of which belongs to some irreducible representation of the crystal point group. Our method of representing these energy levels in terms of a spin-Hamiltonian requires a knowledge of the number of times each irreducible representation is contained within the manifold. To represent the eigenvalues of H_0 we utilize spin s' wavefunctions, where s' is chosen sufficiently large such that $D^{s'}$ contains all the irreducible representations at least as many times as they are contained within the ground state manifold. For example, suppose we wish to represent a manifold of eight levels belonging to the Γ_3, Γ_4 and Γ_5 manifolds of the cubic group.

We would then use $s' = 4$ wavefunctions since $D^4 = \Gamma_1 + \Gamma_3 + \Gamma_4 + \Gamma_5$, contains the irreducible representations within the manifold. We note that by the conventional spin-Hamiltonian description spin $s' = 7/2$ wavefunctions would have been utilized. To represent the energy levels of H_0 is quite simple. H_0 is a scalar and thus belongs, for the example chosen, to the Γ_1, irreducible representation of the cubic group. Its matrix elements, evaluated between Γ_3, Γ_4 and Γ_5 wavefunctions, require three Γ_1 operators chosen from combinations of the irreducible tensor operators S_s^m for $0 \leqq s \leqq 8$; $(2s')$. In all there exist four such operators one each for $s = 0, 4, 6$ or 8. The $s = 0$ operator affects all levels equally and is usually not explicitly included in the spin-Hamiltonian. The $s = 4$ operator is the familiar operator

$$S_{\alpha=1}^1 (4) = \sqrt{\frac{5}{24}} (S_4^4 + S_4^{-4}) + \sqrt{\frac{7}{12}} S_4^0 \tag{13}$$

$$= \frac{1}{4\sqrt{30}} \left[35S_z^4 + 25S_z^2 - 30S(S+1)S_z + 3S^2(S+1)^2 - 6S(S+1) \right.$$

$$\left. + \frac{5}{2} (S_+^4 + S_-^4) \right].$$

The irreducible operators S_s^m have been tabulated for $s \leqq 5$ by Koster and Statz [2], and we have extended the table up to values of $s \leqq 7$. We should like to note the error in S_2^0 in the table of Koster and Statz. The $s = 6$ operator is

$$S_{\alpha=1}^1 (6) = \frac{\sqrt{7}}{4} (S_6^4 + S_6^{-4}) - \frac{\sqrt{2}}{4} S_6^0. \tag{14}$$

These three operators are sufficient to represent any order of the three sets of levels and their respective energies.

Of greater interest are of course the energy levels of the Hamiltonian of an ion in a crystal which contains besides the invariant unperturbed Hamiltonian operator H_0, the operator H_1 which is not invariant under the rotations of the point group. Such an operator will of course split the degenerate levels of H_0. The splitting of these levels will depend a great deal on the spacing of the levels in the manifold from each other and from other nearby levels. We assume that the effect of the levels not included in the manifold is negligible. If this were not so, then the ones whose effect is not negligible should also have been included in the manifold. To compute the effect of the perturbation H_1 on the energy levels, one proceeds as in a degenerate perturbation calculation. That is, one evaluates the matrix elements of $H_0 + H_1$ between the unperturbed eigenfunctions of H_0. The roots of the secular determinant formed with these matrix elements are the eigenvalues of $H_0 + H_1$.

In our "spin-Hamiltonian" description of the energy levels we express H_1 in terms of a sum of the operators O_α^λ,

$$H_1 = \sum_{\alpha,\lambda} A_\alpha^\lambda O_\alpha^\lambda \tag{15}$$

where the A_α^λ are constants. The matrix elements of each O_α^λ in H_1 are then represented by the matrix elements of operators $S_{\alpha,p}^\lambda$ as per Eq. (11).

Suppose for example we perturb the three energy levels considered above by the additional crystalline electric field term

$$f(r) Y_2^0 = A_3^1 O_3^1 . \tag{16}$$

and a magnetic field, **h**, term

$$\mathbf{h} \cdot (\mathbf{L} + 2\mathbf{S}) = A_4^1 O_4^1 + A_4^0 O_4^0 + A_4^{-1} O_4^{-1} \tag{17}$$

For the first term, O_3^1, since

$$\Gamma_3 \times \Gamma_3 = \Gamma_1 + \Gamma_2 + \Gamma_3$$

$$\Gamma_4 \times \Gamma_3 = \Gamma_4 + \Gamma_5 \tag{18}$$

and

$$\Gamma_5 \times \Gamma_3 = \Gamma_4 + \Gamma_5$$

we introduce into our spin-Hamiltonian four even $S_{\alpha=3}^1$ operators, one for the $\Gamma_3 - \Gamma_3$ matrix elements, and one each for the $\Gamma_4 - \Gamma_4$, $\Gamma_5 - \Gamma_5$ and $\Gamma_4 - \Gamma_5$ matrix elements. For $s \leq 8$ there exist five such operators. One each for $s = 2$, 4, or 6, and two for $s = 8$. From these five we require only four.

Similarly for the magnetic term, since

$$\Gamma_3 \times \Gamma_4 = \Gamma_4 + \Gamma_5$$

$$\Gamma_4 \times \Gamma_4 = \Gamma_1 + \Gamma_3 + \Gamma_4 + \Gamma_5 \tag{19}$$

and

$$\Gamma_5 \times \Gamma_4 = \Gamma_2 + \Gamma_3 + \Gamma_4 + \Gamma_5$$

we require five sets of odd $S_{\alpha=4}^\lambda$ operators, one each for the $\Gamma_3 - \Gamma_5$, $\Gamma_3 - \Gamma_4$, $\Gamma_4 - \Gamma_4$, $\Gamma_4 - \Gamma_5$ and $\Gamma_5 - \Gamma_5$ matrix elements. For $s \leq 8$ there exist six such operators, one each for $s = 1$ or 3, and two each for $s = 5$ or 7. All the operators mentioned above are readily constructed through use of a table of the $a_{\alpha\lambda,sm}$ coefficients and a table of S_s^m operators.

IV. Product representation

In Section II we related the matrix elements $\langle \gamma \nu | O_\alpha^\lambda | \beta \mu \rangle$ of the symmetric operator O_α^λ to the matrix elements of irreducible spin operators belonging to the same Γ_α irreducible representation. In this section we shall use the symbol J_α^λ for these operators. The J_α^λ are polynomials in the operators J_z and $J_\pm = J_x \pm iJ_y$. They transform irreducibly like the basis functions of the Γ_α irreducible representation. The matrix elements of these operators are evaluated between the wavefunctions $\phi_\gamma^\nu(j)$ and $\phi_\beta^\mu(j)$, which are constructed from angular momentum j eigenfunctions. Now from the theory of angular momentum we know that angular momentum j eigenfunctions, $\psi_j^{m_j}$ can be constructed from angular momentum l and s eigenfunctions.

$$\psi_j^{m_j}(l, s) = \sum_{m_l m_s} C_{ls}(jm_j | m_l m_s)^* \psi_l^{m_l} \psi_s^{m_s} \tag{20}$$

In a similar manner the operators $J_j^{m_j}$ from which the operators $J_\alpha^\lambda(j)$ are obtained, can be constructed from angular momentum operators $L_l^{m_l}$ and $S_s^{m_s}$.

$$J_j^{m_j}(l, s) = \sum_{m_l m_s} C_{ls}(jm_j | m_l m_s)^* L_l^{m_l} S_s^{m_s} \tag{21}$$

The spin-Hamiltonian representations which utilize the eigenfunctions $\psi_j^{m_j}(l, s)$ and the operators $J_\alpha^\lambda(j | ls) = \sum_{m_j} a_{\alpha\lambda, jm_j} J_j^{m_j}(l, s)$ is referred to as a product representation. It is used for example in the "spin-Hamiltonian" description of the hyperfine splitting of the levels of an ion in a crystal.

REFERENCES

[1]   B. BLEANY AND K. W. H. STEVENS, *Repts. Prog. in Phys.* **16**, 108 (1953);
      K. D. BOWERS AND J. OWEN, *Repts. Prog. in Phys.* **18**, 304 (1955);
      J. S. GRIFFITH, *The Theory of Transition Metal Ions*, Cambridge University Press, 1961.

[2]   G. F. KOSTER AND H. STATZ, *Phys. Rev.* **113**, 445 (1959);
      G. F. KOSTER AND H. STATZ, *Phys. Rev.* **115**, 1568 (1959).

[3]   G. F. KOSTER, *Phys. Rev.* **109**, 227 (1958).

[4]   R. A. SATTEN AND J. S. MARGOLIS, *J. Chem. Phys.* **32**, 573 (1960);
      R. PAPPALARDO, *Phys. Rev.* **109**, 227 (1958).

[5]   W. HAUSER, to be published.

Zero Field Splitting in Atomic Nitrogen

A. S. Chakravarty and R. Bersohn

Department of Chemistry, Columbia University, New York 27, New York

ABSTRACT

The origin of the zero-field splitting of the orbitally non-degenerate ground states of atomic nitrogen ($2p^3, {}^4S_{3/2}$) in crystals is not completely understood. One such contribution linear in field gradient and the dipole-dipole interaction was estimated by Pryce sometime ago for Mn^{2+} ($3d^5, {}^6S$). We have extended his idea for nitrogen atom and deduced a linear relation between the splitting parameters D and E of the conventional spin-Hamiltonian and the field gradients using hydeogenic wavefunctions and $p \to p$ and $p \to f$ excitations. Finally it is shown that reasonable values of the field gradients could give an agreement with the exeprimental D and E.

I. Introduction

In recent years a number of investigations have been reported on the zero field splitting in atoms and ions in crystals (especially the transition metal ions) which necessitate the working out of a theory which would explain, at least qualitatively, the origin of the zero field splitting in the above mentioned atoms and ions, which is not completely understood.

Some time ago Pryce [1] estimated the magnitude of the splitting parameter D in case of Mn^{2+} in a crystalline environment, on the reasonable assumption that the splitting arises due to the combined action of a crystalline field of the form $V_2 = H'(3z^2 - r^2)$ and the spin-spin interaction. In the present paper we have extended his calculation to include the higher excitations. For example, when an atom or an ion is in a p state and is perturbed by a crystal field of the form V_2, the electrons are excited to higher p- as well as f-states. These are represented by $np \to p$, and $np \to f$, where the former is a radial excitation and the latter an angular excitation [2]. Similarly an ion in a d-state will have $nd \to s$, $nd \to d$ and $nd \to g$ excitations. The work on transition metal ions will be reported in another place.

II. The theory

The form of the Hamiltonian representing the crystalline perturbation along the symmetry axis is given by

$$H_1 = - \sum_i \frac{1}{4} (3\cos^2\theta_i - 1) \left(\frac{\partial^2 V}{\partial z^2} \right)_0 r_i^2 \qquad (1)$$

305

and

$$H_1' = - \sum_i \frac{1}{4} \sin^2\theta_i \cos 2\phi_i \left\{ \frac{\partial^2 V}{\partial x^2} - \frac{\partial^2 V}{\partial y^2} \right\}_0 r_i^2 \tag{2}$$

in the plane perpendicular to the symmetry axis, where (r, θ, ϕ) is the position of an electron with respect to the nucleus and $(\partial^2 V / \partial x^2)_0$, $(\partial^2 V / \partial y^2)_0$ and $(\partial^2 V / \partial z^2)_0$ are the field gradients acting on the atom by the surrounding charges along the x, y and z axes respectively.

If the unperturbed ground states of the atom be perturbed by the Hamiltonians (1) and (2), we would get the perturbed states, which we denote by

$$\Psi^{(1)} = \frac{q_\parallel}{e/a_0^3} \Psi_{z^2}^{(1)} \tag{3}$$

and

$$\Psi'^{(1)} = \frac{\xi q_\parallel}{e/a_0^3} \Psi_{x^2-y^2}^{1)} \tag{4}$$

where we write

$$q_\parallel = \left(\frac{\partial^2 V}{\partial z^2} \right)_0$$

and

$$\xi = \frac{\left(\dfrac{\partial^2 V}{\partial x^2} - \dfrac{\partial^2 V}{\partial y^2} \right)_0}{\left(\dfrac{\partial^2 v}{\partial z^2} \right)_0}$$

e is the electronic charge and a_0 is the Bohr radius. We now have to find out the expectation value of the dipole-dipole interaction operator W_{dd} given by

$$W_{dd} = \sum_{i,j} g^2\beta^2 \left[\frac{\mathbf{s} \cdot \mathbf{s}_j}{r_{ij}^3} - \frac{3(\mathbf{s}_i \cdot \mathbf{r}_{ij})(\mathbf{s}_j \cdot \mathbf{r}_{ij})}{r_{ij}^5} \right] \tag{5}$$

between $\Psi^{(0)}$ and $\Psi_1^{(1)}$ and between $\Psi^{(0)}$ and $\Psi_1'^{(1)}$ where β is the Bohr magneton and g is the Landé splitting factor.

The expression (5) can be shown to be reduced to

$$W_{dd} = -\frac{3}{4} g^2\beta^2 \sum_{i<j} \frac{3z_{ij}^2 - r_{ij}^2}{r_{ij}^5} \left(S_z^2 - \frac{1}{3} S(S+1) \right)$$

$$-\frac{1}{4} g^2\beta^2 \sum_{i<j} \frac{3(x_{ij}^2 - y_{ij}^2)}{r_{ij}^5} \left(S_x^2 - S_y^2 \right) \tag{6}$$

where the first term is along the axis of symmetry and the second term in the plane perpendicular to the axis of symmetry.

Following Pitzer et al. [3], we can write

$$W_{ij} = \frac{3z_{ij}^2 - r_{ij}^2}{r_{ij}^5} = \left[\sum_{l=1}^{\infty} \sum_{m=-l+1}^{l-1} \frac{(l-m+1)!}{(l+m-1)!} \frac{r_i^{l-1}}{r_j^{l+2}} P_{l-1}^m (\cos\theta_i) P_{l+1}^m \cdot \right.$$

$$\left. \cdot (\cos\theta_j) e^{im}(\phi_i - \phi_j) \right] \tag{7}$$

and

$$W'_{ij} = \frac{3(x_{ij}^2 - y_{ij}^2)}{r_{ij}^5} = \left[\sum_{l=1}^{\infty} \sum_{m=-l+2}^{l} \frac{(l-m)!}{(l+m-2)!} \frac{r_i^{l-1}}{r_j^{l+2}} P_{l-1}^{m-1}(\cos\theta_i) P_{l+1}^{m+1} \cdot \right.$$

$$\left. \cdot (\cos\theta_j) e^{i(m-1)\phi_i - i(m+1)\phi_j} \right] \tag{8}$$

for $r_i < r_j$. For $r_i > r_j$, we have to interchange i and j on the right hand side of (7) and (8).

Thus we have

$$\langle \Psi^{(0)} + \Psi^{(1)} | W_{dd} | \Psi^{(0)} + \Psi^{(1)} \rangle = 2 \langle \Psi^{(0)} | W_{dd} | \Psi^{(1)} \rangle \tag{9}$$

Similarly,

$$\langle \Psi^{(0)} + \Psi'^{(1)} | W_{dd} | \Psi^{(0)} + \Psi'^{(1)} \rangle = 2 \langle \Psi^{(0)} | W_{dd} | \Psi'^{(1)} \rangle \tag{10}$$

neglecting the second order term which is very small. In Eqs. (9) and (10), $\Psi^{(1)}$ are obtained by perturbing $\Psi^{(0)}$ with (1) and $\Psi'^{(1)}$ are obtained from $\Psi^{(0)}$ by perturbing with (2).

From Eqs. (9) and (10), we get

$$2 \langle \Psi^{(0)} | W_{dd} | \Psi^{(1)} \rangle = \left[-\frac{6}{4} g^2 \beta^2 q_{\parallel} \left(\frac{a^3}{e} \right) \langle \Psi^{(0)} | W_{ij} | \Psi^{(1)} \rangle \cdot \right.$$

$$\left. \cdot \left(S^2 - \frac{1}{3} S(S+1) \right) \right]$$

$$= -\frac{6}{4} g^2 \beta^2 q_{\parallel} \left(\frac{a^3}{e} \right) (DD) \left(S_z^2 - \frac{1}{3} S(S+1) \right) \tag{11}$$

and

$$2 \langle \Psi^{(0)} | W_{dd} | \Psi'^{(1)} \rangle = -\frac{1}{2} g^2 \beta^2 \xi q_{\parallel} \left(\frac{a^3}{e} \right) (EE) \left(S^2 - S^2 \right) \tag{12}$$

where

$$DD = \langle \Psi^{(0)} | W_{ij} | \Psi^{(1)} \rangle \tag{13}$$

and

$$EE = \langle \Psi^{(0)} | W'_{ij} | \Psi'^{(1)} \rangle \tag{14}$$

Comparing Eqs. (11) and (12) with the spin-Hamiltonian

$$\mathcal{H} = D\left(S_z^2 - \frac{1}{3}S(S+1)\right) + E(S_x^2 - S_y^2) \tag{15}$$

we finally get

$$D = -\frac{3}{2}g^2\beta^2 q_{\parallel}\left(\frac{a_0^3}{e}\right) (DD) \tag{16}$$

and

$$E = -\frac{1}{2}g^2\beta^2\xi q_{\parallel}\left(\frac{a_0^3}{e}\right) (EE) \tag{17}$$

The above result applies to any atom with configuration np^3. We now proceed to deal with the specific case of the nitrogen atom.

The ground state of nitrogen atom is $2p^3$, $^4S_{3/2}$. We denote its wavefunctions by

$$a = Y_1^0 u_0'$$

$$b = \frac{1}{\sqrt{2}}\left(Y_1^1 + Y_1^{-1}\right)u_0' \tag{18}$$

$$c = \frac{1}{\sqrt{2i}}\left(Y_1^1 - Y_1^{-1}\right)u_0'$$

where Y_1^m are the normalized spherical harmonics of θ and ϕ and u_0' represents the radial part of the wavefunction and is r-times the zero order wave function. We now perturb these states by the Hamiltonian given by (1), and get the excited states [2].

$$a' = p_{10}Y_1^0 u_{2p\to p}' + p_{30}Y_3^0 u_{2p\to f}'$$
$$b' = p_{11}(Y_1^1 + Y_1^{-1})u_{2p\to p}' + p_{31}(Y_3^1 + Y_3^{-1})u_{2p\to f}' \tag{19}$$
$$c' = p_{11}(Y_1^1 - Y_1^{-1})u_{2p\to p}' + p_{31}(Y_3^1 - Y_3^{-1})u_{2p\to f}'$$

where

$$p_{10} = \frac{1}{5} \qquad p_{11} = -\frac{\sqrt{2}}{20}$$

$$p_{30} = \frac{18}{20\sqrt{21}} \qquad p_{31} = \frac{6}{20\sqrt{7}}$$

Similarly by perturbing the states (18) by the Hamiltonian (2), the excited states are given by

$$a_1' = p_{32}'(Y_3^2 + Y_3^{-2})u_{2p\to f}'$$

$$b_1' = p_{11}'(Y_1^1 + Y_1^{-1})u_{2p\to p}' + p_{31}'(Y_3^1 + Y_3^{-1})u_{2p\to f}'$$

$$\qquad + p_{33}'(Y_3^3 + Y_3^{-3})u_{2\to pf}' \tag{20}$$

$$c_1' = p_{11}'(Y_1^1 - Y_1^{-1})u_{2p\to p}' + p_{31}'(Y_3^1 - Y_3^{-1})u_{2p\to f}'$$

$$\qquad + p_{33}'(Y_3^3 - Y_3^{-3})u_{2p\to f}'$$

where

$$p_{32}' = \frac{1}{\sqrt{280}} \qquad p_{31}' = -\frac{1}{20\sqrt{7}}$$

$$p_{11}' = \frac{\sqrt{2}}{20} \qquad p_{33}' = \frac{\sqrt{3}}{4\sqrt{35}}$$

and, $u_{2p\to p}'$ and $u_{2p\to f}'$ occurring in expressions (19) and (20) are the radial and angular excitations respectively.

The exact forms of $u_{2p\to p}'$ and $u_{2p\to f}'$ can be found analytically by solving the differential equations given by Das and Bersohn (Eq. 3) provided we assume Slater's function for u_0', i.e.

$$u_0' = Nr^2 e^{tr} \tag{21}$$

where $t = \dfrac{(Z-s)\ \text{eff}}{2}$ and N is the normalization factor.

By making use of Eq. (3) of Das and Bersohn [2] we arrive at the required differential equations

$$\phi_{2p\to p}'' - 2t\phi_{2p\to p}' + \left(\frac{4t}{r} - \frac{2}{r^2}\right)\phi_{2p\to p} = -Nr^2(r^2 - \langle r^2 \rangle) \tag{22}$$

and

$$\phi_{2p\to f}'' - 2t\phi_{2p\to f}' + \left(\frac{4t}{r} - \frac{12}{r^2}\right)\phi_{2p\to f} = -Nr^4 \tag{23}$$

where

$$\phi_{2p\to p}\, e^{-tr} = u_{2p\to p}'$$
$$\phi_{2p\to f}\, e^{-tr} = u_{2p\to f}' \tag{24}$$

and

$$\langle r^2 \rangle = \int u'^2 r^2 dr$$

Solutions of (22) and (23) are

$$u'_{2p \to p} = Ne^{-tr} \left(\frac{3}{4t^2} r^4 + \frac{1}{6t} r^5 - \frac{10}{t^4} r^2 \right) \tag{25}$$

and

$$u'_{2p \to f} = Ne^{-tr} \left(\frac{1}{3t^2} r^4 + \frac{1}{6t} r^5 \right) \tag{26}$$

Since we now know exactly the excited states given by (19), we now proceed to find the expressions for DD given by (13) and EE given by (14), which are

$$
\begin{aligned}
DD = & \left(\frac{6}{25} \right) \iint u_0'^2(1) u_0'(2) \frac{1}{r_>^3} u'_{2p \to p}(2) \\
& + \left(\frac{53}{35 \times 5} \right) \iint u_0'^2(1) u_0'(2) \frac{1}{r_>^3} u'_{2p \to f}(2) \\
& - \left(\frac{51}{35 \times 5} \right) \iint u_0'^2(1) u_0'(2) \frac{r_<^2}{r_>^5} u'_{2p \to f}(2)
\end{aligned}
\tag{27}
$$

and

$$
\begin{aligned}
EE = & \left(\frac{3}{25} \right) \iint u_0'^2(1) u_0'(2) \frac{1}{r_>^3} u'_{2p \to p}(2) \\
& + \left(\frac{12}{35} \right) \iint u_0'^2(1) u_0'(2) \frac{1}{r_>^3} u'_{2p \to f}(2) \\
& - \left(\frac{54}{35 \times 5} \right) \iint u_0'^2(1) u_0'(2) \frac{r_<^2}{r_>^5} u'_{2p \to f}(2)
\end{aligned}
\tag{28}
$$

where the numbers in the brackets are the angular factors.

Performing the radial integrations for $t = \dfrac{Z - s}{2} = 1.95$, we get

$$
\begin{aligned}
DD &= -0.347 \times 10^{-2} \left(\frac{1}{a_0^3} \right) \\
EE &= -0.67 \times 10^{-2} \left(\frac{1}{a_0^3} \right)
\end{aligned}
\tag{29}
$$

III. Comparison with experiment

From the recent experiments on the nitrogen atom in potassium azide (KN_3) by Wylie et al. [4], we have

$$
\begin{aligned}
g &= 2.001 \qquad (g_{\parallel} = g_{\perp} = g) \\
D &= +0.0143 \text{ cm}^{-1} \\
E &= -0.002 \text{ cm}^{-1}
\end{aligned}
\tag{30}
$$

Now, at this stage, if the magnitudes of the field gradients ($q_{\parallel}$ and $\xi q_{\parallel}$) at the nitrogen atom in KN_3 were known from a reasonable charge distribution in KN_3, then we would have been able to compare our theoretical values given by (16) and (17) with the experimental values of Wylie et al., but unfortunately, this is not the case. We, therefore, substitute the values of DD, EE and the above experimental values of D and E given by (27), (28) and (30) respectively in our final expressions (16) and (17) and find out the total field gradient tensor. By doing so, we get

$$q_{\parallel} = + 7.606 \times 10^{14} \text{ statcoulomb/cm}^3$$

and   (31)

$$\xi q_{\parallel} = - 1.653 \times 10^{14} \text{ statcoulomb/cm}^3$$

The experiments done by Cole and McConnell [5] on nitrogen atom trapped in a molecular nitrogen matrix give

$$D = + 0.1016 \times 10^{-2} \text{ cm}^{-1} \tag{32}$$

for which we get, proceeding as before,

$$q = 0.54 \times 10^{14} \text{ statcoulomb/cm}^3 \tag{33}$$

A graph showing the variation of $\dfrac{D}{q_{\parallel}}$ and $\dfrac{E}{\xi q_{\parallel}}$ with $t = \dfrac{Z - s}{2}$ for the nitrogen atom is given in Figure 1.

IV. Discussion

This work on the nitrogen atom can formally be extended to other np^3 atoms such as P, As, Sb. When one goes to the elements beyond the first row of the periodic table, there is the problem that spin-orbit coupling may be an important or even the major source of zero-field splitting. With nitrogen one can have fair confidence that only the diplole-dipole interaction produces a torque on the spins.

We come now to the central question which enters in every discussion of the field gradient in solids. Is the distortion of the atom due to the overlap of the immediate neighbors or is it due to the field gradient of the lattice as a whole? Some time ago Bersohn [6] showed that the field gradient in ionic crystals due to the lattice is of the order of 10^{13} statcoulombs/cm^3 which is the correct order of magnitude of the field gradient acting at the nuclei of ions such as Na^+ and Al^{+++}. These calculations did not, of course, prove that the field gradient was not also produced by the overlap of nearest neighbors.

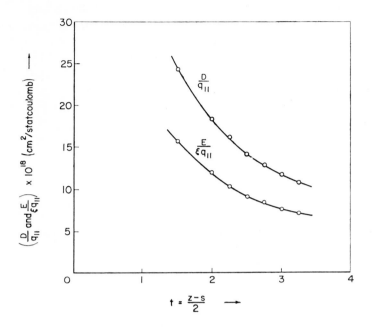

Figure 1

Variation of $D/q_{\|}$ and $E/\xi q_{\|}$ with $t = (z - s)/2$ for nitrogen atom.

In KN_3 a field gradient tensor was calculated for various assumed positions of the N atom i.e., at the central position of N_3^-, at one of the end N positions and at the interstitial position $(1/4, 1/4, 1/4)$. The tensors were sensitive to the assumed charge distribution in N_3^- but in no case did they resemble the experimental tensor as deduced from Eqs. (16), (17), (29), and (30).

The position of the nitrogen atom in solid nitrogen at $4.2°K$ is unknown and it is again difficult to estimate the field gradient. The nitrogen atom cannot be located at the center of a molecular vacancy because this site has cubic symmetry. If we represent each molecule by a point quadrupole of magnitude $eQ = 3 \times 10^{-26}$ statcoulombs cm^2 [7], the field gradient should be of the order eQR^5 where R is the intermolecular spacing in solid N_2, $eQR^{-5} \sim 10^{12}$ statcoulombs/cm^3 which is the order of magnitude of the field gradient inferred in solid N_2. It is reasonable that a nitrogen atom in a light non-polar crystal should be exposed to a much weaker field gradient that in the ionic crystal KN_3.

Effective comparison with experiment must await further experiments in which the location of the nitrogen atom is better known (one such would be the X-irradiation of a single crystal of N_2). Meanwhile it is hoped that the calculattion of D and E will be of conceptual interest.

REFERENCES

[1] M. H. L. PRYCE, *Phys. Rev.* **80,** 1107 (1950).

[2] T. P. DAS AND R. BERSOHN, *Phys. Rev.* **102,** 733 (1956).

[3] R. M. PITZER, C. W. KERN AND W. N. LIPSCOMB, *J. Chem. Phys.* **37,** 267 (1962).

[4] D. W. WHYLIE, A. J. SHUSKUS, C. G. YOUNG AND O. R. GILLIAN, *Phys. Rev.* **125,** 451 (1962).

[5] T. COLE, AND H. M. MCCONNELL, *J. Chem. Phys.* **29,** 451 (1958).

[6] R. BERSOHN, *J. Chem. Phys.* **29,** 326 (1958).

[7] C. H. TOWNES AND A. L. SCHAWLOW, *Microwave Spectroscopy*, McGraw-Hill, New York, 1955, p. 365.

DISCUSSION

G. BURNS, U.S.A.: How will the other contributions to D alter the value of the effective nuclear charge that you obtain for Mn^{2+}?

A.S. CHAKRAVARTY, U.S.A.: One does not know until one knows the sign of the contribution from the spin-orbit interaction.

The Ground State Splitting and Optical Spectra of d^5 Configuration in Cubic Crystalline Fields

W. Low and G. Rosengarten*

Department of Physics, The Hebrew University of Jerusalem, Israel

ABSTRACT

Gabriel et al.[1] have calculated the ground state splitting for Mn^{2+} ions in a cubic field. Using the same Hamiltonian we have calculated the ground state splitting, the energy level scheme and the wavefunction for Mn^{2+} and Fe^{3+} in a number of crystalline environments. Our calculations differ from those of Gabriel[1] that

a) We diagonalize the complete matrix including the spin orbit coupling rather than using a perturbation procedure.

b) We try to get the best fit to the optical spectra and to obtain the corresponding initial splitting.

c) We use 5 parameters including α, the Trees correction.

It is found that using reasonable values of the spin orbit coupling λ and crystal field strength Dq, the optical spectra can be fitted but the initial splitting in all cases is too small.

Introduction

Gabriel et al.[1] have recently calculated the ground state splitting of the Mn^{2+} ions in a cubic crystalline field. They constructed the matrices according to the cubic representation. The largest matrix, the Γ_8 matrix has a dimension of 42×42. This size of the matrix necessitated a perturbation calculation. They constructed a convergent perturbation technique, which was taken to the sixth order in order to find some splitting of the S state. They applied this technique in particular to the case of Mn^{2+} in MgO. This splitting has been measured by Low [2] and found to be $57 \times 10^{-4} \, cm^{-1}$. The optical absorption data on this crystal system are unfortunately not available. The authors used the absorption data of MnO as measured by Pratt and Colhoe [3]. They conclude that they cannot fit the optical spectrum (of MnO) and the ground state splitting (of MgO: MnO) with one set of parameters B, C, Dq, ξ and M_0; M_2. B and C are the electrostatic parameters, Dq the cubic crystal field parameter, λ the spin-orbit coupling, M_0 and M_2 two parameters arising from a spin-spin interaction. A possible fit of the ground state splitting can only be obtained with $Dq > 1100 \, cm^{-1}$ and for

* The research reported in this document has been sponsored in part by the Cambridge Research Laboratories OAR, through the European Office, Aerospace Research, United States Air Force.

$\xi \sim 300$ cm^{-1}. Such an unusual large crystal field would lead to a Stark level $^4\Gamma_4$ at less than 14000 cm^{-1} from the ground state. However, in MnO and in all hydrates this level is found to be 16.000 cm^{-1} or even higher. Gabriel et al. suggest tentatively that a simple crystal field calculation may not be adequate in accounting for the ground state splitting and the optical spectra.

We have independently undertaken a similar calculation as the above mentioned authors. We have used the same Hamiltonian. Nevertheless, our calculations differ in a number of significant aspects. Our largest matrix belongs to the doublet state Γ_8 and is of dimension 25 × 25.

We could diagonalize these matrices without having recourse to a perturbation calculation. Indeed our numerical results differ significantly from those obtained by Gabriel et al. using their parameters. As outlined below our method of fitting the experimental data is different as well. We have extended our computations to the case of Fe IV which was not considered by these authors. However, we concur with their main conclusion that one is unable to fit the optical spectra and the ground state splitting unless one uses a spin-orbit coupling parameter larger than that found in the free ion.

Method of calculation and results

The Hamiltonian consists of

$$\mathscr{H} = H_{\text{atomic}} + \xi \sum l_i s_i + V_{\text{cubic}}$$

where H_{atomic} is of the conventional nonrelativistic central field Hamiltonian. The eigenvalues of this part can be expressed essentially by means of four parameters A, B, C, and α. The parameter A is redundant as long as one considers only transitions within the configuration. B and C are linear combinations of Slater integrals, α the Trees correction (a term which was not taken into account by Gabriel et al.), ξ the spin-orbit coupling constant for the particular crystal, and V cubic crystal field potential given by

$$V_{\text{cubic}} \propto [Y_4^0 + \sqrt{\tfrac{4}{15}} \, (Y_4^4 + Y_4^{-4})].$$

All these four parameters may differ in magnitude from one crystal host to the next and of course also from that of the free ion.

Our calculations consisted in constructing matrices classified according to the Γ_6, Γ_7, Γ_8 representations, which have the following dimensions

Doublet states: Γ_6: 12 × 12; Γ_7: 13 × 13; Γ_8: 25 × 25
Quartet states: Γ_6: 8 × 8 ; Γ_7: 8 × 8 ; Γ_8: 16 × 16

An initial set of parameters was chosen which by inspection would give a reasonable good fit to the optical spectrum. Unfortunately, the optical data are not sufficient to determine all the five parameters. The two smallest parameters ξ and α were arbitrarily fixed, α taking the value α_0, that of the free ion. The spin orbit coupling parameter was varied between ξ_0 the free ion value and $0.7\,\xi_0$. With such an initial set of parameters the matrices were diagonalized. The center of gravity of the various calculated lines split by spin-orbit coupling was determined and this was compared with the broad lines determined from experiment. If necessary a least square fit calculation was made to obtain improved parameters. The matrices were again diagonalized using the new parameters.

There are no reliable optical data for either Mn^{2+} or Fe^{3+} in cubic fields. Probably the best optical data are for MnF_2 as measured by Stout[4]. However, the point symmetry for this crystal system is lower than cubic. We have taken the data of Stout and treated them as if MnF_2 were a cubic crystal. Table I shows the results of these calculations. We list the parameters used for the calculations. The first column gives the designation of the level. It shows the various admixtures from the "parent ionic levels". This admixture is caused in the main by the cubic field and to a lesser extent by the spin-orbit coupling. The next column gives the irreducible representation of the various spin-orbit split levels. The third column lists the calculated energy levels and the fourth column the measured absorption line. The fifth column gives the deviation between the measured and calculated levels. We finally list for comparison the measured absorption lines in various manganese hydrates. The agreement between the measured and calculated level for MnF_2 is remarkably good. The average deviation is less than 200 cm^{-1}. However, the initial splitting is only 10^{-3} cm^{-1}, compared with the initial splitting found in MgO:Mn as 57×10^{-4} cm^{-1} or in most hydrates about 3×10^{-3} cm^{-1}.

TABLE I

Comparison of optical spectra of MnF_2 with calculated values

Parameters all in cm^{-1}	
Crystal parameters	Free ion parameters
$B = 820$	$B_0 = 910$
$C = 3150$	$C_0 = 3270$
$\alpha = 76$	$\alpha_0 = 76$
$\xi = 320$	$\zeta_0 = 320$
$Dq = 750$	

TABLE I CONTD.

Name	Irreducible representation	Calculated value	Exp. value in MnF_2	Deviation	Exp. value in $Mn(6H_2O)^{2+}$
$99.9\%\,{}^{6}_{5}S\Gamma_1 + 0.07\%\,{}^{4}_{3}P\Gamma_4 +$	$\Gamma7$	$-$ 19.574	Initial	$+$ 19.6	
$0.03\%\,{}^{4}_{3}G\Gamma_4$	$\Gamma8$	$-$ 19.573	splitting unknown		
$59\%\,{}^{4}_{5}G\Gamma_4 + 40\%\,{}^{4}_{5}P\Gamma_4$	$\Gamma7$	19510			
	$\Gamma8$ I	19519	19440	$-$ 110	18900
	$\Gamma8$ II	19569			
	$\Gamma6$	19613			
${}^{4}_{5}G\Gamma_5$	$\Gamma7$	23443			
	$\Gamma8$ I	23491	23500	$-$ 30	23000
	$\Gamma6$	23580			
	$\Gamma8$ II	23587			
${}^{4}_{5}G\Gamma_1$	$\Gamma8$	25438			
${}^{4}_{5}G\Gamma_3$	$\Gamma7$	25443	25300	$-$ 19	25000
	$\Gamma6$	25454			
	$\Gamma8$	25455	25500		
${}^{4}_{5}D\Gamma_5$	$\Gamma8$ I	28386	28120		
	$\Gamma6$	28403		$-$ 285	28000
	$\Gamma8$ II	28614			
	$\Gamma7$	28777	28370		
$39\%\,{}^{4}_{5}D\Gamma_5 + 22\%\,{}^{2}_{5}I_{II}\,\Gamma_5$	$\Gamma7$	28699			
	$\Gamma8$	29096			
${}^{4}_{5}D\Gamma_3$	$\Gamma7$	30099			
	$\Gamma8$	30114	30230	$+$ 115	29750
	$\Gamma6$	30132			
$57\%\,{}^{2}_{5}I\Gamma_2 + 40\%\,{}^{2}_{3}F\Gamma_2$	$\Gamma7$	31866			
$61\%\,{}^{2}I\Gamma_4 + 19\%\,{}^{2}_{II}H_{II}\Gamma_4$	$\Gamma8$	32616			
$+ 17\%\,{}^{2}_{3}F\Gamma_4$	$\Gamma6$	32375			
$59\%\,{}^{4}_{3}P\Gamma_4 + 34\%\,{}^{4}_{5}G\Gamma_4$	$\Gamma8$ I	32958			
	$\Gamma7$	32965	33060	$+$ 62	32400
	$\Gamma8$ II	33024			
	$\Gamma6$	33062			
$39\%\,{}^{2}_{5}I_1\Gamma_5 + 26\%\,{}^{2}_{3}F\Gamma_5$	$\Gamma8$	33393			
	$\Gamma7$	33472			
${}^{2}_{5}I\Gamma_3$	$\Gamma8$	35410			
${}^{2}_{5}I\Gamma_1$	$\Gamma6$	37236			
	$\Gamma8$	38164			
$38\%\,{}^{2}_{3}F\Gamma_4 + 23\%\,{}^{2}_{5}G\Gamma_4$	$\Gamma8$	38406			
	$\Gamma6$	38473			
${}^{2}_{5}D\Gamma_5$	$\Gamma8$	38793	39000	$+$ 176	
	$\Gamma7$	38885			
$37\%\,{}^{2}_{5}G\Gamma_5 + 34\%\,{}^{2}_{5}I_1\Gamma_5$	$\Gamma7$	39727			
	$\Gamma8$	39952			

The data on MnF_2 are typical for a whole class of salts containing manganese. We report here only in detail this calculation for MnF_2. Many diagonalizations for different salts were undertaken. A full report containing all these energy levels will be given elsewhere.

Table II gives a comparison of ground state splitting of Mn^{2+} in a number of crystals. It is seen that the main parameters do not differ significantly. Indeed the differences are less than 5%. In all these cases the measured initial splitting is considerably less. Again using these parameters it is found that the calculated initial splitting is less than that found experimentally.

TABLE II

*Comparison of ground state splitting
of Mn^{2+} in various crystals*

	All values in units of cm^{-1}		
Parameter	MnF_2	$MnCl_2$	$Mn(6H_2O)^{2+}$ estimated
B	801 ± 21	758 ± 70	780
C	3158 ± 64	3082 ± 100	3130
a	76	76	76
ξ	320	320	320
Dq	752 ± 18	763 ± 50	575
Initial splitting	1×10^{-3}	$<1 \times 10^{-3}$	$\sim 1 \times 10^{-3}$
Measured splitting			$2–3 \times 10^{-3}$

The situation is not very different in the case of trivalent iron. Table III lists some of the spectra for iron in a number of crystal hosts. The spectra of Fe^{3+} in MgO are very weak and some of the bands may actually belong to Mn^{2+} in this crystal. Again the optical spectrum can be fitted reasonably well but the initial splitting is considerably smaller than that found experimentally.

Table IV summarizes the initial splitting for different sets of parameters. The second and third columns give the parameters which give a reasonable fit to the optical spectrum. These columns list also the calculated initial splitting $3a$ and the eigenfunctions of the ground state corresponding to the set of parameters. Columns three and four list the parameters used by Gabriel et al. with $\alpha = 0$ and $\alpha = 90$ cm^{-1} and the calculated splitting. It is to be noticed that the initial splitting is smaller by about 25% when $\alpha = 90$ cm^{-1}. Our calculated splitting differs from that found by Gabriel et al. who calculated (using the perturbation technique) a splitting of 53.6×10^{-3} cm^{-1} or nearly twice as large as that found by us.

TABLE III

Optical spectra of Fe^{3+} in solids

All levels in units of cm^{-1}				
$Fe(H_2O)_6^{3+}$ [5]	$Fe(H_2O)_6^{3+}$ [6]	Calculated	Fe^{3+} in beryl [7]	Fe^{3+} in MgO
12500	12600	13170	12300	12100
18000–190000	18200	18200		(15200) 18000
24500	24500	{ 24694 24820	-23600	-25500 (?)
27500		{ 26500 27300	{ 26800 28740	
$3a \sim 35 \times 10^{-4}$	35×10^{-4}	16×10^{-4}	45×10^{-4}	61.5×10^{-4}

TABLE IV

Comparison of ground state splitting of Fe^{3+}
as a function of electrostatic parameters

	All values in cm^{-1}			
B	730	750	1100	1100
C	3150	3250	4000	4000
α	90	90	90	0
ξ	300	420	440	440
Dq	1350	1350	2150	2150
$3a$	3×10^{-3}	16×10^{-3}	22×10^{-3}	29×10^{-3}
Admixture	99.88% $^6S\Gamma_1$ + 0.09% $^4P\Gamma$; + 0.02% $^4G\Gamma_4$	99.75% $^6S\Gamma_1$ + 0.19% $^4P\Gamma_4$ + 0.04% $^4G\Gamma_4$		

Experimental value in hydrates	35–45 $\times$ 10^{-3} cm^{-1}	
in MgO	61.5 $\times$ 10^{-3} cm^{-1}	

Since we obtain in our calculations not only the eigenvalue but the eigen-function as well, we can calculate the g-factors. In all cases the g-factors turn out to be smaller than 2.0023. It can, therefore, not explain the g-factors observed for the case of Fe^{3+} in MgO ($g = 2.0037$) or in CaO ($g = 2.0059$) [8]

which are considerably larger than 2.0023. Moreover, even the g-factors of Mn^{2+} cannot be accounted for from the calculated admixture of the ^4P wavefunction. The situation is not much improved when the admixture of the ^4P wavefunction is increased so as to fit the initial splitting.

Conclusion

Our calculations show that one can fit reasonably well the optical spectrum when the total matrix of cubic field and spin orbit coupling is diagonalized. The fit is indeed improved if the spin orbit coupling is diagonalized. The fit is considerably better using the 3 parameters B, C, Dq as freely adjustable parameters than using Stout's technique of including a covalency parameters. Considering the approximation of using cubic field symmetry in crystals of lower symmetry than cubic, the inexact knowledge of selection rules, the agreement is to be considered satisfactory. However, the calculated values of the initial splitting as well as the g-factors both for Mn^{2+} and for Fe^{3+} do not fit the experimental values. Fidone and Stevens[9] have pointed out that covalent bonding may effect considerably the g- factor and may even make it larger than that of the free electron. It is quite likely that covalent bonding may influence to some extent the initial splitting as well, and not only through changes in the parameters B, C and Dq, but through a dmixtures of p states.

Similarly the electron transfer spectrum may cause small admixtures of P wavefunction to the ground state while not affecting appreciably the relative spacing of the energy levels. The ground state splitting and the g-factor of this level is a very sensitive function of such admixtures whereas the other energy levels are not. In addition, the relative optical absorption intensities are affected by the electron transfer spectrum. The much more intense optical absorption for Fe^{3+} compared with Mn^{2+} indicates the stronger influence of the transfer spectrum. Very likely this is one of the causes for the stronger admixture of P and other levels to the ground state and therefore the larger initial splitting of Fe^{3+} in inorganic crystals.

This all points to the fact that the conventional crystal field is only a good first approximation in calculating the gross features of the optical spectrum. Within the framework of the theory one is able to account only in part for the finer details such as initial splittings and g-factors of transition elements. With the simple assumptions of the crystal field theory one should not ask for too much; one should be rather surprised that it can explain so much and calculate energy levels as well as indicated in the case of Mn^{2+} and Fe^{3+}.

We are grateful to Professor G. Racah for considerable assistance in the calculation of the matrices and for many helpful discussions.

REFERENCES

[1] J. R. Gabriel, D. F. Johnston and M. J. D. Powell, *Proc. Roy. Soc.* **A264,** 503 (1961).
[2] W. Low, *Phys. Rev.* **105,** 797 (1957).
[3] G. W. Pratt and R. Colhoe, *Phys. Rev.* **116,** 281 (1959).
[4] J. W. Stout, *J. Chem. Phys.* **31,** 709 (1959).
[5] H. L. Schlafer *Z. Phys. Chem.* Neue Folge **4,** 116 (1955).
[6] O. G. Holmes, D. S. McClure, *Chem. Phys.* **26,** 1688 (1957).
[7] M. Dvir and W. Low, *Phys. Rev.* **119,** 1587 (1960).
[8] W. Low and R. S. Rubins, *Physics Letters* **1,** 316 (1962).
[9] J. Fidone and K. W. H. Stevens, *Proc. Phys. Soc.* **73,** 116 (1959).

The ESR Spectrum of a d^9 Ion in an Octahedral Environment

M. C. M. O'Brien

The Clarendon Laboratory, Oxford

ABSTRACT

The octahedron of ligands surrounding a d^9 ion is distorted by the Jahn-Teller effect, the effective potential energy surface for the distortion having three equal minima with saddle points in between. The dynamics of the model proposed by Opik and Pryce [6] have been used as a basis for a calculation of the spin-Hamiltonian constants, and their variation with temperature. The results of the calculation have been compared with the spectra of the $Cu^{++}(H_2O)_6$ complex, and of Ni^+ as an impurity in the alkali halides. The theory accounts satisfactorily for a ligand hyperfine structure in Ni^+ that would not appear with a static distortion. The variation of the spectra of both ions with temperature cannot be accounted for by a straightforward Boltzmann distribution between the states, and a different spin-lattice relaxation rate for states of different energy is suggested. A calculation of relaxation times is in progress.

It is well known that a d^9 ion at the center of an octahedron of ligands is not in a stable state, and it will distort the octahedron to reach a stable state of lower symmetry. This application of the Jahn-Teller theorem has been discussed by Van Vleck [8], Öpik and Pryce [6], Liehr and Ballhausen [4] and others. It turns out that there are three equivalent distortions by which the complex can lower its energy by an equal amount, and the potential energy barrier between these distortions is relatively small. Experimentally this leads to the appearance of two types of ESR spectra: a low temperature spectrum of tetragonal symmetry, that of the ion when the complex is in one or other of its distorted states, and a high temperature, isotropic spectrum, when the vibrations average out the effects of the three different distortions. These spectra were first reported, for Cu^{++}, by Bijl and Rose-Innes [1] and by Bleaney, Bowers and Trenam [3].

In an attempt to get a better account of what is happening, we use the model of Öpik and Pryce [6]. The distortions of the octahedral complex are described in terms of the normal coordinates of E_g symmetry, Q_2 and Q_3, and only vibrations in which $Q_2^2 + Q_3^2$ is constant are considered. The potential energy for the vibrations is given by

$$V = A \begin{bmatrix} -Q_3 & -Q_2 \\ -Q_2 & Q_3 \end{bmatrix} + \frac{1}{2} M\omega^2(Q_2^2 + Q_3^2) + A_3 Q_3(Q_3^2 - 3Q_2^2) \quad (1)$$

which operates on the column matrix $\begin{bmatrix} a \\ b \end{bmatrix}$, where the electronic state is $a|x^2 - y^2\rangle + b|3z^2 - r^2\rangle$, a linear combination of the two d states of E_g symmetry. The term in A is the Jahn-Teller term, while the rest of V is a classical potential energy expanded in powers of Q_2 and Q_3 to third order. M is the mass of a ligand, and ω is the vibrational frequency for Q_2 and Q_3. We adopt the definitions of Q_2 and Q_3 given by Öpik and Pryce.

The lowest electronic eigenstate of this potential is

$$\cos\frac{\theta}{2}|x^2 - y^2\rangle + \sin\frac{\theta}{2}|3z^2 - r^2\rangle \quad (2)$$

if $Q_3 = \rho\cos\theta$ and $Q_2 = \rho\sin\theta$, and its energy is

$$-A\rho + \frac{1}{2} M\omega^2\rho^2 + A_3\rho^3\cos 3\theta. \quad (3)$$

This energy surface has a trough at $\rho = \rho_0 = A/M\omega^2$, and the bottom of the trough is corrugated by the third order term, $A_3\rho^3\cos 3\theta$, which at constant ρ has three minima and three maxima. We assume the sides of the trough are steep compared with its variations in depth, and hold ρ constant while solving the Schrodinger equation for θ.

The vibrational Hamiltonian to be solved is then

$$\left[\frac{h^2}{2M\rho_0^2}\frac{\partial^2}{\partial\theta^2} - A_3\rho_0^3\cos 3\theta\right]\phi(\theta) = E\phi(\theta). \quad (4)$$

Here the usual approximation has been made, that the electronic states follow the nuclear motion exactly, so that the electronic energy can be regarded as a potential for the nuclear motion. This equation has been solved numerically for a range of values of the parameters. The lowest eigenstates will occur in groups of three nearly degenerate states, corresponding to the three energy minima at $\theta = 0, \pm 2\pi/3$, while higher levels will be singly or doubly degenerate, and will not be concentrated near the energy minima.

The spin-Hamiltonian constants

The constants in the spin-Hamiltonian will be different for different vibrational eigenstates $\phi(\theta)$. In order to calculate them we again make the assumption that the electronic wavefunction follows the nuclear motion exactly. At a fixed value of θ the nuclei are in a position of orthorhombic symmetry, and the formulae given by Bleaney, Bowers and Pryce [2] can be used to give the g-values and other spin-Hamiltonian constants as functions of θ. The following results are obtained:

$$g_z = 2 - 4P(1 + \cos\theta) + 4P^2\left(-\frac{5}{4} - \frac{1}{2}\cos\theta\right) + 4Q(\cos\theta + \cos^2\theta) \quad (5)$$

$$A_z/p = -K - \frac{4}{7}\cos\theta + g_z - 2 + \frac{6}{7}P\cos\theta - \frac{3}{7}Q\cos 2\theta \quad (6)$$

Here g_z and A_z are the constants for the spin-Hamiltonian

$$\mathscr{H} = \beta(g_xH_xS_x + g_yH_yS_y + g_zH_zS_z) + A_xI_xS_x + A_yI_yS_y + A_zI_zS_z \quad (7)$$

under a static distortion of magnitude θ. The principle axes of the g tensor are unaltered by this distortion, and g_x, g_y and A_x, A_y can be found by replacing θ by $\theta \pm 4\pi/3$ in these expressions. p and K are the usual hyperfine interaction constants: $p = 2g_n\beta\beta_n\langle 1/r^3\rangle$ for the d electrons, and K allows for the admixture of unpaired s electron. The parameters P and Q depend on the energies of the excited d states $|xy\rangle$, $|yz\rangle$ and $|zx\rangle$ in the following way: we can write the energies of these states

$$E_{xy} = E - E_1\cos\theta$$
$$E_{yz} = E - E_1\cos\left(\theta + \frac{4\pi}{3}\right)$$
$$E_{zx} = E - E_1\cos\left(\theta - \frac{4\pi}{3}\right). \quad (8)$$

Then we can define P and Q by writing approximately

$$\frac{\lambda}{E_{\alpha y}} = P - Q\cos\theta \text{ etc.} \quad (9)$$

where λ is the spin-orbit coupling. The expressions (5) and (6) are correct to second order in P and first order in Q.

The actual g- and A-values for the spin-Hamiltonian for a given eigenstate $\phi(\theta)$ are then the expectation values of (5) and (6) in $\phi(\theta)$.

The ligand hyperfine structure

Other spin-Hamiltonian constants can be calculated in the same way. The ligand hyperfine structure is of particular interest. The magnitude of the hyperfine structure from a given nucleus will be proportional to the square of the coefficient of an orbital on that nucleus in the linear combination of orbitals describing the electronic state. The squares of these coefficients are given by the following expressions:

$$\frac{1}{6}\left[\eta - \xi\rho_0\cos\left(\theta + \frac{4\pi}{3}\right)\right]^2\left[1 - \cos\left(\theta + \frac{4\pi}{3}\right)\right] \text{ for ions on the x-axis}$$

$$\frac{1}{6} \left[\eta - \xi\rho_0 \cos \left(\theta - \frac{4\pi}{3} \right) \right]^2 \left[1 - \cos \left(\theta - \frac{4\pi}{3} \right) \right] \quad \text{for ions on the } y\text{-axis} \quad (10)$$

$$\frac{1}{6} \left[\eta - \xi\rho_0 \cos \theta \right]^2 \left[1 - \cos \theta \right] \qquad\qquad \text{for ions on the } z\text{-axis}$$

where the admixture of ligand orbital is assumed to depend on the distance of the ligand from the central ion. η is the admixture of ligand orbital when the ligand is at a distance R from the central ion, R being the equilibrium distance in the absence of the Jahn-Teller effect, and $\eta - \xi\delta R$ is the admixture when the ligand is at a distance $R + \delta R$. On this assumption the expressions (10) are correct to second order in η and $\xi\rho_0$, if the effect of spin-orbit coupling is neglected.

Application to experiment

(1) g-Values and central ion hyperfine structure

We see from Eqs. (5) and (6) that the g- and A-values for the spin-Hamiltonian in a given vibrational state depend primarily on the expectation value of $\cos \theta$ in that state. If the energy minima are very pronounced $\phi(\theta)$ will be sharply peaked at the minima, and we have three degenerate states with $\phi(\theta) \cong \delta(\theta)$, $\delta(\theta + 4\pi/3)$ and $\delta(\theta - 4\pi/3)$. The expectation values of $\cos \theta$ in these states are obviously $1, -1/2, -1/2$. Thus

$$g_z \cong 2 - 8P, \; 2 - 2P, \; 2 - 2P,$$
$$A_z \cong -\kappa - \frac{4}{7}, \; -\kappa + \frac{2}{7}, \; \kappa + \frac{2}{7}. \qquad (11)$$

These are recognisable as the approximate spin-Hamiltonian constants for a distorted complex which may have its tetragonal axis along the z, x or y directions, and the spectrum shows three similar ions differently oriented.

As we go to higher vibrational states the wavefunctions become more spread out, and $\langle \cos \theta \rangle$ approaches zero. When this happens

$$g_z = g_x = g_y \cong 2 - 4P$$
$$A_z = A_x = A_y \cong -\kappa. \qquad (12)$$

The spectrum then becomes isotropic, with its g-and A-values the mean of those in the anisotropic spectra.

For vibrational states of intermediate energies the picture is not so clean. This can be demonstrated by supposing we can fasten our attention on a set of three states in three very deep wells, and study their spectra, with a field along a cube axis, as the wells are made shallower. For simplicity we assume the nucleus has no magnetic moment. To begin with we would just see the spectra with the g-values given by Eqs. (11). As the wells become shallower the three degenerate vibrational states split up into a singlet and a doublet, with a splitting we shall call 3Δ. This splitting competes with the splitting by the magnetic field, and when Δ is comparable with the difference between g-values ($\sim 6P$) extra lines appear in the spectrum halfway between the existing lines, with a relative intensity approximately $8\Delta^2/(6P\beta H)^2$. The two lines at $g = 2 - 2P$, previously coincident, are now separated by an amount $4\Delta^2/6P\beta H$, and this effect should be very sensitive for the detection of a small Δ. As Δ increases the new line becomes stronger and splits into two, and two of the original lines disappear. For $\Delta \gg P\beta H$ we should still see three lines, the centre one at $g = 2 - 4P$; but as the wells become shallower the wavefunction, $\phi(\theta)$, becomes more spread out, $\langle \cos\theta \rangle$ decreases, and the three lines coalesce into one at $g = 2 - 4P$.

In a complex there will be many sets of eigenstates $\phi_n(\theta)$ with energies E_n At low temperatures the Boltzmann factor prevents all but the lowest from being occupied. We see the spectrum of the lowest set of three states, and should be able to determine Δ and $\langle \cos\theta \rangle$ for these states. At higher temperatures the spectra of states with higher energies should appear with larger values of Δ and smaller $\langle \cos\theta \rangle$, and the observed spectrum should consist of a superposition of spectra from all states with $E_n \lesssim kT$ Thus as the temperature is raised an isotropic spectrum at $g = 2 - 4P$ should gradually build up, but the low temperature spectrum should never entirely disappear. To account for the fact that the low temperature spectrum disappears, and that above a certain temperature only an isotropic spectrum remains, the relaxation processes must be included, and they will be discussed in a later section.

(2) The ligand hyperfine structure

The expressions (10) for the ligand hyperfine structure take a simple form if the well is very deep. In the state with $\theta = 0$, for instance, the probabilities of finding an electron in a ligand orbital are the following:

$$\frac{1}{6}\left[\eta + \frac{1}{2}\xi\rho_0\right]^2\left[\frac{3}{2}\right] \qquad \text{for ions on the } x\text{-axis}$$

$$\frac{1}{6}\left[\eta + \frac{1}{2}\xi\rho_0\right]^2\left[\frac{3}{2}\right] \qquad \text{for ions on the } y\text{-axis} \qquad (13)$$

$$0 \qquad \text{for ions on the } z\text{-axis.}$$

This corresponds to the fact that the ground state is an $|x^2 - y^2\rangle$ orbital, which bonds equally to the four neighbours in the xy plane, and not all to the neighbours on the z-axis. In this state we should thus expect to see a hyperfine structure from no more than four neighbours. If the well is not so deep, and $\langle \cos\theta \rangle \neq 1$, a hyperfine structure should appear from the other pair of neighbours, with a relative magnitude of about $1 - \langle \cos\theta \rangle$. Such a ligand hyperfine structure has been observed from Ni^+ in alkali halide crystals (Hayes and Wilkens, to be published). It provides the best direct evidence for an expectation value of $\cos\theta$ that is different from that predicted on a static model.

Relaxation

The states ϕ (θ) are states of the complex, but not eigenstates of the whole crystal. The effect of the rest of the crystal on the complex will be to cause transitions between the levels of the complex with some characteristic relaxation time, τ. The result will be similar to motional narrowing of the spectrum. $1/\tau$ will increase with temperature, and when it becomes comparable with the frequency difference between two lines of the spectrum those lines start to disappear, and are replaced by a single line at their mean frequency. As τ will vary rather rapidly with temperature there will be a rather narrow region of temperature in which its effect appears. Below this critical temperature the spectrum should be that of an isolated complex, while above it all irregularities are averaged out, and there will only be an isotropic spectrum with sharp lines.

A line width calculation made by McConnell [5] for a copper ion in solution has been applied by Orton, Auzins, Griffiths and Wertz [7] to the high temperature spectrum of a Cu^{++} ion in a cubic crystal. The significant difference between the two cases is that whereas the ion tumbling in solution takes on all possible orientation with respect to the applied field, the ion whose ligands are oscillating in a Jahn-Teller potential always has the same principal axes. The result is that in the Jahn-Teller case the relaxation only contributes to the line width a term due to frequency interruption, while in the liquid there is also a term due to phase interruption and a contribution to the spin-lattice relaxation rate. In the Jahn-Teller case spin-lattice relaxation will occur through higher states admixed by the spin-orbit coupling, as is usual for paramagnetic ions in crystals, and the vibrations considered here are of the wrong symmetry to produce this relaxation.

Discussion

We see that the resonance spectrum of a d^9 ion in octahedral surroundings depends on the relative values of a few parameters: the depth of the vibrational potential wells, $A_3\rho_0^3$; the effective mass of the system moving in the potential, $M\rho_0^2$; the relaxation time for transitions between vibrational levels, τ; and the spin-lattice relaxation time, T_1. For a low temperature spectrum to be seen $1/\tau$ must be less than $(g_{\parallel} - g_{\perp})\beta H/h$, while the spectra of higher vibrational levels, $\phi_n(\theta)$, will only appear if this condition continues to hold at temperatures such that $kT \cong E_n$. For a high temperature spectrum to appear $1/\tau$ must become comparable with $(g_{\parallel} - g_{\perp})\beta H/h$ at a temperature below that at which $1/T_1$ becomes so large that the spectrum is lost.

REFERENCES

[1] D. BIJL, AND A. C. ROSE-INNES, *Proc. Phys. Soc.* **A, 66,** 954, (1953).
[2] B. BLEANEY, K. D. BOWERS AND M. H. L. PRYCE, *Proc. Roy. Soc.* **A, 228,** 166.
[3] B. BLEANEY, K. D. BOWERS AND R. S. TRENAM, *Proc. Roy. Soc.* **A, 228,** 157 (1955).
[4] A. D. LIEHR AND C. J. BALLHAUSEN, *Ann. Phys.* **3, 304,** (1958).
[5] H. M. MCCONNELL, *J. Chem. Phys.* **25,** 709 (1956).
[6] U. OPIK AND M. H. L. PRYCE, *Proc. Roy. Soc.* **A, 238,** 425 (1957).
[7] J. W. ORTON, P. AUZINS, J. H. E. GRIFFITHS AND J. E. WERTZ, *Proc. Phys. Soc.* **78,** 555 (1961).
[8] J. H. VAN VLECK, *J. Chem. Phys.* **7,** 72 (1939).

Discussion

W. LOW, ISRAEL: Why is there no Jahn-Teller effect observed in the fluorescent spectrum from the ^2E level to the ground state in the case of Cr^{3+} say in the Hl_2O_3?

O'BRIEN, ENGLAND: I have not made the calculations to see whether the effect is small.

Anomalies of g-Factor due to Vibrational Coupling

ROBERT ENGLMAN

Massachusetts Institute of Technology, Cambridge, Mass.

AND

DAVID HORN*

Technion–Israel Institute of Technology, Haifa

ABSTRACT

The vibrational coupling with a degenerate ionic state is analyzed, with special reference to the cupric ion. In the first Part we find that (to some extent and approximately) the g-factor can be uncoupled from the vibrational motion and may be regarded as depending only on the electronic state. In the second Part approximate, analytical solutions are given of a fairly general class of Jahn-Teller problems, on the basis of comparison with computed eigenvalues.

In Part III a simple model is employed to show that a Cu^{2+} ion impurity in some cubic crystals will be subject to a moderate Jahn-Teller effect at higher temperatures and to an extremely strong one at low temperatures. This will give rise to two distinct situations. In the one, at high temperatures, the hole is constrained to rotate in function-space—and also in real space—showing an isotropic g-factor; in the other, in the strong coupling limit, the constraint is largely removed and the hole is partially free to orient itself. This freedom can now be removed by extremely tiny directional effects, as by a minute tetragonal field or even the applied magnetic field. In either case absorptions are anisotropic. The transition temperature depends roughly on the fourth root of the orienting field strength.

I. The g-matrix

The doubly degenerate states of Cu^{2+} in static cubic surroundings and coupled to a doubly degenerate mode of vibration of the neighbors will serve us throughout for illustration. The degenerate electronic states of symmetries $(1/\sqrt{3})(2z^2 - x^2 - y^2)$, $(x^2 - y^2)$ will be denoted alternatively as u, v or $\begin{pmatrix} 1 \\ 0 \end{pmatrix}$, $\begin{pmatrix} 0 \\ 1 \end{pmatrix}$ following Tanabe and Sugano [1] and Öpik and Pryce [2]. (In this representation the basic states of Longuet-Higgins et al. [3] are $(1/\sqrt{2})\begin{pmatrix} 1 \\ i \end{pmatrix}$, $1/\sqrt{2}\begin{pmatrix} i \\ 1 \end{pmatrix}$.) The relevant part of the spin-Hamiltonian is

$$H_i \begin{pmatrix} g_{ij}^u & g_{ij}^{uv} \\ g_{ij}^{uv} & g_{ij}^v \end{pmatrix} S_j \text{ where}$$

---

* Present address: Department of Physics, University of Tel-Aviv, Israel.

$$g_{zz}^u = 2 \qquad\qquad g_{xx}^u = g_{yy}^u = 2 + 6x_2$$

$$g_{zz}^v = 2 + 8x_1 \qquad\qquad g_{xx}^v = g_{yy}^v = 2 + 2x_2$$

$$g_{xx}^{uv} = -g_{yy}^{uv} = 2\sqrt{3}\,x_2$$

The x's are given in Griffith's book [4, p. 343] or in Low's book [5, p. 93] as the spin-orbit coupling constant over the separation from the levels of the $^2F_2$ states. We shall take $x_1 = x_2$.

The g-matrix can be resolved into its isotropic part $(1/2)(g_{ij}^u + g_{ij}^v)$ $\times \begin{pmatrix} 1 \\ & 1 \end{pmatrix}$ and an anisotropic part, with which we shall be mainly concerned.

$$\Theta_{ij} = \frac{1}{2}\left(g_{ij}^u - g_{ij}^v\right)\begin{pmatrix} 1 & \\ & -1 \end{pmatrix} + g_{ij}^{uv}\begin{pmatrix} & 1 \\ 1 & \end{pmatrix}.$$

The Hamiltonian describing the interaction of the electronic states with the vibration will now be written in three ways, for future reference,

1) $-\dfrac{1}{2}\left(\dfrac{\partial^2}{\partial X^2} + \dfrac{\partial^2}{\partial Y^2}\right) + \dfrac{1}{2}\left(w_1^2 X^2 + w_2^2 Y^2\right) + k_1 X\begin{pmatrix} 1 & \\ & -1 \end{pmatrix} + k_2 Y\begin{pmatrix} & 1 \\ 1 & \end{pmatrix}$

(the linear J-T effect)

(we do not write down the most general Hamiltonian, but just the one we shall use).

2) When $w_1 = w_2$, it is useful to write $X = R\sin\phi$, $Y = R\cos\phi$. Then in new units and a changed representation

$$-\frac{1}{2}\left[\frac{\partial^2}{\partial R^2} + \frac{1}{R}\frac{\partial}{\partial R} + \frac{1}{R^2}\frac{\partial^2}{\partial\phi^2} - R^2\right] + kR\begin{pmatrix} & e^{-i\phi} \\ e^{i\phi} & \end{pmatrix}$$

(degenerate modes)

3) The *quadratic* Jahn-Teller effect is represented by

$$\text{Kinetic energy} + \frac{1}{2}(\Omega_1^2 X^2 + \Omega_2^2 Y^2) + k_1 X\begin{pmatrix} 1 & \\ & -1 \end{pmatrix} + k_2 Y\begin{pmatrix} & 1 \\ 1 & \end{pmatrix}$$

where the Ω's are diagonal *matrices*, corresponding to the consideration[6] that the frequencies will depend on the electronic state.

The linear effect will have solutions of the form $\begin{pmatrix} f_n(X,Y) \\ h_n(X,Y) \end{pmatrix}$ having energy, E_n. It is important to realize that these states are still two fold degenerate since the state $\begin{pmatrix} h_n(-X,Y) \\ f_n(-X,Y) \end{pmatrix}$ has the same energy. Nor is the degeneracy removed by the cubic term introduced by Öpik and Pryce [2], it is however absent in the quadratic effect. This is of course the reason why we consider *this*.

Furthermore in the linear effect f_n and h_n may be so chosen as to have opposite parities in Y. Therefore, if we expand f and h in some suitable states (as is done by Longuet-Higgins et al., in a series of harmonic oscillators),

like $\left(\begin{matrix} \sum f_\mu^n | \mu \rangle \\ \sum h_{\mu'}^n | \mu' \rangle \end{matrix} \right)$, the two sets μ and μ' will not mix. Also $\sum_\mu |f_\mu^n|^2 +$

$+ \sum_{\mu'} |h_{\mu'}^n|^2 = 1$.

We shall now consider the temperature dependence of the g-factor for an isolated complex. We shall of course consider statistical averages, so that the pair of degenerate states will enter with the same weight, and any linear combination of them may be chosen. We shall chose the one specified above.

A temporary change of notation will now be introduced. We shall pass from the g-matrix to an operator operating in our two dimensional function-space

$$g_{ij} = 2 - \lambda \sum_k \frac{L_i | K \rangle \langle K | L_j}{E_k - \mathscr{H}}.$$

Since the ground state manifold and the excited states will not be, in general, and certainly not for Cu^{2+}, subject to the same Jahn-Teller effect, there will enter, through the denominator of this expression, a dependence of the g-matrix on the vibrational state of the ground state. (So it turns out now that the notation g'' etc. is insufficient. We shall try to justify it in this section!) However, because of the smallness of the vibrational energy as compared with the crystal field separation, the denominator may be expanded as follows. Suppose we have chosen the vibrational kets $| \mu \rangle$ introduced above to be vibrational eigenstates of the upper manifold. The effect of ignoring the Jahn-Teller effect in *this* manifold may be neglected. Let ε_μ be that part of the total energy E_k of an eigenstate which is due to the vibrations, the remainder, which is essentially the crystal field splitting, being denoted by Δ. Then

$$E_K - \mathscr{H} = \Delta + (\varepsilon_\mu - \mathscr{H})$$

the second term being small compared to the first. Expanding the denominator we have first

$$g_{ij}^0 = 2 - \frac{\lambda}{\Delta} \sum L_i | K \rangle \langle K | L_j$$

which has the following properties: When operating on our special

choice of states, $\left(\begin{matrix} \sum f_\mu^n | \mu \rangle \\ \sum h_{\mu'}^u | \mu' \rangle \end{matrix} \right)$ and its co-degenerate partner, it will be diagonal in the function space and its trace, which is what enters in thermal averages, will be independent of the vibrational state of the ground state. The term in the next order of the expansion will be

$$g_{ij}^{(1)} = - \lambda \Delta^{-2} \sum L_i |K\rangle \langle K| L_j (\mathcal{H} - \varepsilon_\mu)$$

The dependence of this term on the eigenstates can be seen by evaluating the matrix expectation values of $g^{(1)}$. By a simple calculation one finds that only the isotropic part of $g^{(1)}$ contributes. One also sees that, provided that in the absence of the Jahn-Teller effect the vibrational Hamiltonian of the ground states were identical with that in the upper state manifold, the operator $\mathcal{H} - \varepsilon_\mu$ is just the 'pure' Jahn-Teller matrix. Now there does not seem to be any analytical method to obtain the expectation values in any eigenstate, so we proceed as follows. At low or moderate temperatures a few lowest-energy states will sufficiently well represent the behavior of the system and we can calculate the expectation value for each of these numerically since we have an expansion of these state-vectors in vibrational eigenstates. (These were computed by Longuet-Higgins et al., we are indebted to Professor Pryce for letting us have them so readily.) At high temperatures we can do no better than calculate by operational methods the statistical mean and the deviation of the g-factor.

We want to bring our notation in line with the paper cited. Our states n are denoted there by p, m, our vibrational states μ are labelled by $m + k$ ($k = 1, 2, 3 \cdots$) and have energies $(m + k)\hbar w$. The coefficient of the $m + k$'th vibrational state will be denoted by $a_k(p, m)$. Then the expectation value

$$\begin{aligned}\langle \psi_{p,m} | g_{ij}^{(1)} | \psi_{p,m} \rangle &= (g_{ij}^{(is)} - 2\delta_{ij})\Delta^{-1} \sum_{k=1}^\infty [E_{pm} - (m+k)\hbar w] a_k^2(p,m) \\ &= (g_{ij}^{(is)} - 2\delta_{ij})\Delta^{-1}[E_{pm} - mhw - \hbar w \sum k a_k^2(p,m)] \\ &= (2\vartheta_{ij} - g_{ij}^{(is)})\Delta^{-1} \hbar w f(p,m)\end{aligned}$$

In the Table on the next page we show the first twelve values for the case $m = 0$, $k^2 = 5$.

These calculated values do not show any interesting behavior apart from the fact that they are not very far from one another.

The termal average of $g^{(1)}$ is

$$\overline{g^{(1)}} = - (g_{ij}^{(is)} - 2\vartheta_{ij})\Delta^{-1} Tr[F \exp(-\mathcal{H}/kT)] / Tr[\exp(-\mathcal{H}/kT)]$$

$F = - (\mathcal{H} - M)$, where M is the Jahn-Tellerless Hamiltonian, the diagonal part in the representation of the article cited.

p	1	2	3	4
E_{p0}	-1.961	$-.909$	.198	1.358
$f(p,0)$	5.117	5.347	5.708	6.038
p	5	6	7	8
E_{p0}	2.531	3.588	4.443	5.469
$f(p,0)$	5.957	4.472	4.241	5.896
p	9	10	11	12
E_{p0}	6.560	7.475	8.474	9.546
$f(p,0)$	5.060	4.126	5.786	4.966

The average value of F in the subspace m of the Hilbert-space p, m will first be calculated. This is

$$\langle F \rangle_m = Tr_m[F \exp(-\mathscr{H}/KT)]/Tr_m \exp(-H/KT)$$

In the first approximation, which is valid at high temperatures, we can write this as

$$\frac{Tr_m[F \exp(-M/KT)\exp(F/KT)]}{Tr_m[\exp(-M/KT)\exp(F/KT)]}$$

$$\approx \frac{Tr_m[F(1+F/KT)\exp(-M/KT)]}{Tr_m[(1+F/KT)\exp(-M/KT)]} \sim \frac{Tr_m[F^2\exp(-M/KT)]}{KT \cdot Tr_m[\exp(-M/KT)]}$$

$$= k^2 \sum_{n=m+1}^{\infty} n\hbar w \exp(-n\hbar w/KT)/KT \times \sum_{n=m+1}^{\infty} \exp(-n\hbar w/KT)$$

$$= \frac{k^2 \hbar w}{KT} \left[m + 1 + \left(\exp \frac{\hbar w}{KT} - 1 \right)^{-1} \right].$$

For high temperatures, i.e. for $kT > \hbar w(1 + |k|)$, we find that

$$\langle F \rangle_{T \to \infty} \to k^2 \hbar w$$

The breadth of the line of the g-factor can be found by a similar calculation where one looks for the second moment of the distribution of F. The result is now that $\sigma^2 = k^2 \hbar w KT$. These results are independent of m and are therefore generally true. When we look at the table we see that all the values of f lie in the neighborhood of k^2, which in this case is equal to 5, so there is no radical change in the g-factor over a full span of temperatures.

In so far as the limited scale of our calculations allows us to draw conclusions, we conclude that in spite of the Jahn-Teller effect the g-matrix may be regarded approximately as operating in the function space of the electron only. The primary effect of the vibrational coupling will be the reduction of the isotropic part of the g-matrix by a factor of $(1 - k^2 \hbar w \Delta^{-1})$. This result is however only true in terms of an average effective g. There will be a spread of actual values going at high temperatures as $(\hbar w k^2 \cdot KT)^{1/2}$, diminished however by the small factor $\hbar w \Delta^{-1}$.

II. Approximate analytic Jahn-Teller states

The ground state

The following ground-state 'solution' suggests itself for the linear Jahn-Teller effect:

$$\psi_0 = \exp\left\{-\frac{1}{2}w_1\left[X + k_1 w_1^{-2}\begin{pmatrix} 1 \\ & -1 \end{pmatrix}\right]^2 - \frac{1}{2}w_2\left[Y + k_2 w_2^{-2}\begin{pmatrix} & 1 \\ 1 & \end{pmatrix}\right]^2\right\}$$

$$= \exp\left\{-\frac{1}{2}w_1 X^2 - \frac{1}{2}w_2 Y^2 - \frac{1}{2}(k_1^2 w_1^{-3} + k_2^2 w_2^{-3})\right\}$$

$$\times \left\{\cosh w - \left[\frac{k_1 X}{w_1}\begin{pmatrix} 1 \\ & -1 \end{pmatrix} + \frac{k_2 Y}{w_2}\begin{pmatrix} & 1 \\ 1 & \end{pmatrix}\right]\frac{\sinh W}{W}\right\}$$

$$W^2 = \left(\frac{k_1 X}{w}\right)^2 + \left(\frac{k_2 Y}{w_2}\right)^2.$$

This matrix wavefunction is to be understood as operating on a pair of orthogonal linear combination of the states $\begin{pmatrix} 1 \\ 0 \end{pmatrix}$ and $\begin{pmatrix} 0 \\ 1 \end{pmatrix}$ giving rise to a degenerate pair. This solution is the extension from the cases where either the electronic state is non-degenerate or when only one mode operates. The extension is obviously not unique, owing to the fact that the two Pauli matrices do not commute and consequently ψ_0 is not equal, for example, to the product of two "gaussian wave-functions". One of our criteria for suggesting this 'solution' is that its properties and, in particular, its energy expectation values reproduce remarkably well, throughout the range of k, those of the exact solutions in the case of degenerate modes, while alternative extensions are wide of the mark. In this case then

$$\psi_0 = \exp-\frac{1}{2}\left[R + k\begin{pmatrix} & e^{-i\phi} \\ e^{i\phi} & \end{pmatrix}\right]^2$$

$$= \exp-\frac{1}{2}(R^2 + k^2)\left[\cosh kR - \begin{pmatrix} & e^{-i\phi} \\ e^{i\phi} & \end{pmatrix}\sinh kR\right]$$

$$= \frac{1}{2}\exp-\frac{1}{2}(R-k)^2\begin{pmatrix} 1 & -e^{-i\phi} \\ -e^{i\phi} & 1 \end{pmatrix} + \frac{1}{2}\exp-\frac{1}{2}(R+k)^2\begin{pmatrix} 1 & e^{-i\phi} \\ e^{i\phi} & 1 \end{pmatrix}$$

The expectation value of the Hamiltonian has the analytic form

$$\bar{E} = 1 - \frac{k^2}{2} - \frac{ke^{k^2}I(k) - \int_0^k dt e^{t^2} I(t)}{1 + 2ke^{k^2}I(k)}, \quad I(k) = \int_0^k dt e^{-t^2}$$

This is compared in Figure 1 with the exact values obtained computationally

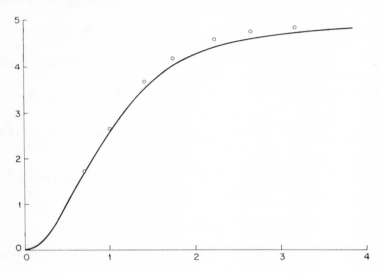

Figure 1

Comparison of approximate analytic energies (full line) and computed values (dots). $-(E - 1 - k^2/2)$ is plotted vs. k.

by Longuet-Higgins et al. The maximum error occurs at about $k^2 = 3$, its magnitude is equal to 6% of the relevant Jahn-Teller stabilization energy. $1 - k^2/2 - E$ is plotted vs. k, so that the exact values lie above ours. This being plotted, the agreement between our and the "experimental" values is perhaps not so impressive, since the 'sting' of the variation of E with high k has largely been removed.

An expansion of our expression gives us

$$E = 1 - k^2 \qquad k \ll 1$$

which is right to this order, and

$$E = \frac{1}{2} - \frac{1}{2}k^2 + \frac{1}{4}\frac{1}{k^2}, \quad k \gg 1$$

where the last term is only qualitatively correct, the right value being $1/8k^2$.

The rationale of these approximate solutions (and of those that follow) is that when vibrations are coupled with electronic states that are degene-ate, the equilibrium position of the mode will adjust itself to the electro-nic state. The solutions are not exact, however, because the electronic state is not a good quantum number. A perturbational correction seems feasible, but has not been developed so far.

A direct generalization of this scheme seems possible for the ground state of other situations subject to a linear Jahn-Teller effect, be they finite systems or crystals; and in the latter case involving either degenerate core electrons or conduction electrons.

If the method is extended to the quadratic effect one obtains a pair of solutions

$$\Phi = \exp\left\{-\frac{1}{2}\Omega_1\left[X + k\Omega_1^{-2}\begin{pmatrix}1 & \\ & -1\end{pmatrix}\right]^2 - \frac{1}{2}\Omega_2\left[4 + k\Omega_2^{-2}\begin{pmatrix} & 1\\ 1 & \end{pmatrix}\right]^2\right\}$$

which operate as before on $\begin{pmatrix}1\\0\end{pmatrix}$ and $\begin{pmatrix}0\\1\end{pmatrix}$. Writing the solution in the form

$e^{\begin{pmatrix}A & C\\ C & B\end{pmatrix}}$, we can find the following closed form

$$\Phi = e^{(1/2)(A+B)}\left\{\cosh W + \left[(A-B)\begin{pmatrix}1 & \\ & -1\end{pmatrix} + 2C\begin{pmatrix} & 1\\ 1 & \end{pmatrix}\right]\frac{\sinh W}{2W}\right\}$$

where $W = \frac{1}{2}\sqrt{(A-B)^2 + 4C^2}$,

which includes the linear effect as a special case. Now, however, the solution pairs are no longer degenerate, as they were in the linear case. To see what happens we return to the degenerate modes. The solutions of the linear effect can be written in the representation of *real* cubic harmonics u, v as

$$N^{-(1/2)}e^{-1/2R^2}\left\{\cosh kR - \begin{pmatrix}\sin\phi & \cos\phi\\ \cos\phi & -\sin\phi\end{pmatrix}\sinh kR\right\}.$$

If there is, in addition, a quadratic term present then in a cubic environ-ment this will be of the form

$$\alpha(X^2 - Y^2)\begin{pmatrix}1 & \\ & -1\end{pmatrix} = -\alpha R^2\cos 2\phi \begin{pmatrix}1 & \\ & -1\end{pmatrix}.$$

We can find the non-vanishing matrix elements of this within the original state. These are

$$\Delta\mathcal{H} = \alpha N^{-1}e^{-R^2}R^2\cos^2 2\phi \sinh^2 kR \begin{pmatrix}1 & \\ & -1\end{pmatrix},$$

showing that the cubic harmonics will be the eigenstates and that u will lie lower if $\alpha < 0$. The energy difference will be to first order in α

$$\Delta E = 2\alpha \frac{\int_0^\infty dx \, x^5 e^{-x^2} \sin h \, kx}{e^{-k^2} + 2kI(k)}$$

For small k this becomes $\Delta E \sim 2\alpha k^2$.

The splitting may have observable effects on the low temperature g-factor of some complexes. The formula

$$\bar{g} = g^{is} + \tfrac{1}{2} (g^u - g^v)(1 - e^{\Delta E/kT})/(1 + e^{\Delta E/kT})$$

is then appropriate.

It may be noted at this stage that an argument is presented in the following Part to the effect that in cubic *crystals* the effect of¦ the quadratic term is negligible.

The excited states

Some arbitrariness is left for the guessing of the excited states which is not present in the ground state. To have some guidance, one would have to conduct some numerical comparisons with the exact solutions available. This we have not done yet. Nevertheless, we believe that the following definition in terms of generating functions is the most suitable.

$$G(t_1 \, t_2) = \exp \left\{ -\frac{1}{2} w_1 \left(X + kw_1^{-2} \begin{pmatrix} 1 \\ & -1 \end{pmatrix} - 2t_1 \right)^2 \right.$$

$$\left. - \frac{1}{2} w_2 \left(Y + kw_2^{-2} \begin{pmatrix} & 1 \\ 1 & \end{pmatrix} - 2t_2 \right)^2 + t_1^2 + t_2^2 \right\}.$$

The individual wavefunctions are of course the coefficients of various powers of t_1 and t_2. These matrices operate on linear combinations of the basic vectors. Now however two orthogonal combinations will not be degenerate, in the sense of their energy expectation values being equal, as was the case in the ground state. There is nevertheless, a two-fold degeneracy discussed in the previous Part, which is, still possessed by these solutions. The appropriate linear combination is found by the diagonalization of the *matrix of the expectation values.*

In the degenerate case one makes the transformations $T^2 = t_1^2 + t_2^2$ and $\tau = \arctan t_1/t_2$. The eigen-solutions will be the coefficients of the powers of $e^{i\tau}$ and of T in the generating function

$$G(T,\tau) = e^{T^2} e^{-(1/2) \, R_t^2} \left[\cosh kR_t - \begin{pmatrix} & e^{-i\theta_t} \\ e^{i\theta_t} & \end{pmatrix} \sinh kR_t \right]$$

where $\theta_t = \arctan(X - 2t_1/Y - 2t_2)$ and $R_t^2 = R^2 + 4T^2 - 2RT \cos (\theta - \tau)$.

These functions have been tested by comparing their energy *expectation* values with the exact results for the limit of small and large coupling constants. In the latter case there is an error in the third term, which is $(1/2)(l^2 + 1/4)/k^2$ in contrast with $l^2 2k^2$, the result obtained by Longuet Higgins et al., Moffit and Thorson [7].

III. The anisotropy-isotropy transition in dilute copper salts

In a crystal a new type of problem makes its appearance, the collective interaction, through vibrations, of different Jahn-Teller sites. Papers by Goodenough et al. [8] and by Wojtowicz [9] are concerned with this problem. This latter disregards, however, interaction of all but neighboring sites due to the lattice modes. A preliminary formulation of the problem in terms of our approximate Jahn-Teller states shows formal similarities with the spin-wave problem. This leads us to expect, on the one hand a possible occurrence of phase-transitions, on the other—great mathematical difficulties in the solution.

However, even in the absence of interaction between sites, the collective nature of the vibrations changes the problem, in a solid from that of a complex, in essentials. This is typified by the anomalous behavior of some dilute copper crystals:

It is found that when the temperature of some copper salts is raised an "interesting transition" [10] takes place. Initially, below about 10°K, the g-factor is anisotropic. Subsequently isotropic lines arise, which then swallow up the anisotropic ones, "however, their appearance is as meagre as heretofore", i.e. no significant temperature broadening is observed. A wholly isotropic g-factor is found at temperatures which are roughly 50°K.

The meaning of this puzzle, like its Biblical predecessor, has claimed many solvers and fewer solutions. The Jahn-Teller effect has been evoked, but not very helpfully since the same cause was supposed to explain the anisotropic part through the elongation of the surrounding octahedron and, 'on alternate days', the isotropic part through the resonance about the various possible equilibrium situations, without indicating the cause of the transition. Indeed, one finds in some textbooks the implication that the isotropic state is the obvious one and the transition to the anisotropic state must be explained, and in others the opposite implication. In the theory we now propose to outline, both states are obvious in their proper domains. These are fixed by reasonable adjustment of some parameters. First we present the main ideas of the theory, then by means of a simple model we establish the results; subsequently we shall put the theory on a more formal footing.

The local Jahn-Teller distortion around the ion implicates *all* modes of a certain type—those which in the terminology of molecular (lattice) vibrations are even (odd) about the ion—. Two factors determine the relative efficiency of the modes: the efficacy of the mode in its zero point motion and the possibility of its excitation to its higher harmonics. This latter shifts the emphasis from higher to lower frequencies as the temperature is lowered. The former factor depends in turn on the extent to which a local distortion affects an infinite wave: this goes linearly with the wave number, i.e. at the start it increases linearly with frequency then it levels off, and also on the softness of the mode, which is inversely proportional to the frequency *squared*. The net result is then that, the lower the frequency of a mode, the more effective it is. This means that as we lower the temperature we find the Jahn-Teller effect enhanced. (We wish to emphasize that we do not bring in some mystical outside effect which gets more or less important as the temperature is changed; no, we rest throughout within the framework of the problem and apply statistical considerations to it.) Now it is a property of the effect (we show this below) that when weak, it will only allow states which represent rotations in the space of the doubly degenerate functions while, when strong, some of the different rotational states are nearly degenerate and many kinds of linear combinations of them may be formed. (We would not know what happens when the Jahn-Teller coupling tends to zero, but this cannot happen even at the highest temperatures since the characteristic frequency must tend to a finite limiting value.) In the former case (weak effect, high temperatures) the paramagnetic resonance transition will be isotropic since only transitions between rotational states can occur and in this representation the anisotropic g-matrix is strictly off-diagonal. In the other case (strong effect, low temperatures) the Jahn-Teller effect will not be definitive in selecting the appropriate combinations of the degenerate functions. These will then be fixed either by a tetragonal field, no matter how small, or, even in the absence of this, by the solutions of the anisotropic g-matrix. Transitions will then take place between levels which are directionally oriented.

It may be asked that if we include such minute terms as $H \cdot g \cdot s$ in the energy matrix, surely, the higher order terms as for example the quadratic Jahn-Teller effect, advocated by Liehr and Ballhausen [6] will be many orders of magnitude more effective. The answer is that at any finite temperature these terms, though individually more effective, will be neutralized by a factor $N^{-1/2}$. (N is the number of sites in the crystal.) This follows from the fact that at any finite temperature there will be about N such quadratic terms whose mean value, when evaluated in any vibrational state, will add up destructively, so that the actual term entering the matrix will be the mean *fluctuation* from exact cancellation, i.e. of the order $N^{-1/2}$. At absolute zero in a cubic crystal these terms add up to zero exactly.

To give a straightforward demonstration of the mechanism of the transition we will continue to consider a single frequency to be operative. This may be the frequency of a mode which typifies the behavior of the crystal. Alternatively we may wish to consider an Einstein model of a crystal, all of whose modes have a common frequency. We can then make a unitary transformation on the modes to the coordinates of vibration of the nearest neighbor octahedron which will be subject to the Jahn-Teller effect and to other modes which will not be. In either case, in order that this single frequency be an *effective* frequency we must take it to be a function of the temperature, $w(T)$, initially increasing with T and then levelling off to the Debye frequency. We next consider

$$K = qk/\hbar\omega = q \langle u \, | \, \partial V / \partial q \, | \, v \rangle / \hbar\omega$$

as a function of frequency and indirectly of temperature. K is the effective strength of the Jahn-Teller effect. We shall further define an instability temperature, by writing K as the ratio of this to the Debye temperature

$$K_\infty = \Theta_I / \Theta_D$$

in the high temperature limit when ω tends to its limiting value. From the definition of K we know that in this limit it is of the order of unity or less. $1/2$ or $1/4$ is the kind of value which is suggested by both the g-factor experiments (Θ_D is probably of the order of 200°K, though we sadly lack information on this point) and a numerical estimate of the matrix element. Anticipating the conclusions that follow, we say that in cases where K_∞ should turn out to be much less than this, the anisotropic region will be at extremely low temperatures. If $K_\infty > 1$ then the high temperature behavior will have to be examined more carefully than done here; for cases however, where $K_\infty \gg 1$ (these are extremely unlikely to occur) we shall conclude that the region of purely isotropic g-factor cannot be reached. Further, generally,

$$K = \frac{k}{\hbar\omega} \sqrt{\frac{\hbar}{M\omega}}$$

where M is the effective mass of the vibration. This result, with a $\omega^{-3/2}$ dependence, is to be used if the single frequency model is strictly taken. When however ω is regarded as a *typical* frequency, then it is better to write

$$K = \bar{U}\, \frac{k}{\hbar\omega}\, \sqrt{\frac{\hbar}{M\omega}}\, .$$

Here $U = 2\pi R \sin\theta\, \omega/v$ (R is the radius of the octahedron, v is the velocity of the wave, θ is a phase factor, and the average is the root mean square value of $\sin\theta$) is a factor introduced by Van Vleck [11] to give the extent to which an infinite wave is affected by a local perturbation. This result is characterized by a weaker frequency dependence, as $\omega^{-1/2}$. Still, there is no qualitative difference between the two models; there will be a difference, however, when we start putting numbers into our results. Until then it is advisable to think in terms of the typical frequency model, it being more conservative and probably also more realistic.

Let us now consider afresh the whole problem—the ion subject to the Jahn-Teller effect and in the presence of an orienting field. This second will comprise the magnetic field entering through the spin-Hamiltonian and some tetragonal field, since only this last counts for an E state. Now we do not know whether this exists or not and what may be its magnitude. We therefore provisionally disregard it in favour of the magnetic field, which is definitely there, adding the reservation that future information on the tetragonal field may require the revision of some details, but not the substance of this theory.

We seek the eigenvalues and eigenvectors of the Hamiltonian in the vector space of $\frac{1}{\sqrt{2}}\,(u \pm iv)$,

$$\mathscr{H} = K \cdot E + \frac{1}{2} M\omega^2 R^2 + kR \begin{pmatrix} & e^{-i\phi} \\ e^{i\phi} & \end{pmatrix}$$
$$+ H \cdot g^{is} \cdot S \begin{pmatrix} 1 & \\ & 1 \end{pmatrix} + H \cdot \begin{pmatrix} & \Gamma \\ \Gamma & \end{pmatrix} \cdot S$$

where g^{is} is the isotropic part, with which we shall not be henceforth concerned, it being already diagonal.

$$\Gamma = \langle u | g_{ij} | v \rangle + i/2 [\langle u | g_{ij} | u \rangle - \langle v | g_{ij} | v \rangle]$$

is the non-isotropic part.

The solutions of the Jahn-Teller Hamiltonian (the first line of $\mathscr{H}$) were given by Longuet-Higgins et al. and by Moffitt and Liehr [12]. These can be written as

$$\psi_{pl} = \begin{pmatrix} f_{pl}(R) & e^{i(l-1/2)\phi} \\ h_{pl}(R) & e^{i(l+1/2)\phi} \end{pmatrix}$$

It is clear that the anisotropic g-matrix will have matrix elements only between states which differ in their l value by one, i.e. we have to write down and then solve the infinite chain of matrix connecting $\psi_{pl}, \psi_{p'l+1}, \psi_{p''l+2}, \cdots$. That part which connects the states p, l and $p', l + 1$ may be written as

$$\begin{pmatrix} E_{pl} & H \cdot \Gamma \cdot S \langle h_{pl} | f_{p'l+1} \rangle \\ H \cdot \overline{\Gamma} \cdot S \langle h_{pl} | f_{p'l+1} \rangle & E_{p'l+1} \end{pmatrix}.$$

First we solve this, then we return to the original matrix of infinite dimensions.

Now since the off-diagonal elements are minute, of the order of .05 cm^{-1} in the situation described by Bleaney et al., in all but a few very exceptional cases the matrix will be well-nigh diagonal. Let us however consider these exceptional cases. Consider first the limit when $K^2 \ll 1$ (high ω, T). Then $E_{pl} = \hbar\omega[p + l - 1/2 \pm (l + 1/2)K^2]$.

For $|E_{pl} - E_{p',l+1}|$ to be small this necessitates $p' = p - 1$, when

$$\Delta E = |E_{pl} - E_{p',l+1}| = \hbar\omega K^2$$

It is of course inconceivable that the least possible value of K, viz. $K_\infty = \Theta_I/\Theta_D$ be small enough for the off diagonal terms to be significant.

In the other extreme $K^2 \gg 1$ (low temperatures, small ω)

$$f_{p,l} = -\hbar_{p,l-1} \propto e^{-1/2(R-k)^2}, \quad \text{for } k > 0,$$

the low lying energies are

$$E_{pl} = \hbar\omega \left[(p - \tfrac{1}{2}) - \tfrac{1}{2}K^2 + l^2/2K^2 \right]$$

so that in the matrix $p = p'$, necessarily and since in our model as $T \to 0$, $\omega \to 0$ and $K^2 \to \infty$, this term will steadily tend to zero. In the intermediate region where $K^2 \sim 1$ we can find $\Delta E = |E_{pi} - E_{p'l-1}|$ either by interpolation between the two limiting cases, or by actual inspection of the eigenvalues given by Longuet-Higgins et al. The result is shown in Figure 2 where the spread in the region $K^2 \sim 1$ arising with different values of l is indicated. We also need the matrix elements $\langle f | h \rangle$. These are just about unity as $K \to 0$ and are $-1/2$ for $K^2 \to \infty$. We shall commit no error worth speaking of if we take it to be uniformly $-1/2$.

The eigenvalues of this matrix are $\pm \sqrt{[(\Delta E)^2 + 1/4 |H \cdot \Gamma \cdot S|^2]}$. This has two values for either sign of the spin S, shown in Figure 3, where we also show the four possible transitions under the application of the microwave field. Two of these transitions $(1 - 4), (2 - 3)$ are anisotropic since there is an energy difference involved which depends on the anisotropic g-matrix. In particular, there is a difference of $\pm 1/2 |H \cdot \Gamma \cdot S|$ in the transition $S_z = -1/2 \to 1/2$ near the origin, which corresponds to the

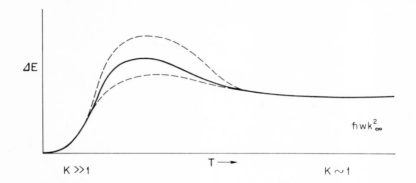

Figure 2

$|\Delta E|$ the difference in energies between states $(l,\ l+1)$ which are coupled by an orienting field, plotted (schematically) vs. temperature T.

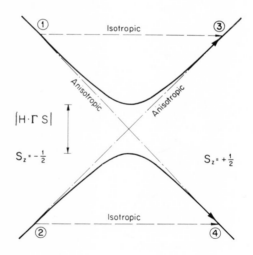

Figure 3

Levels and Zeeman transitions vs. $x = \Delta E/|\ H.\Gamma\ |S\ (|\ x\ |$ is a rapidly increasing function of temperature).

owest temperatures. Of course this energy difference is to be superimposed on the much larger *positive* energy difference which arises from the iso-tropic part. There are also the transitions $(1 - 3)$ and $(2 - 4)$ which are horizontal and necessarily isotropic.

The respective transitions have intensities

$$\left. \begin{matrix} (1-4) \\ (2-3) \end{matrix} \right\} \sin^2 2\theta,$$

$$\left. \begin{matrix} (1-3) \\ (2-4) \end{matrix} \right\} \cos^2 2\theta,$$

where

$$\sin^2 \theta = \frac{1}{(x + \sqrt{1 + x^2})^2 + 1} \qquad x = \frac{2\Delta E}{|H \cdot \Gamma| S}.$$

(see Figure 4). Accordingly at high temperatures, large x, *only* the isotropic transitions will occur, while for small x, at low temperatures, *only* the anisotropic transition will take place with finite intensity.

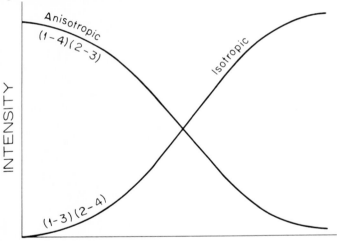

Figure 4

Relative intensities of the transitions depicted in Figure 3, vs. $|x|$.

We must estimate at what temperatures the transition to the anisotropic g-factor is expected, i.e. we must at last make some decision about the variation with temperature of the frequency. Now it will be shown subsequently that for temperatures which are much below both the Debye and the instability temperatures, we must take for our problem

$$\omega \propto T^{5/2} \qquad \text{for the typical frequency model}$$

$$\omega \propto T^{1/4} \qquad \text{for the single} \qquad \text{,,} \qquad \text{,,}$$

This means that

$$\Delta E \simeq l\hbar\omega K^{-2} = l(T/\Theta_D)^5 K\Theta_D^3/\Theta_I^2 \qquad \text{for the t.f.m.}$$

$$= l(T/\Theta_D)^7 K\Theta_D^3/\Theta_I^1 \qquad \text{for the s.f.m.}$$

Computing the former, more conservative model we find that, on the basis of

$$K = \Theta_I/\Theta_D = 1/4, \quad \Theta_D = 200°K, \quad l = 1$$

$$\Delta E = 7 \times 10^{-4} \text{ cm}^{-1} \text{ at } 10°K,$$

which is indeed very small. Actually a more careful (though unfortunately still not absolutely rigorous) procedure would increase this by a numerical factor between one and two orders of magnitude. Even so we find that at these low temperatures ΔE is reduced to or below the anisotropic part of the energy of transition.

$$2|H \cdot \Gamma \cdot S| \simeq 0.03 \text{ cm}^{-1} \text{ at } 0.3 \text{ cm}^{-1} \text{ microwave radiation}$$

$$\simeq 0.08 \text{ cm}^{-1} \text{ at } 0.8 \text{ cm}^{-1} \qquad ,, \qquad\qquad ,,$$

in the situation described by Bleaney, Bowers and Trenam.

Our theory is in error on two counts. One, because it predicts for the low temperature limit eigenvalues of $1/2 \ H\cdot\Gamma\cdot S$, whereas the factor half is obviously wrong; and secondly because only the two by two matrix was diagonalized instead of the infinite one. However, the two errors correct each other. For consider the limit $K^2 \to \infty$. In this limit we shall have a matrix for each p since the off-diagonal matrix-elements vanish if they involve different p's. If the rows of the matrix are labelled according to l, we shall have a bordered matrix whose off-diagonal elements are uniformly $-1/2 \ H\cdot\Gamma\cdot S$, all radial factors being identical, and the diagonal elements effectively zero. Let us terminate the matrix after N rows and columns. We can diagonalize it by means of the wavefunctions

$$\psi_k = \frac{1}{\sqrt{2N}} \sum_{s=0\ldots N-1} \binom{l-1/2+s}{l+1/2+s} e^{2\pi iks/N} \qquad k = 1, \cdots N$$

which has eigenvalues

$$E_k = \pm |H \cdot \Gamma \cdot S| \cos 2\pi k/N$$

On the face of it these form, in the limit $N \to \infty$, a continuous set of eigenvalues. However, the density of eigenvalues and therefore also the intensity of spectral lines is peaked infinitely sharply at the values $E_k = \pm |H \cdot \Gamma \cdot S|$

and drops sharply at any energy a finite distance from these peaks. This follows since the density of eigenvalues will be

$$\frac{1}{N}\frac{dk}{dE} = 1/\left|\sin 2\pi k/N\right| = \left(\left|H\cdot\Gamma\cdot S\right|^2 - E^2\right)^{-1/2}.$$

The lines will have a finite width, due to their wide wings which may possibly be unobservable. They will also be asymmetric. These assertions await experimental verification, as also does the following (which depends on the absence of a tetragonal field):

The transition temperature depends on the strength of the applied contant magnetic field, or equivalently on the microwave frequency, according to some relation like $T \propto H^{1/4}$.

REFERENCES

[1]   Y. TANABE AND S. SUGANO, *J. Phys. Soc. Japan* **9**, 753 (1954).

[2]   U. OPIK AND M. H. L. PRYCE, *Proc. Roy. Soc.* **238**, 425 (1957).

[3]   H. C. LONGUET-HIGGINS, U. OPIK, M. H. L. PRYCE AND R. A. SACK, *Proc. Roy. Soc.* **244**, 1 (1958).

[4]   J. S. GRIFFITHS, *The Theory of Transition Metal Ions*, Cambridge University Press 1961.

[5]   W. LOW, *Paramagnetic Resonance in Solids*, Academic Press, New York, 1960.

[6]   A. D. LIEHR AND C. J. BALLHAUSEN, *Ann. Phys.* **3**, 304 (1958).

[7]   W. MOFFITT AND W. THORSON, *Calcul de Fonction d'Onde*, Ed. Daudeb, CNRS, 1958, Paris.

[8]   J. B. GOODENOUGH, A. WOLD, R. J. ARNOTT AND N. MENYUK, *Phys. Rev.* **124**, 373 (1961).

[9]   P. J. WOJTOWICZ, *Phys. Rev.* **116**, 32 (1959).

[10]   B. BLEANEY, K. D. BOWERS AND R. S. TRENAM, *Proc. Roy. Soc.* **A228**, 157 (1955).

[11]   J. H. VAN VLECK, *Phys. Rev.* **57**, 426 (1940).

[12]   W. MOFFITT AND A. D. LIEHR, *Phys. Rev.* **106**, 1195 (1957).

[13]   A. ABRAGAM AND M. H. L. PRYCE, *Proc. Phys. Soc.* **63**, 409 (1950).

DISCUSSION

N. BLOEMBERGEN, USA: If the damping of the rotational states is taken into account, the region of coexistence postulated by Dr. Englman is washed out. Is there any difference in principle between the case discussed in these two papers and the well known case of the coalescence of two resonances of motional narrowing, as described for example in Abragam's book?

R. ENGLMAN, USA: It is possible that the life-time of organized vibrational motion is short enough for the purposes of NMR for the lattice motion to be regarded as random, Markoffian (as assumed by Abragam) and long enough for the present case to be regarded as organized (as essentially assumed in my work).

It would be very useful to redo the experiments which showed the region of coexistence.

Hyperfine Interactions with Ligand Nuclei in Transition Ion Complexes

W. MARSHALL

Atomic Energy Research Establishment, Harwell, Berkshire

ABSTRACT

Several effects contribute to the hyperfine interaction between an electron spin and the nuclear spin of the surrounding ligands. The main effect is due to the dipole interaction and Fermi contact interaction with the spin density produced on the ligands by the covalent mixing of ligand wavefunctions into the anti-bonding orbitals. But there are several smaller effects of some importance and these are discussed. The direct magnetic interaction can be expressed as an expansion involving various multi-poles of the electron spin and orbital moment distributions on the transition ion: the results are put into the form of equivalent operators. An unquenched orbital magnetic moment proportional to $(g-2)$ also appears on the ligand and gives an appreciable interaction in some cases. The main spin dipole term is also modified by the spin orbit coupling to produce a further correction proportional to $(g-2)$. Finally the spin orbit interaction taken to a second order produces a small anisotropic interaction proportional to a Fermi contact interaction with the spin density at the ligand nucleus. General formulae are given, and these are evaluated in the simple cases of Ni^{++} and Cr^{+++} ions, where it is found that the unquenched orbital moment on the ligand and the corresponding distortion of ligand spin density produce corrections of the order of $(g-2) \simeq 30\%$ for Ni^{++} but that the other terms are only about 1% corrections.

I. Introduction

In order to gain a good understanding of transition ion complexes it has proved very profitable to measure the hyperfine interaction between the electron spin nominally associated with the central ion and the nuclear spins of the surrounding ligands [1; 2]. The experiments so far performed have used F^- as ligands and have either observed the nuclear magnetic resonance of the F^{19} nuclei in the concentrated salt or have observed the electron paramagnetic resonance in the diluted salt [3; 4; 5]. The theory is easy to work out if the central ion has a half closed shell, i.e. Mn^{++}, but the most valuable experiments have proved to be those on other ions and for these several correction terms appear [5]. It is the purpose of this paper to enumerate these corrections and evaluate them in special cases of interest (Cr^{+++}, Ni^{++}, Cu^{++}). It will be concluded that these corrections are small but not so small that they can be neglected in accurate quantitative calculations.

In the conventional theory the unpaired electrons are placed in anti-bonding orbitals formed by a linear combination of the $3d$ orbitals of the central ion with the appropriate $1s$, $2s$ and $2p$ orbitals of the F^- ligands. The F^{19} nucleus is then taken to interact with the spin density on the ligand itself: the contact interaction, acting through the admixture of $1s$ and $2s$ orbitals in the antibonding orbital, gives an isotropic coupling between electron spin S and nuclear spin I whereas the admixture of $2p$ orbitals gives a tensor coupling which is of the same form as the direct dipole inter-action between the electron spin on the central ion and the ligand nucleus. These terms are included in the conventional theory and the correction terms we consider in this paper will now be described.

The spin density on the central ion has spherical symmetry for a half-closed shell (Mn^{++}, Fe^{+++}). In this case it is legitimate to replace it by a point dipole when calculating the direct dipole-dipole interaction. More generally however the spin density has a lower symmetry and the higher multipole corrections to the simple formula must be considered. This point is considered in Section II where it is shown that, in general, correction terms of order $1/R^5$ and $1/R^7$, where R is the central ion-ligand distance, appear. Unquenched orbital moment on the central ion produces inter-action terms like $1/R^3$ and $1/R^5$ which are evaluated in Section III. In Section IV the corresponding terms arising from the overlap region between $3d$ and ligand orbitals are considered using a simple approximation. The spin orbit coupling not only removes the quenching of the orbital moment on the central ion, it also removes the quenching on the ligand ion itself and this is evaluated in Section V; the spin density on the ligand is also affected and this point is discussed in Section VI. To second order in the spin orbit coupling the ligand admixture is asymmetrical in the sense that it depends upon spin orientation. This introduces an anisotropic coupling which is a small fraction of the isotropic coupling arising from the contact interaction; this effect is discussed in Section VII. Finally in Section VIII the particular correction terms appropriate for crystals of $KNiF_3$ and K_2NaCrF_6 are roughly evaluated. We begin by defining the problem and setting up a convenient notation.

The complex we consider with the usual notation [1] of ligands 1, 2 and 3 on the positive x, y and z axis respectively while 4, 5 and 6 are on the negative and x, y, z axes. We construct antibonding orbitals.

$$D_z^2 = N_\sigma \{ d_z^2 + a_\sigma [p_z^3 - p_z^6 - \tfrac{1}{2}p_x^1 + \tfrac{1}{2}p_x^4 - \tfrac{1}{2}p_y^2 + \tfrac{1}{2}p_y^5]$$
$$- a_s [s^3 + s^6 - \tfrac{1}{2}s^1 - \tfrac{1}{2}s^4 - \tfrac{1}{2}s^2 - \tfrac{1}{2}s^5] \}$$

$$D_{x^2-y^2} = N_\sigma\{d_{x^2-y^2} + a_\sigma\tfrac{1}{2}\sqrt{3}[p_x^1 - p_x^4 + p_y^5 - p_y^2] - a_s\tfrac{1}{2}\sqrt{3}[s^1 + s^4 - s^2 - s^5]\}$$

$$D_{xy} = N_\pi\{d_{xy} - a_\pi[p_y^1 + p_x^2 - p_y^4 - p_x^5]\} \qquad (1)$$

$$D_{yz} = N_\pi\{d_{yz} - a_\pi[p_z^2 + p_y^3 - p_z^5 - p_y^6]\}$$

$$D_{zx} = N_\pi\{d_{zx} - a_\pi[p_z^1 + p_x^3 - p_z^4 - p_x^6]\}$$

where, for example, p_z^3 stands for the $2p$ orbital transforming like z on the ligand 3 and s^3 stands for a normalised mixture of s-functions on ligand 3. The normalisation factors are given by

$$N_\sigma = [1 - 6a_\sigma t_\sigma - 6a_s t_s + 3a_\sigma^2 + 3a_s^2]^{-\frac{1}{2}}$$

$$N_\pi = [1 - 8a_\pi t_\pi + 4a_\pi^2]^{-\frac{1}{2}} \qquad (2)$$

where t_s, t_σ and t_π are overlap integrals defined by

$$t_s = \langle d_z^2 | s^3 \rangle, \quad t_\sigma = -\langle d_z^2 | p_z^3 \rangle, \quad t_\pi = \langle d_{zx} | p_x^3 \rangle \qquad (3)$$

The complex can now be described by assigning electrons to these orbitals in the usual way and in any particular case we can immediately write down the main terms of the interaction Hamiltonian between the electron spin and any of the six ligands. For example a $(3d)^9\ {}^2D$ state with a hole in the D_{z^2} orbital has an interaction with ligands 3 and 6 which is

$$\mathscr{H}(3)/2\hbar\gamma\mu_\beta = (3S_\sigma I_\sigma - S \cdot I)[g/2R^3 + 2\langle r^{-3}\rangle a_\sigma^2/s]$$
$$+ S \cdot I(8\pi/3)a_s^2|s(0)|^2 \qquad (4)$$

and with ligands 1, 2, 4 and 5

$$\mathscr{H}(1)/2\hbar\gamma\mu_\beta = (3S_\sigma I_\sigma - S \cdot I)[g/2R^3 + \langle r^{-3}\rangle a_\sigma^2/10] + S \cdot I(2\pi/3)a_s^2|s(0)|^2 \qquad (5)$$

where the expectation value $\langle r^{-3}\rangle$ refers to the p orbitals of the ligand and $s(0)$ refers to the value of the ligand s function at the ligand nucleus. Our objective is to calculate correction terms to such main terms.

II. Spin multipole contributions

In this section we consider the interaction of the ligand nucleus with the magnetic field produced solely by the electron spin distribution on the central ion. The Hamiltonian for this interaction is

$$\mathscr{H} = 2\gamma\hbar\mu_B \sum_i 3(\rho_i \cdot S_i)(\rho_i \cdot I)\rho_i^{-5} - S_i \cdot I \rho_i^{-3} \qquad (6)$$

where

$$\rho_i = R - r_i$$

and the sum over i involves all electrons on the central ion and the ligand concerned is at $\mathbf{R}$ relative to the central ion. By expanding (6) in powers of r_i/R it is straightforward but tedious to derive the result

$$\mathcal{H}/2\gamma\hbar\mu_B$$

$$= \sum_i (3\mathbf{S}_{i\sigma}\mathbf{I}_\sigma - \mathbf{S}_i \cdot \mathbf{I})\left[R^{-3} + 3R^{-5}(3r_{i\sigma}^2 - r_i^2) + (15/8)R^{-7}(35r_{i\sigma}^4 - 30r_{i\sigma}^2 r_i^2 + 3r_i^4)\right]$$

$$+ (\mathbf{S}_{i\pi}\mathbf{I}_\pi - \mathbf{S}_{i\mu}\mathbf{I}_\mu)\left[3R^{-5}(r_{i\pi}^2 - r_{i\mu}^2)/2 + (15/4)R^{-7}(7r_{i\sigma}^2 - r_i^2)(r_{i\pi}^2 - r_{i\mu}^2)\right]$$

$$+ (\mathbf{S}_{i\pi}\mathbf{I}_\sigma + \mathbf{S}_{i\sigma}\mathbf{I}_\pi)\left[-12r_{i\pi}r_{i\sigma}R^{-5} - 15r_i\, r_{i\sigma}(7r_{i\sigma}^2 - 3r_i^2)R^{-7}\right]$$

$$+ (\mathbf{S}_{i\mu}\mathbf{I}_\sigma + \mathbf{S}_{i\sigma}\mathbf{I}_\mu)\left[-12r_{i\mu}r_{i\sigma}R^{-5} - 15r_{i\mu}r_{i\sigma}(7r_{i\sigma}^2 - 3r_i^2)R^{-7}\right] \qquad (7)$$

$$+ (\mathbf{S}_{i\pi}\mathbf{I}_\mu + \mathbf{S}_{i\mu}\mathbf{I}_\pi)\left[3r_{i\mu}r_{i\pi}R^{-5} + 15r_{i\mu}r_i\,(7r_{i\sigma}^2 - r_i^2)R^{-7}\right]$$

where at the ligand we have erected orthogonal right handed axes $\pi\mu\sigma$ with the σ axis along $\mathbf{R}$. In (7) we have retained only even harmonics of $\mathbf{r}_i$ in anticipation that odd harmonics will give zero and we have stopped at harmonics of fourth order in anticipation that higher harmonics will give zero for d electrons. We notice that each term of (7) is of the form

$$\sum_i S_i(1T)\, C_k^t(r_i)$$

where $C_k^t(\mathbf{r}_i)$ is a spherical harmonic of $\mathbf{r}_i$ transforming like Y_k^t.

$$C_k^t(\mathbf{r}) = \{4\pi/(2k+1)\}^{1/2} r^k Y_k^t(\theta,\phi) \qquad (8)$$

Now

$$\langle SMLQ|\ \sum_i S_i(1T)C_k^t(r_i)\,|S'M'L'Q'\rangle =$$

$$\begin{pmatrix} I & S' & S \\ T & M' & -M \end{pmatrix}\begin{pmatrix} k & L' & L \\ t & Q' & -Q \end{pmatrix} n\{(2S+1)(2S'+1)(2L+1)(2L'+1)\}^{1/2}\ (\tfrac{1}{2}\|s\|\tfrac{1}{2})(l\|C_k\|l)$$

$$\sum_{S_1 L_1}(SL\{(S_1 L_1)l)(S'L'\{(S_1 L_1)l)$$

$$\begin{Bmatrix} 1 & \tfrac{1}{2} & \tfrac{1}{2} \\ S_1 & S & S' \end{Bmatrix} \begin{Bmatrix} k & l & l \\ L_1 & L & L' \end{Bmatrix} (-1)^{k - s'_1 + 2 2 s' + \tfrac{1}{2} + L_1 + l + M + Q}$$

where we use Edmonds [6] notation for $3j$ and $6j$ symbols and the fractional parentage [9] coefficients are those for a $(d)^n$ configuration. Because we can ignore mixing of states with a different total spin we only require this expression to be evaluated for $S' = S$ but, in general, that is the only simplification possible because the ground state of the magnetic ion may be a mixture of different L states because of the presence of the cubic field.

However in many cases of interest the ground state of the ion is the state of maximum multiplicity and a pure L state. In that case the spin operators [7] can be replaced by $S/2s$ and the $C_k^t(\mathbf{r}_i)$ can be replaced by equivalent operators. We write

$$
\begin{aligned}
\sum_i C_2^t(\mathbf{r}_i) &\equiv \alpha_L \langle r^2 \rangle C_2^t(\mathbf{L}) \\
\sum_i C_4^t(\mathbf{r}_i) &\equiv \beta_L \langle r^4 \rangle C_4^t(\mathbf{L})
\end{aligned}
\tag{10}
$$

where $C_2^t(\mathbf{L})$ and $C_4^t(\mathbf{L})$ are operators obtained from $C_2^t(\mathbf{r})$ and $C_4^t(\mathbf{r})$ by first writing the latter in a completely symmetrised form with respect to the components x, y and z and then replacing x, y, z by L_x, L_y, L_z respectively. The constants of proportionality α_L and β_L have the values for

$$
\begin{array}{llll}
(d)^1 \text{ or } (d)^9; \; ^2D; & \alpha = -2/21, & \beta = 2/63 \\
(d)^2 \text{ or } (d)^8; \; ^3F; & \alpha = -2/105, & \beta = -2/135 \\
(d)^3 \text{ or } (d)^7; \; ^4F; & \alpha = 2/105, & \beta = 2/315 \\
(d)^4 \text{ or } (d)^6; \; ^5D; & \alpha = 2/21, & \beta = -2/63
\end{array}
\tag{11}
$$

the expectation values $\langle r^2 \rangle$ and $\langle r^4 \rangle$ refer to the d orbitals of the central ion.

Hence [7] becomes

$$
\begin{aligned}
\mathcal{H}/2\gamma\hbar\mu_B &= [3\mathbf{S}_\sigma \mathbf{I}_\sigma - \mathbf{SI}][R^{-3} + (3\alpha/2S)\langle r^2 \rangle R^{-5}\{3L_\sigma^2 - L(L+1)\} \\
&\quad + (15\beta/16S)R^{-7}\{35L_\sigma^4 - 30L_\sigma^2\mathbf{L}^2 + 3\mathbf{L}^4\}] \\
&\quad + [\mathbf{S}_\pi \mathbf{I}_\pi - \mathbf{S}_\mu \mathbf{I}_\mu][(3\alpha/4S)\langle r^2 \rangle R^{-5}\{L_\pi^2 - L_\mu^2\} \\
&\quad + (15\beta/8S)\langle r^4 \rangle R^{-7}\{(7L_\sigma^2 - \mathbf{L}^2)(L_\pi^2 - L_\mu^2)\}] \\
&\quad + [\mathbf{S}_\pi \mathbf{I}_\sigma + \mathbf{S}_\sigma \mathbf{I}_\pi][-(6\alpha/S)\langle r^2 \rangle R^{-5}\{L_\pi L_\sigma\} \\
&\quad - (15\beta/2S)\langle r^4 \rangle R^{-7}\{L_\pi L_\sigma(7L_\sigma^2 - 3\mathbf{L}^2)\}] \\
&\quad + [\mathbf{S}_\pi \mathbf{I}_\sigma + \mathbf{S}_\sigma \mathbf{I}_\pi][-(6\alpha/S)\langle r^2 \rangle R^{-5}\{L_\mu L_\sigma\} \\
&\quad - (15\beta/2S)\langle r^4 \rangle R^{-7}\{L_\mu L_\sigma(7L_\sigma^2 - 3\mathbf{L}^2)\}] \\
&\quad + [\mathbf{S}_\pi \mathbf{I}_\mu + \mathbf{S}_\mu \mathbf{I}_\pi][(3\alpha/2S \langle r^2 \rangle R^{-5}\{L_\mu L_\sigma\} \\
&\quad + (15\beta/2S)\langle r^4 \rangle R^{-7}\{L_\mu L_\pi(7L_\sigma^2 - \mathbf{L}^2)\}]
\end{aligned}
\tag{12}
$$

where every expression appearing between brackets { } should be properly symmetrized. Thus for example

$$\{L_\pi L_\sigma\} = \tfrac{1}{2}[L_\pi L_\sigma + L_\sigma L_\pi]$$

$$\{35L_a^4 - 30L_\sigma^2 L^2 + 3L^4\} = 35L_\sigma - 20L(L+1)L_\sigma^2 + 25L_\sigma^2 - 6L(L+1) +$$
$$+ 3L^2(L+1)^2$$

$$\{(7L_\sigma^2 - L^2)(L_\pi^2 - L_\mu^2)\} = (7/2)[L_\sigma^2 L_\pi^2 + L_\pi^2 L_\sigma^2 - L_\sigma^2 L_\mu^2 - L_\mu^2 L_\sigma^2] \tag{13}$$
$$- [5 + L(L+1)][L_\pi^2 - L_\mu^2]$$

For complexes of high enough symmetry the off diagonal terms of (12) vanish. As examples of the evaluation of (12) let us consider a few explicit examples.

(i) $(d)^9 {}^2D$ with a hole in the d_2^0 orbital. For the interaction with ligand 1 the $\pi\mu\sigma$ axes correspond to yzx respectively and we get

$$\mathscr{H}(1)/2\gamma\hbar\mu_B = [3S_\sigma I_\sigma - S\cdot I][R^{-3} - (6/7)\langle r^2\rangle R^{-5} + (45/28)\langle r^4\rangle R^{-7}]$$
$$+ [S_\pi I_\pi - S_\mu I_\mu][-(3/7)\langle r^2\rangle R^{-5} + (15/14)\langle r^4\rangle R^{-7}] \tag{14}$$

and this also describes the interaction with ligands 2, 4 and 5. For the interaction with ligand 3 the $\pi\mu\sigma$ axes correspond to xyz and we get

$$\mathscr{H}(3)/2\gamma\hbar\mu_B = [3S_\sigma I_\sigma - S\cdot I][R^{-3} + (12/7)\langle r^2\rangle R^{-5} + (30/7)\langle r^4\rangle R^{-7}] \tag{15}$$

(ii) $(d)^9 {}^2D$ with hole in the $(d_2^2 + d_2^{-2})/\sqrt{2}$ orbital. For the interaction with ligand 1 we get

$$\mathscr{H}(1)/2\gamma\hbar\mu_B = [3S_\sigma I_\sigma - S\cdot I][R^{-3} + (6/7)\langle r^2\rangle R^{-5} + (95/28)\langle r^4\rangle R^{-7}]$$
$$+ [S_\pi I_\pi - S_\mu I_\mu][(3/7)\langle r^2\rangle R^{-5} - (15/14)\langle r^4\rangle R^{-7} \tag{16}$$

which also describes the interaction with ligands 2, 4 and 5. For the interaction with ligands 3 and 6 we get

$$\mathscr{H}(3)/2\gamma\hbar\mu_B = [3S_\sigma I_\sigma - S\cdot I][R^{-3} - (12/7)\langle r^2\rangle R^{-5} + (5/7)\langle r^4\rangle R^{-7}] \tag{17}$$

(iii) $(3d)^8 {}^3F$. The interaction with all ligands is similar
$$\mathscr{H}/2\gamma\hbar\mu_B = [3S_\sigma I_\sigma - S\cdot I][R^{-3} + (5/2)\langle r^4\rangle R^{-7}] \tag{18}$$

(iv) $(3d)^3 {}^4F$. Again the interaction with all ligands is similar

$$\mathscr{H}/2\gamma\hbar_{\mu\beta} = [3S_\sigma I_\sigma - S\cdot I][R^{-3} - (5/3)\langle r^4\rangle R^{-7}]$$

For other cases the formulae are more complicated and must be worked out from the general formula (9); for example $(3d)^4$ complexes have a ground state which is a mixture of ^4F and ^4P and we must use the general form; (actually for this particular case it would be simpler to use the form of (9) appropriate for a single d electron and combine this with an expression for the wavefunction expressed in the strong cubic field representation.)

In all the above formulae we recognise that the leading term, that involving $1/R^3$, is the interaction with the spin part of the magnetic moment on the central ion and is therefore included in (4) and (5), the remaining terms are corrections which arise because of the multipole distribution of electron spin on the central ion.

III. Orbital moment multipole contributions

In this section we consider the interaction of the ligand nucleus with that part of the orbital magnetic moment which has not been quenched. For the main part this interaction is accounted for by using the appropriate g-value in (4) and (5) but our purpose is to calculate corrections to this.

The interaction Hamiltonian is

$$\mathscr{H} = -2\gamma\hbar\mu_B\rho^{-3}\,\mathbf{I}\times\boldsymbol{\rho}\cdot\mathbf{P} = 2\gamma\hbar\mu_B\mathbf{I}\cdot\nabla_R(1/\rho)\times\mathbf{P} \tag{20}$$

We now expand

$$1/\rho = \sum_{n=0}^{\infty}(r^n/R^{n+1})P_n(\mu) \tag{21}$$

where $\mu = \cos\theta$ and θ is the angle between $\mathbf{r}$ and $\mathbf{R}$. Because there is no dependence of $1/\rho$ on azimuthal angle ∇_R is effectively

$$\nabla_R = \mathbf{R}R^{-1}[\partial/\partial R - \mu R^{-1}\partial/\partial\mu] + \mathbf{r}(rR)^{-1}\partial/\partial\mu \tag{22}$$

Hence we find

$$\mathscr{H}/2\gamma\hbar\mu_B = \mathbf{I}\cdot[R^{-3}P_1' + r^2R^{-5}P_3' + r^4R^{-7}P_5' + \cdots]\,l$$
$$-\mathbf{I}\cdot[r(2P_1 + \mu P_1')R^{-4} + r^3(4P_3 + \mu P_3')R^{-6} + r^5(6P_5 + \mu P_5')R^{-8}]\mathbf{R}\times\mathbf{P} \tag{23}.$$

where P_n' denotes the differential of P_n with respect to μ. To evaluate this we choose $\mathbf{R}$ as a temporary z axis and rearrange the terms in R^{-3} as

$$R^{-3}[\mathbf{I}\cdot\mathbf{l} - 3(zP_xI_y - zP_yI_x)]$$

and note that

$$zP_x = \tfrac{1}{2}[zP_x - P_zx + zP_x + P_zx] = \tfrac{1}{2}l_y + \tfrac{1}{2}m\,\partial/\partial t(zx) \tag{24}$$

The second term of (24) vanishes hence zP_x is effectively $(1/2)l_y$; similarly zP_y is $-(1/2)l_x$ and then terms in R^{-3} become

$$R^{-3}[3I_zl_z - \mathbf{I}\cdot\mathbf{l}]$$

The other terms in (23) may be treated similarly and in each case the explicit appearance of the momentum operator $\mathbf{P}$ can be eliminated by using a relation such as (24); for example, another such relation required is

$$z^3 P_y = -(3/4)z^2 l_x + (3/4)\,i\hbar zy + (1/4)\,m\,\partial/\partial t(z^3 y) \tag{25}$$

In this way (23) can be rearranged into the form

$$\mathcal{H}(\hbar\gamma\mu_B = R^{-3}[3\mathbf{I}_\sigma l_\sigma - \mathbf{I}\cdot\mathbf{l}] + (3/4)\,R^{-5}(5r_\sigma^2 - r^2)\,[5\mathbf{I}_\sigma l_\sigma - \mathbf{I}\cdot\mathbf{l}]$$
$$- (15/2)\,R^{-5}\,[\mathbf{r}\cdot\mathbf{I} - \mathbf{r}_\sigma \mathbf{I}_\sigma]\,r_\sigma l_\sigma \tag{26}$$

We anticipate that the terms of order R^{-5} will transform like a spherical harmonic of order 3, and those of order R^{-7}, which we have omitted from (26), will transform like a harmonic of order 5 and will therefore have matrix elements all zero for d electrons. It is in fact straightforward but tedious to show that the matrix elements of (26) obey

$$(dm'\,|\,\mathcal{H}\,|\,dm) = \hbar\gamma\mu_B\,R^{-3}(dm'\,|\,3\mathbf{I}_\sigma l_\sigma - \mathbf{I}\cdot\mathbf{l}\,|\,dm) \tag{27}$$

$$- \hbar\gamma\mu_B\langle r^2\rangle R^{-5}12(10/7)^{\frac{1}{2}}\Bigg[I_z(-1)^{2-m'}\begin{pmatrix} 2 & 3 & 2 \\ -m' & 0 & m \end{pmatrix}$$

$$- I_+(3^{\frac{1}{2}}/4)(-1)^{2-m'}\begin{pmatrix} 2 & 3 & 2 \\ -m' & -1 & m \end{pmatrix} + I_-(3^{\frac{1}{2}}/4)(-1)^{2-m'}\begin{pmatrix} 2 & 3 & 2 \\ -m' & 1 & m \end{pmatrix}\Bigg]$$

Hence for states described by a total S and L we have the matrix elements

$$(SML'Q'\,|\,\mathcal{H}\,|\,SMLQ) = \hbar\gamma\mu_B R^{-3}\delta_{L'L}(LQ'\,|\,3\mathbf{I}_\sigma \mathbf{L}_\sigma - \mathbf{I}\cdot\mathbf{L}\,|\,LQ)$$

$$+ \hbar\gamma\mu_B\langle r^2\rangle R^{-5}12(10/7)^{\frac{1}{2}}n(2L'+1)^{\frac{1}{2}}(2L+1)^{\frac{1}{2}}$$

$$\Sigma_{S_1 L_1}(SL\{S_1 L_1)l)(SL'\{(S_1 L)_1 l \begin{Bmatrix} 3 & 2 & 2 \\ L_1 & L' & L \end{Bmatrix}$$

$$(-1)^{L_1+L'} \times \Bigg[I_\sigma(-1)^{L'-Q'}\begin{pmatrix} L' & 3 & L \\ -Q' & 0 & Q \end{pmatrix} \tag{28}$$

$$- I_+(3^{\frac{1}{2}}/4)(-1)^{L'-Q'}\begin{pmatrix} L' & 3 & L \\ -Q' & -1 & Q \end{pmatrix}$$

$$- I_-(3^{\frac{1}{2}}/4)(-1)^{L'-Q'}\begin{pmatrix} L' & 3 & L \\ -Q' & 1 & Q \end{pmatrix}\Bigg]$$

For those cases where only the diagonal element of (28) is required this is more conveniently put into the form of operator equivalents and we have

$$\mathcal{H}/\hbar\gamma\mu_B = R^{-3}(3I_\sigma L_\sigma - I \cdot L)$$

$$+ (3\phi/8)\langle r^2 \rangle R^{-5} \left[I_\sigma L_\sigma(5L_\sigma^2 - 3L(L+1) + 1) \right.$$

$$- (3/16)(I_+ L_- + I_- L_+)(10L_\sigma^2 - 2L(L+1) - 1) \qquad (29)$$

$$- (15/16)(I_- L_+ L_\sigma + I_- L_\sigma L_+ - I_+ L_- L_\sigma - I_+ L_\sigma L_-) \left. \right]$$

where $\phi = -16/21$ for D states, and $+16/105$ for F states.

To illustrate the evaluation of (29) we look at only two cases $Ni^{++}(3d)^8\,{}^3F$ and $Cr^{+++}(3d)^3\,{}^4F$. For both of these ions the ground state is a pure F state with wavefunction

$$\psi_g = (1/2^{\frac{1}{2}})\{|F^2\rangle - |F^{-2}\rangle|5M\rangle \qquad (30)$$

in the absence of spin orbit coupling. In the presence of spin orbit coupling the wavefunction to first order in λ becomes

$$\Psi = [1 - (\lambda/\Delta)\, L \cdot S]\psi_g \qquad (31)$$

where Δ is the splitting to the nearest orbital triplet. Calculating the expectation value of (29) with the wavefunction (31) gives the result

$$\mathcal{H} = \hbar\gamma\mu_B(g-2)R^{-3}[3I_\sigma S_\sigma - I \cdot S][1 - (5/28)\langle r^2 \rangle R^{-2}] \qquad (32)$$

$$- (1/2)\hbar\gamma\mu_B(g-2)\langle r^2 \rangle R^{-5} I \cdot S$$

The isotropic term in (32) is of no real importance because it is small compared with the isotropic term coming from the contact interaction.

IV. Overlap effects

In the previous two sections we discussed multipole contributions to the field at the ligand nucleus assuming these to come from pure d orbitals on the central ion. However the unpaired electrons occupy antibonding orbitals and therefore also have a density on the ligands themselves and in the intermediate overlap region. The density on the ligands gives rise to the main terms in (4) and (5) and the small corrections we describe in V and VI. The overlap density, because it is essentially all inside the magnetic ion to ligand radius is best treated by the multipole type of discussion given in II and III.

To do this we recognise that the overlap densities are of the same symmetry as the d orbitals themselves and that therefore to a good approximation we need only modify our definition of $\langle r^2 \rangle$ and $\langle r^4 \rangle$ to include them in the formulae quoted in II and III. We notice first that these formulae should be multiplied by the appropriate normalisation factors N_σ^2 or N_π^2 and then that adding the overlap effects modifies these factors and gives rise to new definitions $\langle r^2 \rangle$ and $\langle r^4 \rangle$.

In summary: those formulae of II and III which give interactions associated with σ orbitals should be multiplied by $(1 - 3a_\sigma^2 - 3a_s^2)$ and $\langle r^2 \rangle$ and $\langle r^4 \rangle$ should be taken as

$$\langle r^n \rangle = (1 + 6a_\sigma t_\sigma)\langle r^n \rangle_d - 6a_\sigma t_\sigma \langle r^n \rangle_{\text{ov}} \tag{33}$$

where $\langle r^n \rangle_d$ is the value appropriate to pure d orbitals and $\langle r^n \rangle_{\text{ov}}$ is the value appropriate to the overlap density which, from (1), makes a contribution to $|D_{z^2}|^2$ and $|D_{x^2-y^2}|^2$. Similarly the formulae associated with π orbitals should be multiplied by $(1 - 4a_\pi^2)$ and $\langle r^2 \rangle$ and $\langle r^4 \rangle$ should be taken as

$$\langle r^n \rangle = (1 + 8a_\pi t_\pi)\langle r^n \rangle_d - 8a_\pi t_\pi \langle r^n \rangle_{\text{ov}} \tag{34}$$

where $\langle r^n \rangle_{\text{ov}}$ now refers to the overlap density in $|D_{xy}|^2$, $|D_{yz}|^2$ or $|D_{zx}|^2$.

In practice these corrections are likely to be totally obscured by our uncertain knowledge of $\langle r^2 \rangle_d$ and $\langle r^4 \rangle_d$ for d orbitals in crystals.

V. Orbital moment on the ligands

In III we discussed the orbital moment on the central ion: the spin orbit coupling also gives orbital moment on the ligands. The calculation of this effect is straightforward but must be made separately for each case. We shall illustrate it with a few cases of special importance.

(i) $(3d)^9$: hole in D_{z^2} orbital. For this case the ground state in the absence of spin orbit coupling would be $D_{z^2}X_s$ where we refer to the wave-function of the single hole. In the presence of spin orbit coupling the wave-function to first order is

$$\Psi = D_{z^2}(\mathbf{r})X_s - \sum_i E_i^{-1} |i\rangle \langle i | \lambda \mathbf{L} \cdot \mathbf{S} | D_{z^2}X_s \rangle \tag{35}$$

and in cubic symmetry all the E_i are equal, say to Δ, and we get

$$\Psi = [1 - (\lambda/\Delta)\mathbf{L} \cdot \mathbf{S}]D_{z^2}X_s \tag{36}$$

For this case λ is defined positive for $n < 5$.

We now ask for the matrix element of

$$\mathscr{H} = 2\gamma\hbar\mu_B r^{-3}\mathbf{l} \cdot \mathbf{I} \tag{37}$$

where $\mathbf{l}$ and $\mathbf{r}$ are measured relative to the ligand nucleus with spin $\mathbf{I}$ to get

$$\mathcal{H} = -(4\gamma\hbar\mu_B\lambda/\Delta)\langle D_{z^2}X_s|r^{-3}\mathbf{l}\cdot\mathbf{I}\ \mathbf{L}\cdot\mathbf{S}|D_{z^2}X_s \tag{38}$$

We now operate $\mathbf{L}$ and leave $\mathbf{S}$ as an operator to get

$$\mathcal{H} = -(4\gamma\hbar\mu_B\lambda/\Delta)\langle D_{z^2}|r^{-3}\mathbf{l}\cdot\mathbf{I}|i\sqrt{3}S_yD_{zx} - i\sqrt{3}S_xD_{zy}\rangle \tag{39}$$

The r^{-3} term insures that only admixtures of wavefunctions from that particular ligand will make a significant contribution to (39). For ligand 1 this is

$$\mathcal{H}(1) = -(4\gamma\hbar\mu_B\lambda/\Delta)\langle -\tfrac{1}{2}a_\sigma P'_{x,}|r^{-3}\mathbf{l}\cdot\mathbf{I}_1| - i\sqrt{3}S_ya_\pi P'_z\rangle \tag{40}$$

Hence

$$\mathcal{H}_{1,4} = (2\sqrt{3}\gamma\hbar\mu_B\lambda/\Delta)a_\sigma a_\pi\langle r^{-3}\rangle S_y(I_{1y} + I_{4y}) \tag{41}$$

For ligands 2 and 5 the interaction is

$$\mathcal{H}_{2,5} = (2\sqrt{3}\gamma\hbar\mu_B\lambda/\Delta)a_\sigma a_\pi\langle r^{-3}\rangle S_x(I_{2x} + I_{5x}) \tag{42}$$

For ligand 3, (39) becomes

$$\mathcal{H}(3) = (4\gamma\hbar\mu_B\lambda/\Delta)\langle a_\sigma P_z^3|r^{-3}\mathbf{l}\cdot\mathbf{I}_3| - i\sqrt{3}a_\pi S_yP_x^3 + i\sqrt{3}a_\pi S_xP_y^3\rangle \tag{43}$$

Hence

$$\mathcal{H}_{3,6} = (4\sqrt{3}\gamma\hbar\mu_B\lambda/\Delta)a_\sigma a_\pi\langle r^{-3}\rangle[S_y(I_{3y} + I_{6y}) + S_x(I_{3x} + I_{6x})] \tag{44}$$

(ii) $(3d)^9$: hole in $D_{x^2-y^2}$ orbital. For this case in place of (39) we get

$$\mathcal{H} = -(4\gamma\hbar\mu_B\lambda/\Delta)\langle D_{x^2-y^2}|r^{-3}\mathbf{l}\cdot\mathbf{I}|2iS_zD_{xy} - iS_yD_{zx} - iS_xD_{zy}\rangle \tag{45}$$

Hence

$$\mathcal{H}(1) = -(4\gamma\hbar\mu_B\lambda/\Delta)(a_\sigma\sqrt{3}/2)\langle P'_x|r^{-3}\mathbf{l}\cdot\mathbf{I}_i| - 2iS_za_\pi P'_y + iS_ya_\pi P'_z\rangle \tag{46}$$

and

$$\mathcal{H}_{1,4} = (2\sqrt{3}\gamma\hbar\mu_B\lambda/\Delta)a_\sigma a_\pi\langle r^{-3}\rangle[2S_z(I_{1z} + I_{4z}) + S_y(I_{1y} + I_{4y})] \tag{47}$$

Similarly

$$\mathcal{H}_{2,5} = (2\sqrt{3}\gamma\hbar\mu_B\lambda/\Delta)a_\sigma a_\pi\langle r^{-3}\rangle[2S_z(I_{2z} + I_{5z}) + S_x(I_{2x} + I_{5x})] \tag{48}$$

and $H_{3,6}$ is zero.

(iii) $(3d)^8$; ^3F. For this case we can simply add the results of (i) and (ii) to give

$$\mathcal{H} = -(\sqrt{3}\gamma\hbar\mu_B(g-2)/2)a_\sigma a_\pi\langle r^{-3}\rangle[\mathbf{S}\cdot\mathbf{I} - S_\sigma I_\sigma] \tag{49}$$

for the interaction with each ligand.

(iv) $(3d)^3$; ^4F. The expression (49) applies exactly but for this case, of course, $g - 2$ is negative.

VI. Spin orbit modification of dipole interaction on ligands

The spin orbit coupling also modifies the spin density on the ligands. The appropriate Hamiltonian is worked out as in V.

(i) $(3d)^9$: hole in D_{z^2} orbital. By analogy with (40) we have

$$\mathscr{H}_1 = (-4\gamma\hbar\mu_B\lambda/\Delta)(i\sqrt{3}/2)a_\sigma a_\pi \langle P'_x | 3(\mathbf{r}\cdot\mathbf{S})(\mathbf{r}\cdot\mathbf{I})r^{-5} - (\mathbf{S}\cdot\mathbf{I})r^{-3} | P'_z \rangle S_y \quad (50)$$

Hence

$$\mathscr{H}_{1,4} = (3\sqrt{3}/5)(\gamma\hbar\mu_B\lambda/\Delta)a_\sigma a_\pi \langle r^{-3}\rangle [S_z(I_{1z} + I_{4z}) - S_x(I_{1x} + I_{4x})] \quad (51)$$

Similarly

$$\mathscr{H}_{2,5} = (3\sqrt{3}/5)(\gamma\hbar\mu_B\lambda/\Delta)a_\sigma a_\pi \langle r^{-3}\rangle [S_z(I_{2z} + I_{5z}) - S_y(I_{1y} + I_{4y})] \quad (52)$$

and

$$\mathscr{H}_{3,6} = -(6\sqrt{3}/5)(\gamma\hbar\mu_B\lambda/\Delta)a_\pi a_\sigma \langle r^{-3}\rangle [3S_z(I_{3z} + I_{6z}) - \mathbf{S}\cdot(\mathbf{I}_3 + \mathbf{I}_6)] \quad (53)$$

(ii) $(3d)^9$: hole in $D_{x^2-y^2}$ orbital: By analogy with (46)

$$\mathscr{H}_1 = -(3\sqrt{3}/5)(\gamma\hbar\mu_B\lambda/\Delta)a_\sigma a_\pi \langle r^{-3}\rangle [-2S_y I_{1y} + 3S_x I_{1x} - S_z I_{iz}] \quad (54)$$

with a similar interaction with ligand 4. Similarly

$$\mathscr{H}_2 = -(3\sqrt{3}/5)(\gamma\hbar\mu_B\lambda/\Delta)a_\sigma a_\pi \langle r^{-3}\rangle [-2S_x I_{2x} + 3S_y I_{2y} - S_z I_{2z}] \quad (55)$$

with a similar interaction with ligand 5. The interaction with ligands 3 and 6 is zero.

(iii) $(3d)^8$; ^3F. Adding the results of (i) and (ii) gives for all ligands

$$\mathscr{H} = (3\sqrt{3}/5)(\gamma\hbar\mu_B\lambda/\Delta)\,a_\sigma a_\pi \langle r^{-3}\rangle (3S_\sigma I_\sigma - \mathbf{S}\cdot\mathbf{I}) \quad (56)$$

$$= [3\sqrt{3}\,\gamma\hbar\mu_B(g-2)a_\sigma a_\pi \langle r^{-3}\rangle/40](3S_\sigma I_\sigma - \mathbf{S}\cdot\mathbf{I}) \quad (57)$$

(iv) $(3d)^3$; ^4F. The formula is

$$\mathscr{H} = [\sqrt{3}\,\gamma\hbar\mu_B(g-2)\,a_\sigma a_\pi \langle r^{-3}\rangle/20][3S_\sigma I_\sigma - \mathbf{S}\cdot\mathbf{I}] \quad (58)$$

VII. Effects of order $(\lambda/\Delta)^2$

There are, of course, many effects of order $(\lambda/\Delta)^2$ but most of them will be quite insignificant and we shall ignore them. The only effect of this order which we will consider is an anisotropic interaction produced through the joint action of the spin orbit coupling and the isotropic contact interaction on the ligands. We can visualize this effect as follows: the spin orbit interaction produces an anisotropy in the electron density relative to the spin direction and therefore the electron density on a particular ligand depends upon the spin orientation relative to the bond direction. The effect vanishes for spin 1/2 complexes and we calculate it only for the case of Ni^{++}, $(3d)^8$ ^3F.

In the absence of spin orbit coupling the ground state of the Ni^{++}, $(3d)^8$ ^3F ion is

$$\psi(1,2) = \{D_{z^2}(1) D_{x^2-y^2}(2)]\} X_s \quad (59)$$

where { } stands for a properly constructed determinant. In the presence of spin orbit coupling the ground state wavefunction becomes

$$\Psi = [1 - 4\lambda^2/\Delta^2) + (\lambda/\Delta)\mathbf{L}\cdot\mathbf{S}]\psi(1,2) + O(\lambda/\Delta)^2 \qquad (60)$$

where the terms of $(\lambda/\Delta)^2$ which have not been written explicitly have at least one orbital different from $\psi(1,2)$. Using this wavefunction we must calculate the expectation value of

$$\mathbf{I}\cdot\mathbf{S}_1 O(\mathbf{r}_1) + \mathbf{I}\cdot\mathbf{S}_2 O(\mathbf{r}_2) \qquad (61)$$

where, if we take $\mathbf{I}$ to refer to ligand 3, the operator $O(r)$ has only one nonzero element.

$$\langle D_{z^2}|(Or)|D_{z^2}\rangle = (16\pi\gamma\hbar\mu_B/3)|a_s|^2 |s(0)|^2 = \langle 0\rangle \qquad (62)$$

Because all other matrix elements of $O(r)$ are zero the neglected terms in (60) cannot give the effects to order $(\lambda/\Delta)^2$. The expectation value of (61) becomes

$$\mathscr{H} = \tfrac{1}{2}\langle 0\rangle\mathbf{I}\cdot\mathbf{S} + (\lambda^2/2\Delta^2)\langle 0\rangle[4\mathbf{S}_\sigma(\mathbf{I}\cdot\mathbf{S})\mathbf{S}_\sigma + \mathbf{S}_\pi(\mathbf{I}\cdot\mathbf{S})\mathbf{S}_\pi + \mathbf{S}_\mu(\mathbf{I}\cdot\mathbf{S})\mathbf{S}_\mu - 8(\mathbf{I}\cdot\mathbf{S})] \qquad (63)$$

where we now use a notation applicable to all the ligands. The first term of (63) is the usual result and the second gives anisotropic terms. (63) is more conveniently written as

$$\begin{aligned}
\mathscr{H} = &\tfrac{1}{2}\langle 0\rangle(1 - 8\lambda^2/\Delta^2)\mathbf{I}\cdot\mathbf{S} + (\lambda^2/2\Delta^2)\langle 0\rangle[3S_\sigma^2 + 1]S_\sigma I_\sigma \\
&+ (\lambda^2/4\Delta^2)\langle 0\rangle[\{5 - 3S_\pi^2 + 3(S_\sigma^2 - S_\mu^2)\}S_\pi - 3i(S_\sigma S_\mu + S_\mu S_\sigma)]I_\pi \quad (64) \\
&+ (\lambda^2/4\Delta^2)\langle 0\rangle[\{5 - 3S_\mu^2 + 3(S_\sigma^2 - S_\pi^2)\}S_\mu + 3i(S_\sigma S_\pi + S_\pi S_\sigma)]I_\mu
\end{aligned}$$

Because this expression is not linear in S it must be evaluated with care and with particular reference to the method of experiment which is used to measure the hyperfine interaction. In an NMR experiment on a paramagnetic material an external field is applied successively along the crystal axes. This external field gives the main part of the energy and the hyperfine interaction gives small shifts in the NMR resonance. Noting that if H is along σ then in these conditions, because $S = 1$, $\langle S_\sigma^3\rangle = \langle S_\sigma\rangle$ and the interaction is effectively

$$\mathscr{H} = \tfrac{1}{2}\langle 0\rangle(1 - 8\lambda^2/\Delta^2)I_\sigma\langle S_\sigma\rangle + (2\lambda^2/\Delta^2)\langle 0\rangle I_\sigma\langle S_\sigma\rangle \qquad (65)$$

whereas if H is along π

$$\mathscr{H} = \tfrac{1}{2}\langle 0\rangle(1 - 8\lambda^2/\Delta^2)I_\pi\langle S_\pi\rangle + (\lambda^2/2\Delta^2)\langle 0\rangle I_\pi\langle S_\pi\rangle \qquad (66)$$

with a similar term for H along σ. Hence under these circumstances we may take $\mathscr{H}$ as

$$\mathscr{H} = \tfrac{1}{2}\langle 0 \rangle [1 - 6\lambda^2/\Delta^2]\mathbf{I}\cdot\langle\mathbf{S}\rangle + (\lambda^2/2\Delta^2)\langle 0 \rangle [2I_\sigma\langle S_\sigma \rangle - I_\pi\langle S_\pi \rangle - I_\mu\langle S_\mu \rangle] \quad (67)$$

VIII. Ni^{++} and Cr^{+++} complexes

In this section we assemble and discuss the results for these two cases which are of special interest because they have been investigated by Shulman and Knox [5] in $KNiF_3$ and K_2NaCrF_6 respectively. For these complexes the interaction with each ligand is similar and of the form

$$\mathscr{H} = A_s\mathbf{S}\cdot\mathbf{I} + A_\sigma(2S_\sigma I_\sigma - S_\pi I_\pi - S_\mu I_\mu) \quad (68)$$

Our results for A_s and A_σ are as follows.

For Ni^{++}

$$A_s/\gamma\hbar\mu_B = (8\pi/3)a_s^2\,|\,s(0)\,|^2(1 - 6\lambda^2/\Delta^2)(1 - 3a_\sigma^2 - 3a_s^2)$$
$$- (g - 2)\langle r^2 \rangle\,|\,2R^5 - (g - 2)a_\sigma a_\pi\langle r^{-3} \rangle/\sqrt{3}$$

$$A_\sigma/\gamma\hbar\mu_B = 2a_\sigma^2\langle r^{-3} \rangle/5 + gR^{-3}\{1 - 3a_\sigma^2 - 3a_s^2\} + 5\langle r^4 \rangle R^{-7}$$
$$- 5(g - 2)\langle r^2 \rangle R^{-5}/28 + (g - 2)a_\sigma a_\pi\langle r^{-3} \rangle/2\sqrt{3}$$
$$+ 3\sqrt{3}(g - 2)a_\sigma a_\pi\langle r^{-3} \rangle/40 + (\lambda^2/\Delta^2)(A_s/\gamma\hbar\mu_B) \quad (69)$$

For Cr^{+++}

$$A_s/\gamma\hbar\mu_B = -(g - 2)\langle r^2 \rangle/2R^5 \quad (70)$$

$$A_\sigma/\gamma\hbar\mu_B = -4a_\pi^2\langle r^{-3} \rangle/15 + gR^-\{31 - 4a_\pi^2\} - 10\langle r^4 \rangle R^{-4}/3$$
$$- 5(g - 2)\langle r^2 \rangle R^{-5}/28 + (g - 2)a_\sigma a_\pi\langle r^{-3} \rangle/2\sqrt{3}$$
$$+ \sqrt{3}(g - 2)a_\sigma a_\pi\langle r^{-3} \rangle/20 \quad (71)$$

where $\langle r^{-3} \rangle$ refers to the $2p$ orbitals of the F^- and $\langle r^2 \rangle$ and $\langle r^4 \rangle$ refer to the combined electron density of $3d$ electrons plus overlap density as discussed in IV. We have neglected an anisotropic term of order $(\lambda/\Delta)^2$ for Cr^{+++} because, for this ion, λ is quite small. The calculations of Froese [7] for F^- give

$$\langle r^{-3} \rangle = 6.405\,a_0^{-3} \quad (72)$$

and of Watson [8] for Ni^{++} and Cr^{+++} give

$$\langle r^2 \rangle = 1.130\,a_0^2, \qquad \langle r^4 \rangle = 3.003\,a_0^4 \quad \text{for } Ni^{++}$$
$$\langle r^2 \rangle = 1.447\,a_0^2, \qquad \langle r^4 \rangle = 4.297\,a_0^4 \quad \text{for } Cr^{+++} \quad (73)$$

Using just the main terms of (70) and (72), Shulman and Knox have deduced a_σ^2 is $\simeq 0.05$ for $KNiF_3$ and a_π^2 is $\simeq 0.05$ for K_2NaCrF_6. We shall use these values to give a rough assessment of the correction terms in (70) and (72). We notice immediately that the fifth and sixth terms of of (70) together give a correction which is a factor $(29\sqrt{3}/48)(g-2)a_\pi/a_\sigma$ of the leading term. Using $a_\pi \simeq a_\sigma$ this fraction is roughly $(g-2)$: hence these two terms together can give corrections of the order of 30% and are of such a sign that a_σ^2 should be smaller than would be deduced by the simple theory. The corresponding terms in (72) are very much smaller because g is so close to 2 for Cr^{+++}.

The last term of (70) is a fraction $(g-2)^2 A_s/64A_\sigma$ of the main term; using $(g-2) \simeq 0.3$ and $A_s/A_\sigma \simeq 4$ this gives only a 1% effect. The spin and orbital moment multipole terms in (70) and (72) give corrections which are also of the order of 1% in these cases. The correction terms to the isotropic interaction given by (69) are also quite small.

For these particular cases therefore the only corrections which are worth attention are those arising from the spin orbit interaction producing unquenched orbital moment on the F^- ligands and also modifying the spin distribution on the ligands.

REFERENCES

[1]   K. W. H. STEVENS, *Proc. Roy. Soc. (London)* **219**, 542 (1953).
[2]   J. OWEN, *Proc. Roy. Soc. (London)* **227**, 183 (1954).
[3]   R. SHULMAN AND V. JACCARINO, *Phys. Rev.* **108**, 1219 (1957).
[4]   A. M. CLOGSTON, J. P. GORDON, V. JACCARINO, M. PETER AND L. R. WALKER, *Phys. Rev.* **117**, 1222 (1960).
[5]   R. SHULMAN AND KNOX, *Phys. Rev. Letters* **4**, 603 (1960).
[6]   A. R. EDMUNDS, *Angular Momentum in Quantum Mechanics*, Princeton University Press.
[7]   C. FROESE, *Proc. Cambridge Phil. Soc.* **53**, 206 (1957).
[8]   R. E. WATSON, M.I.T. Technical Report. Number 12, 1959.

Exchange Splittings of L-S Multiplets
of Rare Earth Ions in Crystals

G. F. KOSTER

Massachusetts Institute of Technology, Cambridge, Massachusetts

AND

H. STATZ

Raytheon Company, Waltham, Massachusetts

ABSTRACT

The general form of the exchange interaction between rare earth ions and other magnetic ions in crystalline lattice will be discussed. It will be shown the ordinary Heisenberg form of the exchange interaction is, in general, not applicable, to these cases. The form of the interaction will be presented and used to discuss some of the magnetic properties of rare earth ions in the garnets.

Introduction

In this note we will summarize some results we have obtained concering exchange interactions in the rare earth iron garnets.. In these crystals, there is a strong exchange interaction between the iron atoms corresponding to a Curie temperature of about $500°K$ [1] and a weaker exchange interaction between the iron and the rare earth ions. The latter interaction is roughly ten times weaker than the former and it is this interaction that we wish to discuss. Information about this interaction has recently been obtained by measurements by Wicherskeim [2] and Tinkham [3] on ytterbium iron garnet. These workers have measured the splitting of the ground doublet of the Yb^{3+} ion in the exchange field set up by the Fe^{3+} ions which at the temperatures at which they work, acts as a rigid unit. They find that this splitting depends on the direction of the iron sub-lattices magnetization and that it can be described by a G tensor whose principal values are in the ratio $1:0.86:0.39$. If the exchange interaction between the rare earth ion and the iron ions were an isotropic exchange interaction of the standard Dirac form [4]

$$\text{const} \times \mathbf{S}_{Fe} \cdot \mathbf{S}_{RE} \tag{1}$$

it is not hard to show that the effect, as far as the ratios of the splittings for the magnetization along the principal directions is concerned, should be the same as those obtained by the applicatiom of an external magnetic field. Whereas no measurements appear to have been made where simultaneously the exchange field and external magnetic field are present there have been paramagnetic resonance measurements in crystals where the Fe^{3+} ion has been replaced by a diamagnetic ion such as gallium or aluminum. For Yb^{3+} in such crystals the ratios of the splitting factors, as measured by paramagnetic resonance techniques give typically [5], are 1:.96:.77. These ratios are fairly independent of what replaced the iron ion. This would tend to indicate that the wavefunction of the ground doublet of Yb^{3+} in these substances is relatively insensitive to what atom is at iron sites. If this is true and (1) is the correct form of the exchange interaction, then the discrepancy between the splitting factors in the iron rare earth garnet and the diamagnetically substituted garnet is hard to understand. We believe that the discrepancy is due to the lack of validity of (1) for this case [6].

That the exchange interaction between an iron ion and a rare earth ion should be more complex than (1) indicates is not surprising. Through the large spin orbit interaction in the rare earth ions the orbital motion of the electrons is strongly coupled to their direction of their spin. The constant that multiplies (1) is some exchange integral. For different directions of the spin of the rare earth this exchange integral will be different because the orbital state of the electrons will change and the degree of interaction between the rare earth and the iron atom must surely depend on the orbital state of the rare earth. In what follows, we will show in summary form how this interaction may be described. In a publication to appear, the missing details of this discussion will be presented along with a discussion of the more complex case of rare earth–rare earth exchange interactions.

Form of the exchange interaction

Let us consider then, in particular, the case of an Fe^{3+} ion interacting with a Yb^{3+} ion. Fe^{3+} is in a d^5 configuration and its ground state is a ^6S. Yb^{3+} has 13 f electrons and its ground state is a $^2F_{7/2}$ state. For Yb^{3+} there is a single hole in the f shell. It is possible, for the purposes of this paper, to treat it as if it had a single f electron rather than a single hole. The wavefunction for this single f electron we shall call ϕ_{M_J}, the index denoting the component of the total angular momentum 7/2 along the z axis which we assume lies in the direction of the Fe^{3+} ion. The wavefunction for the Fe^{3+} ion we call ψ_{M_S}. For the combined system we take a wavefunction which is a product of the two above. We must, of course antisymmetrize the product wavefunction with respect to all of the electron coordinates.

We will assume that the iron wavefunction is already antisymmetric with respect to its coordinates. We put electrons 2 through 6 on the iron and the first electron on the Yb^{3+}. (We need not concern ourselves with the electrons in closed shells in either iron.) Our combined wavefunction is therefore

$$A\psi_{M_S}(2\cdots6)\phi_{M_J}(1) \qquad (2)$$

(Here the arguments indicate the space and spin coordinate of the elecrons.) A is the antisymmetrizer which makes our product wavefunction antisymmetric

$$A = \Sigma(-1)^P P \qquad (3)$$

P is a permutation operator permuting space and spin coordinates of electrons 1...6 and the summation goes over all 6 permutations. If we assume that the one electron d wavefunctions on the iron, are orthogonal to the f wavefunctions it is not hard to show that (2) will be normalized if it is multiplied by $(5!6!)^{-1/2}$.

Having the form of the approximate wavefunction what we wish to do is to take matrix elements of the Hamiltonian representing the interaction between the electrons on the two atoms. Thus we wish to evaluate

$$(1/5!6!)\int[A\psi_{M_S}(2\cdots6)\phi_{M_S}(1)]^* \sum_{i>j}(e^2/r_{ij})A\psi_{M_S'}(2\cdots6)\phi_{M_J}(1)d\tau_1\cdots d\tau_6 \quad (4)$$

The form of this matrix element can be greatly simplified due to the orthogonality of our wavefunctions and, as far as an interaction between the two atoms is concerned, is the same as the following

$$5\int\psi_{M_S}^*(2\cdots6)\phi_{M_J}(1)[(e^2/r_{12}) - (e^2P_{12}/r_{12})]\psi_{M_S}(2\cdots6)\phi_{M_J'}(1)d\tau_1..d\tau_6 \quad (5)$$

In reducing (4) to (5) one makes use of orthogonality and the antisymmetry of the iron wavefunctions. Let us consider the two terms in the square bracket. The first term is the coulomb interaction between the charge density of iron atom and that of the rare earth. This will not couple the angular momentun of the two atoms and is really part of the crystalline field which removes the eightfold degeneracy of the $J = 7/2$ state on the Yb^{3+} ion. These crystalline field effects will be taken into account when we determine the ground state wavefunction of the rare earth under the influence of solely the cystalline field. The second term is the matrix element of $-e^2P_{12}/r_{12}$. P_{12} is the operator which permutes both the space and the spin coordinates of electrons 1 and 2 and can be written as

$$P_{12} = P_{12}^s[1/2 + 2\mathbf{S}_1\cdot\mathbf{S}_2] \qquad (6)$$

P_{12}^s is the operator which permutes spatial coordinates and in (6) the term

in the square brackets is the term which permutes spin coordinates written
using the Dirac [4] identity. If we put (6) into the second term in (5) we
again get two terms one of which is $-e^2 P^s_{12}/r_{12}$. Once again this does not
couple the spin on the iron with the angular momentum of the rare earth.
We need only consider the term in (5)

$$- 10 \int \psi^*_{M_S}(2\cdots 6)\phi^*_{M_S}(1)[(e^2 P^s_{12}/r_{12})\mathbf{S}_1 \cdot \mathbf{S}_2]\psi_{M'_S}(2\cdots 6)\phi_{M'_J}(1)d\tau_1\cdots d\tau_6 \quad (7)$$

It is clear that the interaction (7) must be ultimately expressable in terms
of exchange integrals between the iron d wavefunctions and rare earth
f wavefunctions.

$$(m_d m_f/m'_f m'_d) = \int v^*_{md}(1)v_{mf}(2)(e^2/r_{12})v'_{md}(2)v_{M'_J}(1)d\tau_1 d\tau_2 \quad (8)$$

Here v_{md} is the standard central field d wavefunction with magnetic quantum
number m_d and v_{mf} the central field f wavefunction. The v_{mf} when coupled
with the spin give the wavefunction ϕ_{M_J} which have the total angular
momentum as a good quantum number. What we would like to do now is to
write the matrix element (7) in terms of matrix elements, of an operator depending on the angular momenta of the two interacting atoms and constants
depending on the exchange integrals (8) just as is done for the ordinary
Dirac vector model which results in expression (1). This can be done in
complete analogy to the way Racah treats the exchange interaction between
the d electrons and the p electrons in a configuration d^2p (7). Instead of the
operator in the square brackets of (7) we can use an equivalent operator

$$\mathbf{S}_1 \cdot \mathbf{S}_2 \sum_q c_q \mu^q_0 (1) \quad (9)$$

The c's are constants related to the exchange integrals (8) by a relation
given below and the $u^q_m(1)$ are irreducible tensor operators defined by Racah.
The summation extends over q even running from 0 through 6. The irreducible tensor operators transform like an angular momentum q (magnetic
quantum number m) under rotations of the spatial coordinates of electron 1.
They are defined to coincide with Eq. 58 of Racah's paper. They can, if we
wished, be expressed in terms of polynomials in the orbital angular momentum operator of an electron 1. For example for f electrons

$$u^0_0(1) = 1$$

$$u^1_0(1) = l_z\sqrt{3(4)7} \quad (10)$$

$$u^2_0(1) \approx 3l^2_z - l^2$$

It is not hard to show that the relation between the c's in Eq. 9 and the basic exchange integrals (8) is

$$c_q = \sqrt{2q+1} \sum_{\substack{m_d \\ m_f}} (-1)^{2-m_d}(-1)^{3-m_f} \begin{pmatrix} 2 & 0 & 2 \\ -m_d & 0 & m \end{pmatrix} \times \begin{pmatrix} 3 & q & 3 \\ -m_f & 0 & m_f \end{pmatrix} (m_d m_f/m_f m_d) \tag{11}$$

The quantities in the curved brackets are the familiar Wigner $3j$ symbols excellently tabulated by Rotenberg, Bivins, Metropoulis and Wooten [8]. The first of these has the simple value

$$\begin{pmatrix} 2 & 0 & 2 \\ -m_d & 0 & m_d \end{pmatrix} = (-1)^{-m_d}(5)^{-1/2}$$

We see from this that what we have accomplished is the expression of the exchange interaction between the two atoms in terms of the angular momentum vectors of the two atoms (Eq.(9)). Two points are worth mentioning. We see first that the interaction is inherently anisotropic and that it is no longer linear in the angular momentum operators of the rare earth atoms. The term $q = 0$ gives an isotropic interaction but the terms $q = 2,4,6$, (involving the three constants c_2, c_4 and c_6) give rise to an isotropic interaction.

What we must do is to take matrix elements of the form (7) where we replace the square brackets by (9). This, however, is a problem that can be handled by the standard tensor operator techniques developed by Racah [7;9] and discussed in a number of references [8;10;11]. The only difficulty in taking the matrix element of (9) is that, as far as the rare earth electron is concerned, it is in a state of good total angular momentum $j = 7/2$ whereas the operator $\mathbf{s}_1 \Sigma c_q u_0^q$ (1) is not an irreducible tensor operator as far as simultaneous rotations of spin in spare coordinates are concerned. This, however, is easily remedied by introducing instead of the $x,y,$ and z components of the spin of electron 1 the operators

$$d_1^1(S_1) = -\frac{S_{1x}+iS_{1y}}{2}$$

$$d_0^1(S_1) = S_{1z} \tag{11}$$

$$d_{-1}^1(S_1) = \frac{S_{1x}-iS_{1y}}{2}$$

and then defining irreducible tensor operators

$$O_k^p = \sum_{\substack{m_s \\ m}} \sqrt{2p+1} \, (-1)^{q-k+1} \begin{pmatrix} 1 & 8 & p \\ m_s & m & -k \end{pmatrix} d_{m_s}^1 \, \mu_m^8 \tag{12}$$

This is nothing more than the Clebsch Gordan combination of angular momentum one, with an angular momentum q to give an angular momentum $p = q$, $q + 1$, $q - 1$. Using the Wigner Eckart theorem [10;11] matrix elements of O_k^p will be just the same as operator equivalents [12] made out of polynomials of $j_1 = l_1 + s_1$ (as far as matrix elements diagonal in j are concerned). Now, by using the inverse of (12) and expressing the $d^1_{ms} u^q_m$ on the right hand side in terms of a linear combination of the operators in this left hand side, it is possible to calculate the matrix elements of (9) in terms of standard formulae. The result is

$$16 \sum_{m_s} (-1)^{m_s} \sum_8 c_q \sum_p \sqrt{2p+1} \begin{pmatrix} 1 & q & p \\ -m & 0 & m_s \end{pmatrix} d^1_{-m_s}(\mathbf{S}_{Fe}) \times$$

$$(-1)^{7/2 - M_J} \begin{pmatrix} 7/2 & p & 7/2 \\ -M_J & m_s & M_J' \end{pmatrix} \begin{Bmatrix} 1/2 & 1/2 & 1 \\ 3 & 3 & q \\ 1/2 & 1/2 & p \end{Bmatrix} \qquad (13)$$

In 13 we have not taken the matrix element as yet with respect to the iron wavefunctions and have used the fact that as far as those matrix elements are concerned $5\, \mathbf{S}_1 = \mathbf{S}_{Fe}$ where $\mathbf{S}_{Fe}$ is the total spin operator for the Fe^{3+} ion. The quantity in the curly brackets is a $9j$ symbol (16) and is given in terms of tabulated [8] $6j$ symbols by

$$(-1)^{p+q} \begin{Bmatrix} 7/2 & 7/2 & p \\ 1/2 & \dfrac{q+p}{2} & 3 \end{Bmatrix} \begin{Bmatrix} 3 & 3 & p \\ y_2 & \dfrac{q+p}{2} & 7/2 \end{Bmatrix} \Bigg/ 3 \begin{Bmatrix} q & p & 1 \\ y_2 & y_2 & \dfrac{q+p}{2} \end{Bmatrix} \qquad (14)$$

It can be shown that only terms in p odd arise p taking on the values 1, 3, 5, 7. Eq. 13 must appear somewhat cumbersome until one realizes that all the quantities appearing in it are tabulated. The same result would be obtained by taking the matrix elements of an operator of the form

$$\sum_{m_s} A^p_{m_s} u^p_{m_s}(\mathbf{j}_1) d^1_{-m_s}(\mathbf{S}_{Fe}) \qquad (14)$$

where $p = 1, 3, 5, 7$; $m_s = 0, \pm 1$, but it has the virtue of involving only four constants rather than the 6 constants in (14). Put another way (13) enables us to express the constants in (14) in terms of the more fundamental constants in (13). Eq. (14) is nontheless interesting since written out and expressed in terms the x, y, and z components of the angular momenta involved it would be

$$(15)$$

$$A'_\perp(s_x j_x + s_y j_y) + A'_\parallel(s_z j_z) + \text{terms in the third, fifth and seventh power of } j_1.$$

Again we see that this exchange interaction in inherently anisotropic even in the terms linear in j_1 and in addition involves terms in higher orders of j_1.

At this point the reader may object to the fact that we have considered only direct exchange. Due to the large distances involved in the rare earth iron garnets almost surely there is involved some superexchange mechanism involving the oxygen atoms in this crystal. The point is, however, that we have not really made use of the form of the $1/r_{12}$ interacting in our argument and any effective Hamiltonian involving interaction through excited states would be equally good. There is one special feature of the $1/r_{12}$ interaction that we did use however. That is the cylindrical symmetry of this interaction in using in (9) only the u_m^q with $m = 0$. For a general superexchange interaction one would have to include terms in m which would be appropriate for the reduction of the cylindrical symmetry appropriate for the diamagnetic ions lying between the two paramagnetic ions. We will see in the next section that even for a superexchange mechanism in the ytterbium iron garnet one can get some idea as to the anisotropy that the exchange interaction possesses.

The case of ytterbium iron garnet

Ytterbium iron garnet is a cubic crystal with space group O_h^{10} [13]. The ytterbium ions in the unit cell find themselves at sites of D_2 symmetry. What we would like to know is the linear combination of the M_J levels of the $j = 7/2$ state of Yb^{3+} which make up the ground doublet. If we knew this we could use formula (13) to calculate the anisotropy of the exchange splitting as the spin of the iron atom (magnetization of the iron sublattice) points in various directions. If we assume that the ground state of the Yb^{3+} atom in the iron garnet is the same as in an aluminum or a gallium garnet, we can use the observed g-values for the latter case to compute the wavefunction for the former case.

It is not hard to see that for D_2 symmetry the ground doublet must consist of

$$C_1\phi_{1/2} + C_{-3}\phi_{-3/2} + C_5\phi_{5/2} + C_{-7}\phi_{-7/2} \tag{16}$$

and degenerate with it

$$C_1\phi_{-1/2} + C_{-3}\phi_{3/2} + C_5\phi_{-5/2} + C_{-7}\phi_{7/2}$$

If we take the g_x, g_y and g_z values for Yb^{3+} in the ytterbium aluminum garnet [5], namely

$$g_x = 3.87$$

$$g_y = 3.78 \tag{17}$$

$$g_z = 2.47$$

we can easily find that a good fit to the observed g- values is given by

$$C_1 = C_{-7} = 0$$

$$C_{-3} = -.60 \tag{18}$$

$$C_5 = -.80$$

The g-values calculated from this are

$$g_x = g_y = 3.80$$

$$g_z = 2.42. \tag{19}$$

Van Vleck [6] has pointed out that average to the g's in Eq. 17 is close to the isotropic value found for a Γ_7 state in a cubic field. We might note in passing that the coefficients (18) are also close to the values appropriate for cubic symmetry which are

$$C_1 = C_{-7} = 0$$

$$C_{-3} = -.50 \tag{20}$$

$$C_5 = -.85$$

One could now use the wavefunctions (16) and expression (13) to calculate the anisotropy in terms of the parameters C_2, C_4 and C_6 of (9). To see how this works out in practice let us try the following. Let's assume that only one of the basic exchange integrals in (8) is non vanishing namely that one which gives the maximum overlap between the iron and the ytterbium wavefunctions which is $(00|00)$. If we call this integral J and assume all others are zero we obtain using (11)

$$C_0 = (1/\sqrt{35})J$$

$$C_2 = (-2/\sqrt{21})J$$

$$C_4 = (9\sqrt{2}/\sqrt{5(7)11})J \tag{21}$$

$$C_6 = (-2\sqrt{13}/\sqrt{3(7)11})J$$

J now governs the magnitude of the exchange splitting but ratios of the splittings in various directions are independent of the magnitude of J.

With these assumptions and the known wavefunction (18) the two by two secular equation governing the splitting of the ground doublet is given by

$$\text{const.} \times \begin{pmatrix} M_z(.77) - E & M^-(.28) \\ M^+(.28) & M_z(-.77) - E \end{pmatrix} \tag{22}$$

Here we have replaced S_{Fe} by a constant times the magnetization M of the iron ions. ($M^\pm = M_x \pm i\, M_y$). From this we see that the anisotropy of this splitting would be in the ratio of $1 : .36 : .36$. The order in which we have written these ratios is arbitrary since we have no way of knowning if the x, y and z directions which we tacitly assumed in calculating the wavefunction (18) are not permuted from those along which the exchange splittings are measured [14]. It is clear that these ratios bear little resemblance to the observed ratios of the exchange splittings $(1 : .86 : .39)$ mentioned in the Introduction. This is not surprising since almost certainly the exchange mechanism is not direct. Let us look at the situation in ytterbium iron garnet in more detail.

Let us assume that the coupling of the iron magnetization to the angular momentum of the Yb^{3+} ion is through the O^{--} ions which are nearest neighbors of the Yb^{3+}. If the Yb^{3+} ion is placed at the origin of a cubic unit cell there are four nearest neighbor oxygen ions at positions [13]

$$
\begin{matrix}
-.1008 & .0572 & .1524 \\
.0572 & -.1008 & -.1524 \\
.1008 & -.0572 & .1524 \\
-.0572 & .1008 & -.1524
\end{matrix}
\tag{23}
$$

Here distances are expressed in terms of the unit cubic cell dimensions. We assume further that the principal interaction will occur for that orbital state of the f electron that puts the maximum of the wavefunction in the direction of these nearest neighbor oxygen atoms. This is the wavefunction with $m_f = 0$ where the axis of quantitization is in the direction of the particular O^{--} ion under consideration. We assume further that superexchange interactions involving other orbital states of the f electron vanish. Using this argument and the fact that the Fe^{3+} is in an orbital S state it is possible to show that once again it is possible to restrict ourselves to one constant as in (21) if we only assume that our axis of quantitization is along the

$Yb^{3+} - O^-$ axis under consideration. If we use the fact that there are 4 O^{--} atoms through which this exchange interaction can pass it can be shown that the G values appropriate for this situation can be expressed in terms of the G values calculated from (22). (Call these $G_{||}$ and $G_{\perp}$) by the formulas

$$G_z \approx G_{||} \gamma^2 + G_{\perp}(1 - \gamma^2)$$
$$G_y \approx G_{||} \alpha^2 + G_{\perp}(1 - \alpha^2)$$
$$G_x \approx G_{||} \beta^2 + G_{\perp}(1 - \beta^2) \qquad (23)$$

the proportionality constant is the same in the three cases and α, β and γ are the cosines of the angles that the principal axes (D_2 -axes) make with respect to the nearest neighbor oxygen directions. The square of these cosines is the same no matter which nearest neighbor oxygen we talk about since the principal values of the G tensor lie along the [110], [1$\bar{1}$0], and [001] directions. Using (23), one can easily show that

$$G_z : G_y : G_x = 1 : .76 : .49 \qquad (24)$$

These ratios are nearer to the observed ratios $(1 : .86 : .39)$ than those from the direct exchange mechanism. The x, y, and z axes are the same as those defining the paramagnetic resonance g-values which for the same Yb^{3+} were functions (18) have the ratios (19)

$$g_z : g_x : g_y = 2.42 : 3.80 : 3.80 \qquad (25)$$

If the ordering of the axes is the same for the measured paramagnetic g as for the measured exchange G, then the results of the theoretical calculation (24) would be permuted and the agreement would be poor. This could be checked by measuring the splitting of the ground doublet as a function of magnetic field when an exchange field is simultaneously present. If it turns out that the axes are not permuted with respect to one another one could take into account a superexchange mechanism going through second nearest neighbor oxygens and use a two parameter fit involving both first and second nearest neighbor oxygens. This is currently under investigation.

REFERENCES

[1]   R. PAUTHENET, *Ann. de Phys. et de Chim.* **3**, 424 (1958).
[2]   K. A. WICHERSHEIM, *Phys. Rev.* **122**, 1376 (1961).
[3]   M. TINKHAM, *Phys. Rev.* **124**, 311 (1961).
[4]   P. A. M. DIRAC, *Proc. Roy. Soc. (London)* **123A**, 714 (1929).

[5] W. P. WOLF, M. BALL, M. T. HUTCHINGS, M. J. M. LEACH AND A. F. G. WYATT, to appear in *Journ. Phys. Soc. of Japan.* (Report on International Conference on Magnetism and Crystallography, Kyoto, 1961.) See this article for comparitive paramagnetic resonance data and further references.

[6] See the report of J. H. VAN VLECK in the conference mentioned in Ref. 5. This author has looked into this same problem independently in an article to appear in la Revista de la Universidad Nacional de Tuciman.

[7] G. RACAH. *Phys. Rev.*, **62**, 438 (1942).

[8] M. ROTENBERG, R. BIVINS, N. METROPOULIS AND J. K. WOOTEN, JR., *3j and 6j Symbols*, Technology Press, Cambridge, 1959.

[9] G. RACAH, *Phys. Rev.* **63**, 367 (1943).

[10] A. R. EDMONDS, *Angular Momentum in Quantum Mechanics*, Princeton University Press, 1957.

[11] M. E. ROSE, *Elementary Theory of Angular Momentum*, John Wiley and Sons, New York, 1957.

[12] For a tabulation of operator equivalents see G. F. KOSTER AND H. STATZ, *Phys. Rev.* **113**, 445 (1959).

[13] Structure determination of ytterbium iron garnet: private communication F. EULER AND J. BRUCE (to be published). For a structure determination of ytterbium iron garnet, see S. GELLER, M. A. GILLEO, *J. Phys. and Chem. Solids* **3**, 30 (1957); **9**, 235 (1959).

A Theoretical Investigation of Some Spectroscopic and Magnetic Properties of Rare Earth Ions

A. J. FREEMAN

Materials Research Laboratory, Watertown, Massachusetts

AND

R. E. WATSON

A.E.R.E. Harwell, Didcot, Berks, England

We are reporting on investigations of some spectroscopic and magnetic properties of rare earth ions based on approximate Hartree-Fock calculations. First, a set of conventional, nonrelativistic Hartree-Fock wavefunctions were obtained for nine ions of the series; second, calculations were carried out in which spin orbit coupling was directly included in the conventional Hartree-Fock equations in order to obtain some estimate of wavefunction dependence on J and the resulting effects on experimental quantities; and third, spin polarized *and* "orbitally" polarized Hartree-Fock calculations were done for free ions and ions in an external V_2^0 point charge potential.

We shall discuss spin orbit splittings, the Slater $F^k(4f,4f)$ integrals, the crystal-field parameters, $V_n^m = A_n^m \langle r^n \rangle$, and hyperfine interactions, all of which depened fairly critically on the precise form of the $4f$ wavefunctions. Comparisons will be made with experiments and with the results of previous theoretical investigations which relied on approximate wavefunctions or semiempirical parametrizations. We find that the usual spin orbit formula, $(1/r) \, dV/dr$,does not give agreement with experiment and our investigation presents some evidence indicating the importance of including exchange terms between the $4f$ electrons and the core. Our $\langle r^n \rangle$ are found to be in good agreement for $n=2$, 4, and 6 with the Elliott and Stevens parametrization formula but the assumption of constancy with Z of the A_n^m is not valid, as is shown by analysis of the trichloride and ethyl sulphate data. Our $\langle r^{-3} \rangle$ values agree very closely (i.e., to within five percent) with Bleaney's values and hence so do our estimates for the hyperfine interactions. Finally, we discuss aspherical distortions and spin-polarizations effects by means of m_s and m_l "unrestricted" Hartree-Fock calculations and their implications for the interpretation of observed rare earth spectroscopic and magnetic properties.

The Direct Magnetic Contribution to the Transferred Hyperfine Interaction for Trivalent Rare Earth Ions

D. F. Johnston

Theoretical Physics Division
Atomic Energy Research Establishment, Harwell, England

ABSTRACT

Formulae are given for each of the trivalent rare earth ions, which give the f-shell electronic orbital and spin contributions to the magnetic field B due to the ion, at an arbitrary point $\mathbf{R}$ relative to the ion. The energy of interaction $(-\boldsymbol{\mu} \cdot \mathbf{B})$ with a nuclear moment μ at $\mathbf{R}$ can thus be calculated for any crystal symmetry.

I. Introduction

The transferred hyperfine interaction is important in two experimental situations,

(a) electron paramagnetic resonance of an electronic system perturbed by the magnetic fields of neighboring magnetic nuclei,

(b) nuclear magnetic resonance of a magnetic nucleus perturbed by the magnetic fields of neighboring magnetic atoms.

An analysis of such situations requires a knowledge of the direct magnetic contribution to the transferred hyperfine interaction. In the case of the trivalent rare earth ions the interaction between a nuclear moment and the orbital magnetic moment of the rare earth ion may be larger than the spin–spin interaction. In addition, it is necessary to know the relative importance of the higher multipole parts of the interaction when compared with the dipole term. To a good approximation for the present purpose, the electronic ground-state of a trivalent rare earth ion in a crystal can be represented by a linear combination of wavefunctions of the form $|f^n \beta SLJM\rangle$, where the particular combination over the magnetic quantum numbers M depends on the local crystal symmetry. If $\mathbf{B}(\mathbf{R})$ denotes the operator corresponding to the magnetic field due to the ion, at a point $\mathbf{R}$, the interaction $(-\boldsymbol{\mu} \cdot \mathbf{B} = \sum_{\alpha=1}^{\alpha=-1} (-1)^{\alpha} \mu_{-\alpha} B_{\alpha})$ with a nuclear moment μ at $\mathbf{R}$ is known if we know the matrix elements

$$\langle f^n \beta SLJM \,|\, B_{\alpha} \,|\, f^n \beta SLJ'M' \rangle. \tag{1}$$

374

Calculation shows that both the electronic orbital and spin contribution to the magnetic field can be expressed in the operator form

$$B_\alpha = \left(\frac{e\hbar}{m_0}\right) \sum_{k=1}^{K=2l+1} \frac{\langle r^{K-1}\rangle}{R^{K+2}} c(K) \sum_{Q,Q'} \sqrt{\pi}\; Y_Q(\hat{\mathbf{R}}) T_{Q'}^k \; \langle(K+1),Q; K,Q' \,|\,1,\alpha \rangle.$$

The integer K takes only odd values. The operators $T_{Q'}^K$ are defined such that

$$\langle J,M \,|\, T_{Q'}^K \,|\, J',M'\rangle = \langle K,Q'; J',M' \,|\, J,M\rangle.$$

The moments $\langle r^{k-1}\rangle$ are defined by

$$\langle r^{k-1}\rangle = \int_0^\infty r^{K+1} f^2(r)\,dr,$$

where $f(r)$ is the radial part of the one-electron f-shell wavefunctions.

The coefficients $C(K)$ are given by the following general expressions for n-electronic states of the form $|\,l^n\beta S L J M\rangle$. The numbers $\langle(\alpha_1 S_1 L_1)l\,|\}\alpha S L\rangle$ are coefficients of fractional percentage.

Orbital $C(K) = C_1(K)C_2(K)C_3(K)$

$$C_1(K) = (2K+1)^2\sqrt{2(2K+3)} \begin{pmatrix} K+1 & K & 1 \\ 0 & 0 & 0 \end{pmatrix} \begin{Bmatrix} K+1 & K & 1 \\ 1 & 1 & K \end{Bmatrix}$$

$$\times \sqrt{2l+1} \left[(2l-K)(2l-1)\begin{pmatrix} l & l-1 & 1 \\ 0 & 0 & 0 \end{pmatrix}\begin{pmatrix} l & l-1 & K \\ 0 & 0 & 0 \end{pmatrix}\begin{Bmatrix} l & l & K \\ K & 1 & l-1 \end{Bmatrix} \right.$$

$$\left. -(2l+K+2)(2l+3) \begin{pmatrix} l+1 & l & 1 \\ 0 & 0 & 0 \end{pmatrix}\begin{pmatrix} l+1 & l & K \\ 0 & 0 & 0 \end{pmatrix}\begin{Bmatrix} l & l & K \\ K & 1 & l+1 \end{Bmatrix}\right]$$

$$C_2(K) = n\sqrt{(2l+1)(2L+1)} \sum_{\alpha_1 S_1 L_1} |\langle(\alpha_1 S_1 L_1)l\,|\}\alpha S L\rangle|^2 \begin{Bmatrix} K & l & l \\ L_1 & L & L \end{Bmatrix}(-1)^{K+l+L_1+L}$$

$$C_3(K) = \sqrt{(2L+1)(2J'+1)} \begin{Bmatrix} K & L & L \\ S & J & J' \end{Bmatrix}-(1)^{(K+S+J'+L)}$$

Spin $C(K) = C_1(K)C_2(K)C_3(K)$

$$C_1(K) = (-1)^l \sqrt{(2l+1)(2K-1)^2(2K+1)(2K+3)}$$

$$\times \begin{pmatrix} K & 1 & K+1 \\ 0 & 0 & 0 \end{pmatrix}\begin{pmatrix} K & 1 & K-1 \\ 0 & 0 & 0 \end{pmatrix}\begin{pmatrix} l & K-1 & l \\ 0 & 0 & 0 \end{pmatrix}$$

$$C_2(K) = n\sqrt{(2s+1)(2S+1)(2l+1)(2L+1)}\,(-1)^{K+l+\frac{1}{2}+L+S}$$

$$\times \sum_{\alpha_1 S_1 L_1} |\,\langle (\alpha_1 S_1 L_1)l\,|\}\,\alpha\,SL\rangle\,|^2 \begin{Bmatrix} 1 & \frac{1}{2} & \frac{1}{2} \\ S_1 & S & S \end{Bmatrix} \begin{Bmatrix} (K-1)\,l & l \\ L_1 & L\,L \end{Bmatrix} (-1)^{L_1+S_1}$$

$$C_3(K) = \sqrt{(2S+1)(2L+1)(2J'+1)(2K+1)}\,\begin{Bmatrix} 1 & K-1 & K \\ S & L & J' \\ S & L & J \end{Bmatrix}$$

For $K = 1$, the expressions for $C(K)$ condense to the simple form

$$C(1)\ \text{orbital} = -\frac{1}{\sqrt{2J(J+1)}}\,[L(L+1)+J(J+1)-S(S+1)],$$

$$C(1)\ \text{spin} = -\frac{2}{\sqrt{2J(J+1)}}\,[S(S+1)+J(J+1)-L(L+1)],$$

and thus lead to the dipole contribution

$$B_\alpha = -\frac{1}{R^3}\,(\mathbf{M}-3\hat{\mathbf{R}}\hat{\mathbf{R}}\cdot\mathbf{M})_\alpha,$$

with

$$\mathbf{M} = -\frac{e\hbar}{2m_0}\,(\mathbf{L}+2\mathbf{S}),$$

on using the identity

$$(\mathbf{M}-3\hat{\mathbf{R}}\hat{\mathbf{R}}\cdot\mathbf{M})_\alpha = \sqrt{8\pi}\sum_{Q,Q'} Y_Q^2(\hat{\mathbf{R}})M_{Q'}\langle 2,Q;1,Q'\,|\,|1,\alpha\rangle$$

II. The coefficient $C(K)$

The numerical values of $C(K)$ for the ground-states of the trivalent rare-earths are given in Tables I and II, with the exception of europium and gadolinium which are treated separately below. In the case of samarium, additional coefficients are given to facilitate the construction of matrix elements between the $J = 5/2$ and $J = 7/2$ states, since the spin-orbit splitting is relatively small for this ion. The cross-term coefficients are related by the Hermitian condition

$$\frac{C(K,J,J')}{C(K,J',J)} = (-1)^{J-J'}\sqrt{\frac{(2J'+1)}{(2J+1)}}\,.$$

Europium $f^6\ {}^7F$

For europium there is no contribution from the $J = 0$ ground state. For the $J = 1$ state only the $K = 1$ coefficients are non-zero. The $\langle J=0\,|\,J=1\rangle$

TABLE I

The orbital and spin contributions to the coefficients C(K)

	Cerium (f^1) $^2F_{5/2}$	Praseodymium (f^2) $^3H_4$	Neodymium (f^3) $^4I_{9/2}$	Promethium (f^4) $^5I_4$	Samarium (f^5) $^6H_{5/2}$	Samarium $(J=5/2\mid J=7/2)$ cross-terms	Samarium (f^5) $^6H_{7/2}$
Orbit $K=1$	$-4\sqrt{\dfrac{10}{7}}$	$-12\sqrt{\dfrac{2}{5}}$	$-21\sqrt{\dfrac{2}{11}}$	$-14\sqrt{\dfrac{2}{5}}$	$-6\sqrt{\dfrac{10}{7}}$	$2\sqrt{\dfrac{15}{7}}$	$-\dfrac{37}{3}\sqrt{\dfrac{2}{7}}$
spin	$2\sqrt{10}$	0	$-\dfrac{392}{11}\sqrt{\dfrac{2}{143}}$	$-\dfrac{392}{11}\sqrt{\dfrac{2}{165}}$	$5\sqrt{\dfrac{10}{7}}$	$-4\sqrt{\dfrac{15}{7}}$	$\dfrac{11}{3}\sqrt{\dfrac{2}{7}}$
Orbit $K=3$	$-\dfrac{4}{5}\sqrt{10}$	$4\sqrt{\dfrac{2}{5}}$	$9\sqrt{\dfrac{2}{11}}$	$8\sqrt{\dfrac{2}{5}}$	$\dfrac{26}{9}\sqrt{\dfrac{2}{5}}$	$-\dfrac{1144}{135\sqrt{15}}$	$-\dfrac{1575}{\sqrt{11}}$
spin		$-\dfrac{364}{15}\sqrt{\dfrac{2}{165}}$	$-\dfrac{98}{11}\sqrt{\dfrac{2}{143}}$	$\dfrac{98}{11}\sqrt{\dfrac{2}{165}}$	$\dfrac{260}{33\sqrt{21}}$	$-\dfrac{1300}{99\sqrt{7}}$	$-\dfrac{10}{3}\sqrt{\dfrac{26}{21}}$
Orbit $K=5$	$-\dfrac{20}{\sqrt{21}}$	$\dfrac{40}{33\sqrt{26}}$	$-\dfrac{7140}{363\sqrt{39}}$	$-\dfrac{7140}{1089}\sqrt{\dfrac{2}{13}}$	0	$-\dfrac{7826}{1575\sqrt{11}}$	$-\dfrac{424}{99}\sqrt{\dfrac{26}{21}}$
spin	$\dfrac{10}{\sqrt{21}}$	$-\dfrac{20}{33\sqrt{26}}$	$-\dfrac{4760}{363\sqrt{39}}$	$\dfrac{4760}{1089}\sqrt{\dfrac{2}{13}}$	$\dfrac{130}{33\sqrt{21}}$	$-\dfrac{832}{99\sqrt{7}}$	
$K=7$ spin	0	$-\dfrac{4760}{99\sqrt{143}}$	$-\dfrac{13300}{1573\sqrt{143}}\sqrt{\dfrac{85}{143}}$	$\dfrac{226100}{4719\sqrt{13}}$	0	0	$-\dfrac{476}{99}\sqrt{\dfrac{26}{11}}$

TABLE II

The orbital and spin contributions to the coefficients C(K)

	Ytterbium $(f^{13})^2 F_{7/2}$	Thulium $(f^{12})^3 H_6$	Erbium $(f^{11})^4 I_{15/2}$	Holmium $(f^{10})^5 I_8$	Dysprosium $(f^9)^6 H_{15/2}$	Terbium $(f^8)^7 F_6$
Orbit $K=1$	$-9\sqrt{\dfrac{2}{7}}$	$-5\sqrt{\dfrac{7}{3}}$	$-2\sqrt{\dfrac{102}{5}}$	-9	$-\sqrt{\dfrac{170}{3}}$	$-\sqrt{21}$
spin	$-3\sqrt{\dfrac{2}{7}}$	$-2\sqrt{\dfrac{7}{3}}$	$-\sqrt{\dfrac{102}{5}}$	-6	$-\sqrt{\dfrac{170}{3}}$	$-2\sqrt{21}$
Orbit $K=3$	$2\sqrt{11}$	0	$-2\sqrt{\dfrac{323}{65}}$	$-\sqrt{19}$	0	$\dfrac{28}{\sqrt{33}}$
spin	$2\sqrt{11}$	$\dfrac{28}{\sqrt{33}}$	$\dfrac{4}{5}\sqrt{\dfrac{323}{65}}$	$-\dfrac{2}{5}\sqrt{19}$	$-2\sqrt{\dfrac{323}{65}}$	$-\dfrac{28}{\sqrt{33}}$
Orbit $K=5$	$-5\sqrt{\dfrac{26}{21}}$	$\dfrac{15}{33}\sqrt{238}$	$-\dfrac{10}{11}\sqrt{\dfrac{646}{39}}$	$-5\sqrt{\dfrac{19}{39}}$	$\dfrac{15}{11}\sqrt{\dfrac{646}{39}}$	$-\dfrac{5}{33}\sqrt{238}$
spin	$-15\sqrt{\dfrac{26}{21}}$	$\dfrac{20}{33}\sqrt{238}$	$\dfrac{15}{11}\sqrt{\dfrac{646}{39}}$	$-\dfrac{15}{2}\sqrt{\dfrac{19}{39}}$	$-\dfrac{20}{11}\sqrt{\dfrac{646}{39}}$	$\dfrac{5}{11}\sqrt{238}$
$K=7$ spin	$350\sqrt{\dfrac{2}{143}}$	$-\dfrac{3500}{429}\sqrt{\dfrac{323}{33}}$	$\dfrac{700}{429}\sqrt{\dfrac{14858}{39}}$	$\dfrac{700}{39}\sqrt{\dfrac{437}{13}}$	$\dfrac{350}{429}\sqrt{\dfrac{14858}{39}}$	$-\dfrac{700}{429}\sqrt{\dfrac{323}{33}}$

cross-terms are $C(1) = 2\sqrt{6}$ for the orbital coefficient and $C(1) = -4\sqrt{6}$ for the spin coefficient.

Gadolinium f^7 $^8S_{7/2}$

In the Russel-Saunders approximation used here, the gadolinium ion is a classical spin dipole with $\mathbf{M} = -(e\hbar/m_0)\mathbf{S}$.

Acknowledgment

The author would like to thank Dr. Martin Blume for invaluable discussion.

Resonant Harmonic Generation by Paramagnetic Ions

I. R. SENITZKY

U.S. Army Signal Research and Development Laboratory
Fort Monmouth, New Jersey

ABSTRACT

Resonant harmonic generation and frequency mixing in a three level system are discussed. An expression is obtained for the field energy in a cavity at the harmonic or the mixed frequency.

If three energy levels of an atomic system are equally spaced and none of the corresponding three matrix elements of the dipole moment vanish, and if the atomic system is coupled to a field of frequency corresponding to the spacing of adjacent levels, the system will generate twice this frequency. This phenomenon is a special case of resonant frequency mixing [1], and has recently been observed experimentally in ruby [2].

Let us consider the following situation: A paramagnetic crystal occupies a small part of the volume of a microwave cavity. The concentration of paramagnetic ions is sufficiently small so that spin-spin coupling may be neglected; there is, however, inhomogeneous broadening. The paramagnetic ions have at least three energy levels ($E_1 < E_2 < E_3$) and none of the corresponding dipole matrix elements vanish. The cavity has modes which resonate at the three frequencies determined by these levels.

Let the microwave magnetic field of a mode be described by $\mathbf{H}(\mathbf{r}, t) = \mathbf{u}(\mathbf{r})q(t)$, where $\mathbf{u}$ is normalized over the volume of the cavity by $\int_v u^2 d^3\mathbf{r} = 1$. If the modes of frequencies v_{21} and v_{32} are driven by

$$q_{21}(t) = \tilde{q}_{21}\cos(w_{21}t + \theta_{21}), \qquad q_{32}(t) = \tilde{q}_{32}\cos(w_{32}t + \theta_{32}),$$

third order perturbation theory in which both cavity loss and spin-lattice relaxation are taken into account shows that the mode of frequency v_{31} is excited, the field being proportional to

$$\tilde{q}_{21}\tilde{q}_{32}\sin(w_{31}t + \theta_{21} + \theta_{32}).$$

The energy of this field is given approximately by

$$E_{31} = \frac{8\pi^3 N^2 Q^2 T_1{}^2}{\hbar^4(\Delta v)^2}(u_{21}u_{32}u_{31})^2\,|\gamma_{21}\gamma_{32}\gamma_{31}|^2(2P_2 - P_1 - P_3)^2 E_{21}E_{32},$$

380

where E_{21} and E_{32} are the field energies of the two driven modes, respectively, N is the number of paramagnetic ions, γ_{ij} is the matrix element of the field-parallel component of magnetic dipole moment of the ion, u_{ij} is the (normalized) field strength of the ij'th mode at the position of the ions, Δv is the (largest) inhomogeneous broadening, Q is the cavity quality factor (at v_{31}) and P_i is the occupation number of the i'th energy level, averaged over the ions. The spin lattice relaxation time T_1 is assumed, for simplicity, to be approximately equal at all three frequencies. If saturation effects are negligible, and if only three energy levels are occupied, then, for $hv_{ij} \ll kT$,

$$(2P_2 - P_1 - P_3)^2 = \begin{cases} \dfrac{1}{9}\left[\dfrac{h(v_{21}-v_{32})}{kT}\right]^2, & v_{21} \neq v_{32}; \\[3mm] \dfrac{1}{9}\left(\dfrac{hv}{kT}\right)^4, & v_{21} = v_{32} = v. \end{cases}$$

For $v_{21} \neq v_{32}$, we have frequency mixing, and for $v_{21} = v_{32}$ we have harmonic generation. In the former case, conversion with gain is a possibility. The present theory, however, is essentially a small-signal theory, and will cease to be applicable for sufficiently large driving energy at one of the frequencies.

REFERENCES

[1] I. R. SENITZKY, in *Quantum Electronics*, edited by C. H. Townes, Columbia University Press, New York, 1960, p. 212.
[2] C. KELLINGTON, *Phys. Rev. Letters* 9,57 (1962).

Muon Resonance*

VERNON W. HUGHES

Yale University

ABSTRACT

The availability of polarized muons and the ability to detect the spin direction, which are provided by parity nonconservation in the decays of the pi meson and the muon, have made possible magnetic resonance experiments on the muon, on muonium, and on mu-mesic atoms. The study of muon magnetism has advanced our knowledge of the properties of the muon, of relativistic and other higher order effects in atomic magnetism including solid state effects, and of nuclear structure.

I. Introduction

Nonconservation of parity in the weak interactions[1;2;3] involved in the decays of the pi and mu mesons has provided the tool for magnetic resonance studies of muons, mu mesonic atoms, and muonium. In the pion decays

$$\pi^+ \to \mu^+ + \nu_\mu$$

$$\pi^- \to \mu^- + \bar{\nu}_\mu$$

(1)

(ν is a neutrino and $\bar{\nu}$ is an antineutrino), in the rest frame of the pion the positive (negative) muon will have its spin angular momentum directed opposite (parallel) to its momentum. (This correlation of the directions of the linear momentum and of the spin angular momentum indicates directly a violation of parity conservation.) Hence polarized positive and negative muons are available with the polarization direction related to the direction of motion in the rest frame of the decaying pions. The muon decays into a positron (or electron) and two neutrinos:

* This research has been supported in part by the Air Force OSRD, the National Aeronautics and Space Administration, and the National Science Foundation.

$$\mu^+ \rightarrow e^+ + \nu_e + \bar{\nu}_\mu \tag{2}$$

$$\mu^- \rightarrow e^- + \nu_\mu + \bar{\nu}_e$$

Due to parity nonconservation in these decays the positron (or electron) is not emitted isotropically with respect to the muon spin direction but asymmetrically according to

$$I_{e^+}(\theta) \propto 1 + A\cos\theta$$
$$I_{e^-}(\theta) \propto 1 - A\cos\theta \tag{3}$$

in which θ is the angle between the directions of the muon spin and the direction of emission of the positron (electron) and $A \simeq +1/3$. The asymmetry in the decay positron (electron) angular distribution provides the means for detection of the muon spin direction.

II. The positive muon

The original experiment on parity nonconservation in the pion and muon decays involved the observation of the Larmor precession of the positive muon[4]. The experimental arrangement is shown in Figure 1. Pi mesons are produced when the 380 Mev proton beam of the Columbia University synchrocyclotron strikes an internal target. The pi mesons can decay to form muons. The momentum analyzed incoming meson beam consists of both pi mesons and muons. Because of their greater mass the pi mesons lose more energy in the carbon absorber due to ionization than do the muons, and hence they are stopped in the absorber whereas the muons pass through and are indicated by coincident 12 counts from the scintillation counters. A muon can stop in the carbon target and then it decays into a positron and two neutrinos with a mean life of 2.2 μsec. The positron is indicated by a coincident 34 count.

If the muon from pi meson decay is polarized as indicated above, the muons in the incoming beam will also be polarized, though somewhat less in the laboratory frame than in the rest frame of the pi meson. Then if the muon decay leads to an asymmetric positron angular distribution as given in Eq. (3), the positrons will be emitted preferentially in the direction opposite to that of the incoming beam. This behavior can be confirmed in an elegant and unambiguous way by the use of a magnetic field perpendicular to the plane of the diagram. In the presence of the magnetic field a muon should precess with the Larmor frequency characteristic of the muon, which will be 13.5 kc/sec-gauss if the muon has a spin of 1/2 and a

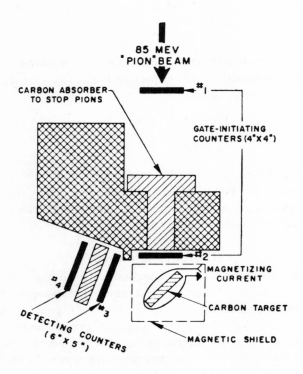

Figure 1

Arrangement of Garwin-Lederman-Weinrich experiment. The magnetizing coil was wound directly on the carbon to provide a uniform vertical field of 79 gauss per ampere. Cross-hatched material is lead shielding.

magnetic moment of 1 muon magneton, $eh/2m_\mu c$. If the muons have a net polarization and if the decay positron angular distribution is correlated with the muon spin direction, then the number of positrons seen by the fixed counter telescope 34 as a function of time after the arrival of the muon should be an exponential function with the time constant of the muon life modulated by $\cos \omega_L t$, where ω_L is the muon Larmor frequency. The actual experimental arrangement involved the observation of the positron counts in a time interval (gate) of 1.25 μsec delayed by 0.75 μsec after the arrival of the muons, as a function of magnetic field. The results are shown in Figure 2. They confirm in a most spectacular way the parity nonconservation in the pi meson and muon decays.

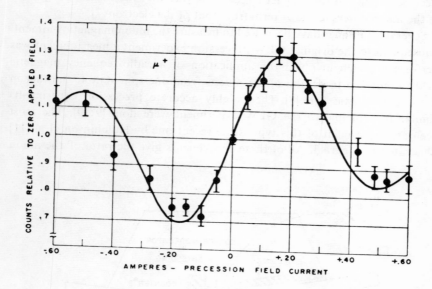

Figure 2

Variation of gated 3–4 counting rate with magnetizing current in GLW experiment. The solid curve is computed from an assumed electron angular distribution, $1 + 1/3 \cos \theta$, with counter and gate-width resolution folded in.

The GLW experiment also provided the first measurement of the spin magnetic moment of the muon. Their data gave $g = 2.0 \pm 10\%$. With the availability of polarized muons and the tool for detecting the spin direction through the asymmetry in the decay positron angular distribution, the way was opened for further work on the spin magnetic moment of the muon. Because of the great interest to elementary particle physics of the properties of the muon, extensive and progressively more accurate measurements of the muon spin magnetic moment have been made.

If the muon obeys the modern quantum electrodynamics of a Dirac particle its g-value will be [5;6]

$$g_{\text{theor}} = 2 \left(1 + \frac{\alpha}{2\pi} + 0.75 \, \frac{\alpha^2}{\pi^2} \right) = 2(1.001165) \tag{4}$$

The difference of g_{theor} from 2 is called the anomalous g-value of the muon, and it arises from the virtual radiative contributions of quantum electrodynamics to the magnetic moment. Note that the theoretical g-value of the muon differs in the α^2 term from that of the electron [7].

Several techniques have been used to measure the muon magnetic moment. Subsequent to the original GLW precession experiment a measurement was performed which involved the application of a radiofrequency magnetic field to induce a transition of the muons from one spin state to another in a static magnetic field [8]. Then highly accurate precession experiments similar in principle to the GLW experiment were done [9;10]. The most accurate experiment of this type is the recent one by Hutchinson el al.[11] illustrated in Figure 3. All of these experiments give the ratio of the muon

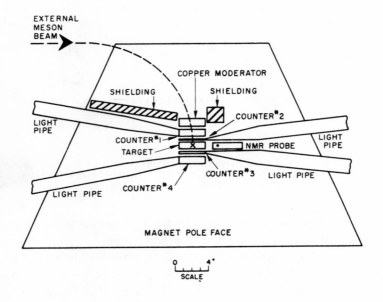

Figure 3

Experimental arrangement of Hutchinson et al. The meson beam from the Nevis cyclotron enters at the left, and is brought to rest in the target. Decay electrons emitted into counters No. 3 and No. 4 are analyzed.

spin resonance frequency in a certain magnetic field to the proton resonance frequency in the same field, which will be the ratio of the magnetic moment of the muon to that of the proton apart from magnetic shielding effects. The positive muons were stopped in water and the assumption is made that the positive muon substitutes for a proton and hence sees the same magnetic shielding as does a proton in a water molecule. On the basis of this assumption[12],

$$\frac{g_{\mu^+}}{g_p} = (3.18338 \pm 0.00004) \frac{m_\mu}{m_p} \tag{5}$$

(m_p = proton mass; m_μ = muon mass)

Considerable data were also taken on muons stopping in various solids including some of the alkali metals, and the results are shown in Table I[12].

TABLE I

Environmental effects on resonance frequency of positive muons

Target Substance	Z	Frequency Shift*		% of Knight Shift	Knight Shift**
			ppm		
Mg	17	+	87 ± 10	6.2%	+ 1400 ppm
Cu	29	+	81	3.5%	+ 2320
Pb	82	+	132	11.0%	+ 1200
Ca	20	+	420	13.5%	+ 3100***
Li	3	+	11	4.4%	+ 249
K	19	+	88	3.1%	+ 2900***
Na	11	+	79	7.0%	+ 1130
C	6	+	380	—	—

  * All frequency shifts indicate paramagnetism.
 ** Knight shift values from table W. D. Knight, *Solid State Physics* **2**, 122 (1956).
*** Predicted values.

It is seen that the observed shifts in resonance frequency are in the sense of paramagnetic effects. The shifts, except for the case of C, are considerably smaller than the Knight shift and have not yet received a quantitative explanation.

In order to obtain g_{μ^+} itself, the ratio of the muon mass to the proton (or electron) mass must be known. The mass ratio m_μ/m_e is found from studies of the mesonic X-ray for the $3D \to 2P$ transition in mu-mesonic phosphorus[13;14;15]:

$$\frac{m_\mu}{m_e} = 206.76 \pm 0.02 \tag{6}$$

Use of Eqs. (5) and (6) gives

$$g_{\mu^+} = 2(1.0011 \pm 0.0001) \tag{7}$$

in good agreement with the theoretical value of Eq. (4)

A much more precise value of the anomalous g-value for the muon has been achieved in an experiment at CERN [16] which measures directly the quantity $g-2$. This is done, as illustrated in Figure 4, by measuring the difference between the orbital cyclotron frequency and the spin precession

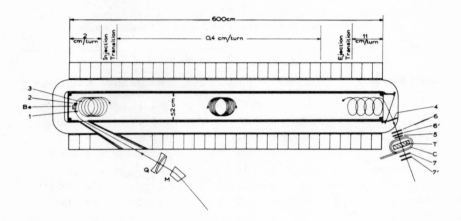

Figure 4

General plan of the $g-2$ experiment showing the 6-meter magnet. M: bending magnet; Q: pair of quadrupoles; 1, Be, 2, 3: injection assembly consisting of Be-moderator and counters 1, 2, 3; T: methylene-iodide target; counters 66′, 77′: "backward" and "forward" electron telescopes. A stored and ejected muon is registered as a coincidence 4, 5, 66′ 7, gated by a 1, 2, 3 and by either a forward or backward electron signal.

frequency in an experiment similar in principle to the free electron $g-2$ experiment [17]. The most recent experimental value [18] for $g-2$ is

$$\frac{(g-2)_{\text{muon}}}{2} = 0.001162 \pm 0.000005 \tag{8}$$

in excellent agreement with the theoretical value.

III. Muonium

A magnetic resonance experiment has also been done on muonium, which is the atom consisting of a positive muon and an electron. Muonium is formed in its ground $n=1$ state when positive muons are brought to rest in argon gas, through the charge capture reaction:

$$\mu^+ + A \rightarrow \mu^+ e^- + A^+ \tag{9}$$

The muonium will be polarized since the incident muons are polarized. Thus, for example, if a strong magnetic field antiparallel to the direction of incidence of the muon beam is present, then of the four hyperfine structure magnetic substates only the two with $M_\mu = +1/2$ will be formed ($M_\mu =$ magnetic quantum number of muon). The formation of muonium was first established [19] through the observation of the characteristic Larmor precession frequency:

$$f = \frac{\mu_0 H}{h} = 1.39 \, H \text{ Mc/sec} \tag{10}$$

of a triplet state of muonium ($\mu_0 =$ Bohr magneton) in an experiment of the GLW type. Indeed the observation of the characteristic Larmor precession frequency of muonium provides the most definitive proof that the spin quantum number of the muon is 1/2.

Muonium is of interest principally because it is the simplest system involving a muon and an eletron and hence the most suitable one for the precise study of the interaction of these two elementary particles. The hyperfine structure splitting in the ground $n=1$ state is the interesting quantity to measure as a test of the muon-electron interaction. If the muon is a particle which obeys the modern Dirac theory and which differs from the electron only in its mass value, then the hfs of muonium can be calculated from the quantum electrodynamic theory of the muon, electron, and photon fields. The result can be expressed as a power series in the small parameters α and m_e/m_μ and to terms of order α^2 and $\alpha(m_e/m_\mu)$ is given by [20]:

$$\Delta v(\text{theor}) = \left(\frac{16}{3}\alpha^2 c R_\alpha \frac{\mu_\mu}{\mu_0}\right)\left(1 + \frac{m_e}{m_\mu}\right)^{-3}\left(1 + \frac{3}{2}\alpha^2\right)\left(1 + \frac{\alpha}{2\pi} - 0.328 \frac{\alpha^2}{\pi^2}\right)$$

$$\times \left(1 + \frac{\alpha}{2\pi} + 0.75 \frac{\alpha^2}{\pi^2}\right)(1 - 1.81\alpha^2)\left(1 - \frac{3\alpha}{\pi}\frac{m_e}{m_\mu}\ln\frac{m_\mu}{m_e}\right) \tag{11}$$

in which $\alpha =$ fine structure constant, $c =$ velocity of light, $R_\infty =$ Rydberg constant for infinite mass, $\mu_\mu =$ muon magneton ($e\hbar/2m_\mu c$), $\mu_0 =$ electron Bohr magneton, $m_e =$ electron mass, and $m_\mu =$ muon mass. The first bracketed factor is the Fermi value for the hfs; the second factor is a reduced mass correction; the third factor is the Breit relativistic correction; the fourth and fifth factors are the $g/2$ values for the electron and the muon; the sixth factor is a second order radiative correction; the seventh factor is a relativistic recoil factor. Use of the best modern values of the fundamental atomic constants gives

$$\Delta\nu(\text{theor}) = 4463.13 \pm 0.10 \text{ Mc/sec.} \tag{12}$$

The hyperfine structure splitting $\Delta\nu$ has been measured by a magnetic resonance experiment in which a transition is induced under strong static magnetic field conditions between the two hfs states $(M_J, M_\mu) = (+1/2, +1/2)$ $\leftrightarrow (+1/2, -1/2)$. The microwave frequency was 1850 Mc/sec and the static magnetic field was about 5700 gauss. Figure 5 shows the experimental

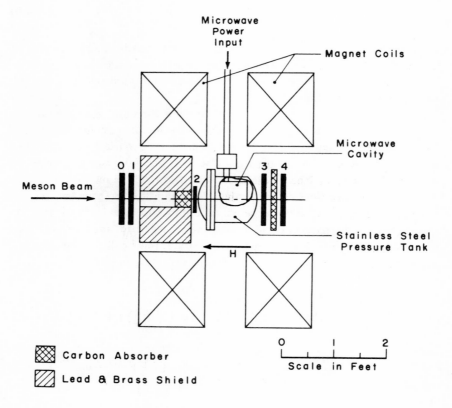

Figure 5

Experimental arrangement for muonium hfs measurement. 0, 1, 2, 3, and 4 are plastic scintillation counters.

arrangement. The muon spin flip is observed through the resulting change in the angular distribution of the decay positrons. A resonance curve is shown in Figure 6. From the observed resonance values of microwave frequency

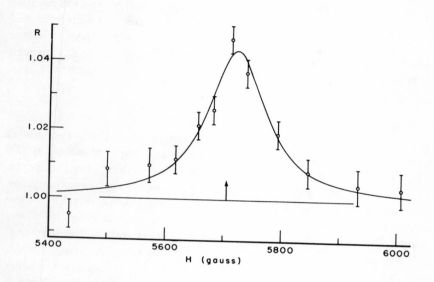

Figure 6

Experimental values in muonium hfs experiment of R (the ratio of positron counts 34 with microwaves on to those with microwaves off) vs static magnetic field for a microwave frequency of 1850.08 Mc/sec, and with an argon pressure of 55 atm. The solid curve is a least-squares fit Lorentzian curve with $H_{center} = 5725$ gauss and with width = 120 gauss. Error flags are ± (one sample standard deviation). The arrow indicates the theoretical line center, ignoring the pressure shift.

and static magnetic field, $\Delta\nu$ is calculated by use of the Breit-Rabi formula to obtain

$$\Delta\nu(\text{expt.}) = 4461.3 \pm 2.2 \text{ Mc/sec}, \tag{13}$$

where the uncertainty is determined by the inhomogeneity of the static magnetic field and an estimated upper limit for a possible pressure shift. The experimental value agrees with the theoretical value and thus provides further proof for the presently held theory of the muon.

IV. Mu-mesonic atoms

A negative muon stopped in matter behaves quite differently than does a positive muon. A positive muon may remain essentially free in matter or it may form muonium or enter into some chemical reaction, since it is quite similar chemically to a proton. The positive muon will decay into a positron and two neutrinos. On the other hand, a negative muon will always be rapidly captured by an atom in the matter and will quickly enter a low-lying level of a mu-mesonic atom composed of the nucleus and the negative muon [21]. The initial capture of the muon will occur to a high orbit and the subsequent cascade to a low-lying orbit will take place through Auger transitions and radiative transitions. The negative muon may decay through the reaction of Eq. (2) or it may undergo a nuclear capture reaction:

$$\mu^- + p \rightarrow n + \nu_\mu \tag{14}$$

With low Z nuclei the negative muon will rapidly enter the $1s$ state about the nucleus and will decay primarily via the muon decay reaction of Eq. (2).

Recently, precise magnetic resonance experiments have been done on negative muons by Hutchinson et al. [11] in the same experimental arrangement they used for positive muons shown in Figure 3. The results of their experiment are given in Table II. The principal interest is in the effects of atomic binding on the g-values and the chemical and solid state effects.

TCP invariance [2] requires that a free positive muon and a free negative muon, as particle and and antiparticle, shall have equal magnetic moments or g-values. However, a negative muon bound in a mu-mesonic atom will have a g-value different from that of a free positive muon due to a number of effects. For a mu-mesonic atom with a zero-spin nucleus and surrounded by a zero-spin electronic cloud the corrections [22] to the gyromagnetic ratio of a Dirac particle ($g_0 = 2$) are as follows:

1. radiative correction, g_1;
2. binding correction to radiative correction, g_2;
3. direct binding correction, g_3;
4. nuclear polarization, g_4;
5. electronic polarization correction, g_5;
6. electronic diamagnetic shielding correction, g_6;
7. center-of-mass correction, g_7.

The radiative correction, g_1, applies equally to the free positive and negative muons, of course. The radiative correction and the binding correction to the radiative correction are:

$$g_1/g_0 = \alpha/2\pi + 0.75\alpha^2/\pi^2 = 0.001165 \tag{15}$$

$$g_2/g_0 = (26/15\pi)\alpha \langle V \rangle / m_\mu c^2, \tag{16}$$

TABLE II

Corrections to gyromagnetic ratio of bound negative muon

Element	g_2/g_0	g_3/g_0 **	g_4/g_0	g_6/g_0	$\frac{1}{2}(g-g_+)\times 10^4_{\text{theor}}$ ***	$\frac{1}{2}(g-g_+)\times 10^4_{\text{expt}}$ ****
${}_2$He	-0.000001	-0.000071 (0)	~ 0	0	-0.72	
${}_2$He*	0	-0.000018 (0)	~ 0	0	-0.18	
${}_6$C	-0.000008	-0.000629 (0)	$+0.000004$	-0.00019	-8.2	
${}_6$C*	-0.000002	-0.000159 (0)	~ 0	-0.00019	-3.5	-7.5 (7)
${}_8$O	-0.000013	-0.001104 (1)	$+0.000012$	-0.00032	-14.3	-9.3 (10)
${}_{12}$Mg	-0.000029	-0.002379 (6)	$+0.000053$	-0.00062	-29.8	-26.3 (7)
${}_{14}$Si	-0.000040	-0.003172 (10)	$+0.000090$	-0.00079	-39.1	-36.1 (11)
${}_{16}$S	-0.000051	-0.004035 (15)	$+0.00014$	-0.00096	-49.1	-48.1 (16)
${}_{20}$Ca	-0.000076	-0.005883 (31)	$+0.00029$	-0.00133	-70.0	
${}_{24}$Cr	-0.000105	-0.00795 (5)	$+0.00051$	-0.00171	-92.6	
${}_{30}$Zn	-0.000153	-0.01126 (10)	$+0.00089$	-0.00238	-129.0	
${}_{42}$Mo	-0.000259	-0.01769 (22)	$+0.0020$	-0.00384	-197.9	
${}_{50}$Sn	-0.000331	-0.02146 (30)	$+0.0028$	-0.0049	-238.9	
${}_{64}$Gd	-0.000449	-0.02659 (44)	$+0.0040$	-0.0069	-299.4	
${}_{82}$Pb	-0.000605	-0.03248 (62)	$+0.0046$	-0.0098	-382.9	

* Muon in 2S state of mu-mesonic atom.

** Numbers in parentheses are uncertainties arising from 2% uncertainty in nuclear radius.

*** g does not include electronic polarization correction, g_5.

**** Numbers in parantheses are quoted experimental errors of reference [11].

where $\langle V \rangle$ is the expectation value of the potential energy and m_μ is the muon mass. The direct binding correction, g_3, is computed from a relativistic treatment of the magnetic moment of a Dirac particle in a central field. The result is

$$g_3/g_0 = -(4/3)\int F^2 dr, \qquad (17)$$

where F is the small component of the radial wavefunction of the muon in the Coulomb field of a nucleus with finite size. Both the corrections g_2 and g_3 have been obtained from the relativistic bound-state muon wavefunctions calculated on an IBM-704 computer. The nuclear charge distribution is taken to be

$$\rho(r) = (Ze/4\pi r_1^3 N_0)(1 - \tfrac{1}{2}e^{-n(1-x)}) \qquad \text{for } x < 1,$$

$$\rho(r) = (Ze/4\pi r_1^3 N_0)(\tfrac{1}{2}e^{-n(x-1)}) \qquad \text{for } x \geq 1, \qquad (18)$$

where $x = r/r_1$ and

$$N_0 = \frac{1}{3} + 2n^{-2} + n^{-3}e^{-n}.$$

The parameters r_1 and n, which characterize the nuclear radius and surface thickness, were chosen to be those which have been used to fit high-energy electron scattering results [23].

A significant nuclear polarization correction term, g_4, arises in second order perturbation theory from the magnetic interaction between the muon and the nucleus together with the magnetic interaction of the nucleus in the external static magnetic field. In an approximate calculation the term g_4 can be related to M1 nuclear gamma ray transition rates. Similarly, an electronic polarization correction term, g_5, arises in second order perturbation theory from the magnetic interaction between the muon and the electrons together with the magnetic interaction of the electrons in the external static magnetic field. The correction term g_5 is negligible unless the ground electronic state has fine structure levels.

The usual diamagnetic shielding by the atomic electrons will be very nearly the same for the muon as it is for the nucleus. This effect can be expressed by a correction term, g_6;

$$g_6/g_0 = -\frac{1}{3}\alpha^2 \sum_i \langle a_0/r_i \rangle, \qquad (19)$$

in which the sum is taken over all the electrons and a_0 is the hydrogen Bohr radius. The center-of-mass correction g_7 is negligibly small.

Table II lists theoretical corrections to the g-values of a bound negative muon for elements from He to Pb. The term g_5/g_0 is omitted because of its dependence on chemical and solid state effects. (For an isolated atom in a $^1S_0$ state g_5 vanishes.) The theoretical error in $g_3 + g_2$ is less than 1×10^{-6} for He and increases gradually to about 10^{-3} for Pb. The error in g_4 is roughly g_4 itself, about 8×10^{-6} for C up to 1×10^{-2} for Pb. The experimental values which have been measured are also listed.

The experimental and theoretical g-values agree rather well, particularly in view of uncertainties about the electronic state of the mu-mesonic atom, about chemical effects [24; 25], and about solid state effects such as the Knight shift [26]. The effect of nuclear size on g_3 is significantly larger than the experimental error for $Z \geqq 12$. The binding effect on the radiative correction, g_2, and the nuclear polarization correction, g_4, are about the size of the present experimental error. The chemical shift and the Knight shift are paramagnetic effects and have the same sign as that required to account for the small remaining discrepancies.

The substantial agreement of experimental and theoretical g-values sets a limit on any anomalous behavior of the muon such as its polarization in the strong electric field of the nucleus. Indeed, according to a crude model for polarization effects, the anomalous "size" of the muon must be less than 10 fermi.

REFERENCES

[1] T. D. LEE AND C. N. YANG, *Phys. Rev.* **104**, 254 (1956).

[2] T. D. LEE AND C. N. YANG, "Elementary Particles and Weak Interactions", Brookhaven National Laboratory 443(T–91), 1957.

[3] J. J. SAKURAI, *Prog. in Nuc. Physics* **7**, 243 (1959).

[4] R. L. GARWIN, L. M. LEDERMAN AND M. WEINRICH, *Phys. Rev.* **105**, 1415 (1957). Hereafter referred to as GLW.

[5] H. SUURA AND E. H. WICHMANN, *Phys. Rev.* **105**, 1930 (1957).

[6] A. PETERMANN, *Phys. Rev.* **105**, 1931 (1957).

[7] C. M. SOMMERFIELD, *Phys. Rev.* **107**, 328 (1957); *Ann. Phys.* **5**, 26 (1958).

[8] T. COFFIN, R. L. GARWIN, L. M. LEDERMAN, S. PENMAN AND A. M. SACHS, *Phys. Rev.* **106**, 1108 (1957).

[9] R. A. LUNDY, J. C. SENS, R. A. SWANSON, V. L. TELEGDI AND D. D. YOVANOVITCH, *Phys. Rev. Letters* **1**, 38 (1958).

[10] R. L. GARWIN, D. P. HUTCHINSON, S. PENMAN AND G. SHAPIRO, *Phys. Rev.* **118**, 271 (1960).

[11] D. P. HUTCHINSON, J. MENES, G. SHAPIRO, A. M. PATLACH AND S. PENMAN, *Phys. Rev. Letters* **7**, 129 (1961).

[12] The most recent figures are a private communication from D. P. Hutchinson and J. Menes.

[13] J. LATHROP, R. A. LUNDY, V. L. TELEGDI, R. WINSTON AND D. D. YOVANOVITCH, *Nuovo Cimento* **17**, 109 (1960).

[14] J. LATHROP, R. A. LUNDY, S. PENMAN, V. L. TELEGDI, R. WINSTON, D. D. YOVA-NOVITCH AND A. J. BEARDEN, *Nuovo Cimento* **17**, 114 (1960).

[15] S. DEVONS, G. GIDAL, L. M. LEDERMAN AND G. SHAPIRO, *Phys. Rev. Letters* **5**, 330 (1960).

[16] G. CHARPAK, F. J. M. FARLEY, R. L. GARWIN, T. MULLER, J. C. SENS, V. L. TE-LEGDI AND A. ZICHICHI, *Phys. Rev. Letters* **6**, 128 (1961).

[17] A. A. SCHUPP, R. W. PIDD AND H. R. CRANE, *Phys. Rev.* **121**, 1 (1961).

[18] G. CHARPAK, F. J. M. FARLEY, R. L. GARWIN, T. MULLER, J. C. SENS AND A. ZI-CHICHI, *Physics Letters* **1**, 16 (1962).

[19] V. W. HUGHES, D. W. McCOLM, K. ZIOCK AND R. PREPOST, *Phys. Rev. Letters* **5**, 63 (1960).

[20] K. ZIOCK, V. W. HUGHES, R. PREPOST, J. BAILEY AND W. CLELAND, *Phys. Rev. Letters* **8**, 103 (1962).

[21] E. FERMI AND E. TELLER, *Phys. Rev.* **72**, 399 (1947).

[22] K. W. FORD, V. W. HUGHES AND J. G. WILLS, *Phys. Rev. Letters* **7**, 134 (1961). Also article submitted to *Physical Review*.

[23] U. MEYER-BERKHOUT, K. W. FORD AND A. E. S. GREEN, *Ann. Phys.* **8**, 119 (1959).

[24] N. F. RAMSEY, *Phys. Rev.* **78**, 699 (1950).

[25] N. F. RAMSEY, *Phys. Rev.* **86**, 243 (1952).

[26] W. D. KNIGHT, *Solid State Physics*, Academic Press, New York, 1956, Vol. 2, p. 93.

RETURN TO ➡ CHEMISTRY LIBRARY
100 Hildebrand Hall
642-3753

LOAN PERIOD 1	2	3
████████	1 MONTH	
4	5	6

ALL BOOKS MAY BE RECALLED AFTER 7 DAYS
Renewable by telephone

DUE AS STAMPED BELOW

JUL 1 3 1988		
No card		